Applied Clay Mineralogy

INTERNATIONAL SERIES IN THE EARTH SCIENCES

ROBERT R. SHROCK, *Consulting Editor*

Applied Clay Mineralogy

RALPH E. GRIM

RESEARCH PROFESSOR OF GEOLOGY
UNIVERSITY OF ILLINOIS
URBANA, ILLINOIS

McGRAW-HILL BOOK COMPANY, INC.

New York   Toronto   London

1962

APPLIED CLAY MINERALOGY

Garrie L. Tufford
MNO 620900 8199

PREFACE

For many years the author has been interested in the widespread use of clays in industry and the problems encountered in engineering construction because of the varying properties of clays and soils. The present volume is the result of an effort through the years to gather together pertinent information on this subject. Particular attention is given to the type and properties of clays required for specific uses and to the fundamental factors of structure and composition of the clay minerals that determine properties and, in turn, specific uses. An attempt is made to derive from the data on various properties, concepts to explain the properties based on the structure of the clay minerals. The concepts are obviously theoretical and express essentially the opinion of the author. Some readers may not agree with them; however, a volume such as this has, in the author's opinion, little value unless an attempt is made to interpret the data along fundamental lines. In every case an attempt is made to designate the line between fact and explanatory theory.

Information on the many uses of clays in industry is widely scattered, and it is possible that much has been missed. It is hoped that no pertinent data have been overlooked.

The volume is very uneven in that some uses are considered in much more detail than others. This is regrettable but unavoidable as there is substantially no technical literature about some uses. In many cases information concerning the required specifications of clays and the contribution that particular clays make to the product properties is a trade secret. In some cases where the information was not secret the author has been able to fill in the gaps from personal knowledge; there are, therefore, many statements for which no references can be given. The volume is also uneven because the author's background and experience have been much more adequate and thorough in some areas than in others. This fact inevitably shows through in the consideration of some subjects. The coverage is particularly uneven and perhaps incomplete in the section Clays in Miscellaneous Uses. For example, not all the

v

uses of clays in pharmaceutical and cosmetic preparations can be given, but it is hoped that the general classes of such preparations have been covered.

In some fields in which clays are used, temperatures are designated in the centigrade scale; in other fields the Fahrenheit scale is followed. In the present volume either scale may be used to conform to the usage in the field under consideration.

It is desired to acknowledge with grateful thanks the help of C. G. Albert, D. U. Deere, W. L. Haden, J. W. Jordan, P. A. Witherspoon, P. Wheeler, and M. R. J. Wyllie, who have read various parts of the manuscript and have offered many valuable suggestions for corrections and additions. However, except where indicated by specific references, the author is solely responsible for the statements made herein.

Ralph E. Grim

Contents

Preface   v

Chapter 1. Introduction   1

Chapter 2. Structure and Properties of the Clay Minerals   7

Introduction. Structure and Composition. Ion Exchange. Clay-water Systems. Changes on Heating. Clay Mineral-Organic Reactions. Miscellaneous Properties. Origin and Occurrence. Clay Mineral Analyses. References.

Chapter 3. Clays in Ceramic Products 52

Introduction. Plasticity. Green Properties. Drying Properties. Firing Properties. Miscellaneous Properties. Clay Materials Used for Various Ceramic Products. References.

Chapter 4. Clays in Foundry Molding Sands 141

Introduction. Types of Clay Used in Molding Sands. Properties of Various Types of Clays. Sands Bonded with Mixtures of Clay Types. Character of the Clay Coating of Sand Grains and Distribution. Concept of the Bonding Action of Clay in Molding Sands.

Chapter 5. Clay Mineralogy in Relation to the Engineering Properties of Clay Materials 204

Introduction. Atterberg Limits. Liquidity Index. Unconfined Compression Strength. Shear Strength. Sensitivity. Permeability. Frost Heaving. Water Adsorption and Swelling. Compressibility and Consolidation. Preconsolidation under Load. Drying. Penetration Resistance. Density. Soil Stabilization. Factors of Particular Significance in Controlling Soil Properties. References.

Chapter 6. Clays in the Discovery and Recovery of Petroleum . . . 278

Introduction. Search for Petroleum. Drilling Fluids. Well Logging. Producing Operations. References.

Chapter 7. Clays in Refining and Preparation of Organic Materials . 307

Catalysis. Petroleum Cracking Catalysts for the Manufacture of Gasoline. Catalysts in Miscellaneous Organic Reactions. Decolorization. Miscellaneous Applications. References.

Chapter 8. Clays in Miscellaneous Uses 333

Introduction. Adhesives. Alsifilm. Aluminum Ore. Animal Bedding. Atomic (Radioactive) Waste Disposal. Cement, Mortar, and Aggregates. Clarification of Wines, Cider, Beer, etc. Coating Seed. De-inking Newsprint Paper. Desiccants, Absorbents, and Molecular Sieves. Emulsifying, Suspending, and Stabilizing Agents. Fabrics. Fertilizers. Miscellaneous Fillers. Floor Absorbent. Food. Grease. Ink. Leather. Medicines, Pharmaceuticals, and Cosmetics. Paint. Paper. Pelletizing Ores, Fluxes, Fuels, etc. Pesticides. Plastics. Plasticizing Agents. Rubber. Soaps and Cleaning and Polishing Compounds. Therapeutic Muds. Water Clarification. Water Impedance. References.

Index 411

CHAPTER 1

Introduction

The expression *clay material* is used herein for any fine-grained, natural, earthy, argillaceous material. It includes clays, shales, and argillites of the geologists. It also includes soils as defined by geologists, engineers, and agronomists, if such materials are argillaceous.

A review of the literature prior to 1920 reveals many different concepts of the fundamental composition of clay materials. Chemical analyses had shown that such materials were composed in general of alumina, silica, and water, with iron, alkalies, and alkaline earths also sometimes present in varying amounts. Various concepts offered many different ideas about how these chemical constituents were organized in the clay materials (Grim, 1953). One idea was that they were present in amorphous mixtures without any definite composition or structure. Another was that the mineral kaolinite was the essential constituent of all clay materials and that any elements not fitting into the composition of kaolinite were present as impurities. Another suggestion was that particle size was the major factor and that, in fact, clay materials could be composed of almost any minerals if they were fine enough—about 1 μ was considered the upper limit—and still another idea was that zeolite-like minerals were the essential constituents of clay materials.

For many years some students of clay materials had suggested that such materials were composed of extremely small particles of a limited number of crystalline minerals. For example, LeChatelier (1887) and Lowenstein (1909) arrived at this conclusion many years ago. This is the clay mineral concept, but prior to 1920 there were no adequate research tools to provide positive evidence for it. The clay mineral concept, therefore, is not new; rather, it has been well established and generally accepted in recent years.

In 1923 Hadding in Sweden and in 1924 Rinne in Germany, working quite independently, published the first X-ray diffraction analyses of clay materials. Both these investigators found crystalline material in the finest fractions of a series of clays and also found that all samples studied seemed to be composed of particles of the same small group of minerals.

1

About 1924 Ross and various colleagues (1926, 1928, 1931, 1934, 1945) began a study of the mineral composition of clays that led to a series of monumental papers on the subject. They showed that the components of clay materials were essentially crystalline and that there was a limited number of such crystalline components to which the name *clay minerals* was applied. Since that time a vast number of workers in many countries have obtained results which verify this conclusion (Grim, 1953).

According to the clay mineral concept, clay materials are essentially composed of extremely small crystalline particles of one or more members of a small group of minerals that are commonly known as the clay minerals. These minerals are essentially hydrous aluminum silicates, with magnesium or iron proxying wholly or in part for the aluminum in some minerals, and with alkalies or alkaline earth also present as essential constituents in some of them. Some clays are composed of a single clay mineral, but in many there is a mixture of them. In addition to the clay minerals some clays contain varying amounts of so-called nonclay minerals such as quartz, calcite, feldspar, and pyrite. Also, many clay materials contain organic material and water-soluble salts. According to the clay mineral concept, the crystalline clay minerals are the essential constituents of nearly all clays and, therefore, the components which largely determine their properties.

Some clay materials do contain material which is noncrystalline on the basis of diffraction analyses, e.g., allophane (see Chap. 2). There are examples known (Grim, 1948) in which allophane is a major component of a clay material. However, such examples are rare, and in general clay materials are composed wholly or predominantly of crystalline components. As will be shown in Chap. 2, the perfection of the crystallinity of the clay minerals varies considerably in various clay materials.

The factors controlling the properties of clay materials may be classified as follows:

Clay Mineral Composition. This refers to the identity and relative abundance of all the clay minerals present. It will be shown later that very small amounts of certain clay mineral constituents may exert a large influence on physical properties. Also, the perfection of the crystallinity is important. Thus, two clays both composed wholly of kaolinite will have somewhat different properties if the kaolinite in one is well organized and in the other poorly ordered. Further, somewhat different properties will accrue if the several clay minerals in a clay material are a mixture of discrete particles or an intimate interlayer mixture. It is important that a clay mineral analysis be complete in that *all* components be determined and their crystallinity evaluated.

Nonclay Mineral Composition. This refers to the identity of the nonclay minerals, their shape and relative abundance, and the particle-size distribution of the individual species. In general, nonclay minerals must be present in more than trace amounts before they influence properties. This is not always true, however, as traces of components may significantly influence the properties of clays developed on firing to elevated temperatures (see Chap. 3). Also traces of elements and minerals present in very small amounts may be of great importance in geologic studies of clay materials in such matters as correlation, determination of condition of deposition, and location of the source area.

Organic Material. This refers to the kind and amount of organic material contained in the clay material. In general, organic material occurs in two forms: it may be present as discrete particles of wood, leaf matter, spores, etc., or it may be present as organic molecules adsorbed on the surface of the clay mineral particles.

It is of great significance that the clay minerals may influence the nature of the organic material associated with them, i.e., have catalytic properties toward the organic, and also under some conditions the presence of organics may greatly change the properties of the clay. This latter fact is made use of at the present time in the preparation of clays composed of organic-clad clay minerals with special properties for particular commercial uses.

Exchangeable Ions and Soluble Salts. Some clay materials contain water-soluble salts which may have been entrained in the clay at the time of accumulation or may have developed subsequently as a consequence of ground-water movement and weathering or alteration processes. The clay minerals and some organic material found in clay materials also may carry adsorbed cations and anions which are exchangeable (see pages 29–34) for other ions by simple treatment, as, for example, in a water solution.

The physical properties of clay materials depend to some extent on the nature of the adsorbed exchangeable ions carried by the clay mineral components. Thus, a sodium clay is likely to have different plastic properties than one with calcium. This difference will be great or small depending on the cation-exchange capacity of the constituent clay minerals. Also the relative abundance of the adsorbed ions present in any particular clay material is important in determining its properties.

The fact that adsorbed ions may influence significantly the properties of a clay material provides a possible way of altering or controlling properties to suit particular conditions.

Texture. The textural factor refers to the particle-size distribution of the constituent particles, the shape of the particles, the orientation of the particles in space with respect to each other, and the forces tending to bind them together. Obviously, as the amount of nonclay minerals increases, their importance in determining properties increases. The influence of the nonclay minerals on the properties of clay materials is beyond the scope of this volume; however, it is desired to indicate its complexity. Thus, the presence of nonclay material in a ceramic clay which is unsorted may in many cases produce desirable shrinkage properties, whereas the same amount of nonclay in particles of a fine-silt size may make the clay almost unusable. Similarly, coarse particles of some nonclay minerals may make a clay material usable as a refractory, whereas the same amount of the same nonclay mineral in a very fine-particle size may so reduce the fusion point of the clay that it can no longer be classed as refractory.

So far as the texture of the clay minerals themselves is concerned, there are few pertinent data. The size of the clay minerals is important in determining properties but only in relation to the ease of the breakdown and dispersion of the clay minerals. Thus, a particle-size analysis of a clay mineral sample is often only a measure of the degree of disaggregation in making the analysis and portrays little regarding the size of particles in the natural clay. This is not to say that data measuring the ease of dispersion of a clay may not be pertinent to its use.

In some clay materials there is a preferred general orientation of the clay mineral particles; for example, in many shales the basal-plane surfaces have parallel orientation. Again this attribute would have little significance if it were lost in the utilization of the clay.

Obviously, a major factor regarding texture is the bond between particles. Very little is known of this matter; indeed, the whole field of the texture of clay materials in their natural state (not after dispersion) is relatively untouched and much in need of study. However, some consideration will be given to the bond properties of the clay minerals later in relation to specific uses.

Clay materials are utilized in the manufacture of a large number and variety of products—ceramics, paper, rubber, catalysts, etc. Clay materials play a significant role in many professions and fields of endeavor such as agriculture and engineering. In general, for each particular use the required specifications pertain to a different set of properties. Thus, for some uses plastic characteristics are important, for others they make little difference. Also, for each use, clays of a particular composition may be required. In many uses the clay is the raw material which is processed by treatment, e.g., chemically or by firing, so that the pertinent properties determining use are those that result from such treatment.

The object of the present volume is to assemble pertinent data on the types of clay materials used in various fields and on the relationship of the fundamental characteristics of the clay minerals to the properties of clay materials that determine their use in particular fields or the properties that are significant when they are encountered in engineering construction activities. It is proposed to assess the data in the literature in an effort to unearth fundamental generalities as to why only certain clays are valuable for certain usages and why certain clay materials are likely to cause difficulties when they are encountered in engineering practice.

As noted above, factors other than clay mineral composition may influence the properties of clay materials, and such factors may in some instances be more important than the clay mineral composition. In general, such factors will be considered only in so far as they influence the role of the clay minerals in determining the physical attributes of clay materials.

A detailed review of the properties of clay-water systems which have relatively large amounts of water, i.e., systems which are essentially fluid, is considered beyond the scope of the present volume. There is an abundant literature, particularly from the point of view of colloid chemistry, on this subject. The interested reader can study the works of Hauser (1939), Marshall (1949), and many others. Also, the application of clay mineralogy in problems of the utilization of agricultural soils is not considered in the present work. Again there is an abundant literature in the field of agronomy which should be consulted. Many of these matters have not been in the author's particular field of interest.

Only cursory attention is paid to the mode of occurrence of various types of clay materials. This very important subject is considered beyond the scope of the present book and deserves special treatment in a separate volume.

REFERENCES

Grim, R. E., Some Factors Influencing the Properties of Soil Materials, *Proc. Second Intern. Congr. Soil Mechanics*, **3**, 8–12 (1948).

———, "Clay Mineralogy," McGraw-Hill Book Company, Inc., New York (1953).

Hadding, A., Eine röntgenographische Methode kristalline und kryptokristalline Substanzen zu identifizieren, *Z. Krist.*, **58**, 108–112 (1923).

Hauser, E. A., "Colloidal Phenomena," McGraw-Hill Book Company, Inc., New York (1939).

LeChatelier, H., De l'action de la chaleur sur les argiles, *Bull. soc. franç. minéral*, **10**, 204–211 (1887).

Lowenstein, E., Ueber Hydrate deren Dampfspannung sich Kontinuerlich mit den Zusammensetzung andert, *Z. anorg. Chem.*, **63**, 69–139 (1909).

Marshall, C. E., "The Colloid Chemistry of the Silicate Minerals," Academic Press, Inc., New York (1949).

Rinne, F., Röntgenographische Untersuchungen an einigen feinzerteilten Mineralien Kunsprodukten und dichten Gesteinen, *Z. Krist.*, **60**, 55–69 (1924).

Ross, C. S., The Mineralogy of Clays, *Proc. First Intern. Congr. Soil Sci.*, **4**, 555–556 (1928).

—— and S. B. Hendricks, Minerals of the Montmorillonite Group: Their Origin and Relation to Soils and Clays, *U.S. Geol. Survey Profess. Paper* 205-B, pp. 23–77 (1945).

—— and P. F. Kerr, The Clay Minerals and Their Identity, *J. Sediment. Petrol.*, **1**, 55–65 (1931).

—— and ——, The Kaolin Minerals, *U.S. Geol. Survey Profess. Paper* 165-E, pp. 151–175 (1931).

—— and ——, Halloysite and Allophane, *U.S. Geol. Survey Profess. Paper* 185-G, pp. 134–148 (1934).

—— and E. V. Shannon, Minerals of Bentonites and Related Clays and Their Physical Properties, *J. Am. Ceram. Soc.*, **9**, 77–96 (1926).

CHAPTER 2

Structure and Properties
of the Clay Minerals

INTRODUCTION

For a detailed review of the structure, composition, properties, and occurrence of the clay minerals the reader should consult the works of Grim (1953), which is the companion volume to the present work, Marshall (1949), Brindley et al. (1951), Jasmund (1955), and Sudo (1959). In the present chapter only a brief review of these matters will be given to prepare readers who are relatively unfamiliar with clay mineralogy with information necessary to understand the remainder of this volume.

At present there is no general agreement on a classification of the clay minerals or nomenclature of species and groups. However, it is possible to describe the clay minerals under a few general headings, and such grouping is adequate for the considerations in the remainder of the present volume.

STRUCTURE AND COMPOSITION

General Statement

The atomic structures of the common clay minerals have been determined in considerable detail by numerous investigators, who based their studies on the generalizations of Pauling (1930) with regard to the structure of the micas and related minerals. Much, however, remains to be learned about the detailed structure of the clay minerals. The fact that they occur in extremely small particles, so that individual crystals cannot be studied, limits the fundamental data that can be obtained concerning their structure. As a consequence, while the broad outlines of their structural attributes can be considered well established, much detail concerning their structural characteristics remains in the realm of speculation and theory.

Two units are involved in the atomic structure of most of the clay minerals. One unit consists of two sheets of closely packed oxygens or

7

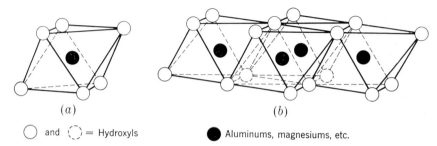

(a)   (b)

○ and ⊙ = Hydroxyls   ● Aluminums, magnesiums, etc.

FIG. 2-1. Diagrammatic sketch showing (a) single octahedral unit and (b) the sheet structure of the octahedral units.

hydroxyls in which aluminum, iron, or magnesium atoms are embedded in octahedral coordination, so that they are equidistant from six oxygens or hydroxyls (Fig. 2-1). When aluminum is present, only two-thirds of the possible positions are filled to balance the structure, which is the gibbsite structure and has the formula $Al_2(OH)_6$. When magnesium is present, all the positions are filled to balance the structure, which is the brucite structure and has the formula $Mg_3(OH)_6$. The normal oxygen to oxygen distance is 2.60 A, and a common hydroxyl to hydroxyl distance is about 3 A; in this structural unit, however, the OH to OH distance is 2.94 A, and the space available for the atom in octahedral coordination is about 0.61 A. The thickness of the unit is 5.05 A in clay mineral structures.

The second unit is built of silica tetrahedrons. In each tetrahedron a silicon atom is equidistant from four oxygens, or hydroxyls if needed to balance the structure, arranged in the form of a tetrahedron with the silicon atom at the center. The silica tetrahedral groups are arranged to form a hexagonal network, which is repeated indefinitely to form a sheet of the composition $Si_4O_6(OH)_4$ (Fig. 2-2). The tetrahedrons are arranged so that the tips of all of them point in the same direction, and

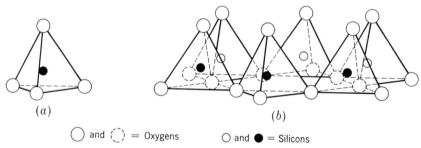

(a)   (b)

○ and ⊙ = Oxygens   ○ and ● = Silicons

FIG. 2-2. Diagrammatic sketch showing (a) single silica tetrahedron and (b) the sheet structure of silica tetrahedrons arranged in an hexagonal network.

the bases of all tetrahedrons are in the same plane (there may be exceptional cases in which some of the tetrahedrons are inverted). The structure can be considered as made of a perforated plane of oxygens which is the plane of the base of the tetrahedral groups; a plane of silicon atoms with each silicon in the cavity at the junction of the three oxygen atoms and therefore forming a hexagonal network; and a plane of hydroxyl atoms with each hydroxyl directly above the silicon at the tip of the tetrahedrons. The open hexagonal network can be considered as composed of three strings of oxygen atoms intersecting at angles of 120°. The oxygen to oxygen distance in the silica tetrahedral sheets is 2.55 A, and the space available for the atom in tetrahedral coordination is about 0.55 A. The thickness of the unit is 4.93 A in clay mineral structures.

Some of the clay minerals are fibrous and are composed of different structural units from those noted above. These minerals resemble the amphiboles in their structural characteristics, and the basic structural unit is composed of silica tetrahedrons arranged in a double chain of the composition Si_4O_{11}, as shown in Fig. 2-3. The structure is similar to that

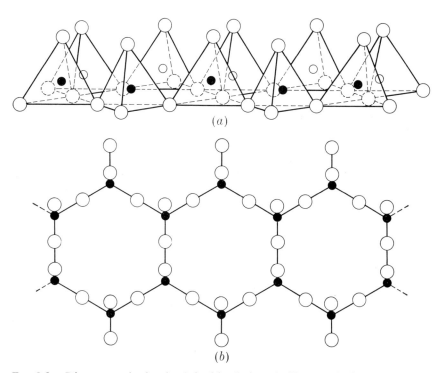

(a)

(b)

Fig. 2-3. Diagrammatic sketch of double chains of silica tetrahedrons, as in the amphibole structural type of clay minerals: (a) in perspective, (b) projected on the plane of the base of the tetrahedrons.

of the sheet of silica tetrahedrons in the layer minerals except that it is continuous in only one direction.   In the other direction it is restricted to a width of about 12 A.

The chains are bound together by atoms of aluminum and/or magnesium placed so that each such atom is surrounded by six "active" oxygen atoms.   The active oxygens are those with only one link to silica and hence are those at the edges of the chains and at the tips of the tetrahedrons.

Allophane Minerals

By definition the allophane clay minerals are those constituents of clay materials which are amorphous to X-ray diffraction.   This does not mean that such materials have a complete absence of any structural organization.   Rather, it means that the arrangement of tetrahedral and octahedral units with respect to each other is not sufficiently regular to permit diffraction or the individual units, which may be well ordered. are too small in size to yield diffraction effects; in the latter case electron diffraction sometimes reveals order.

Allophane components have no general definite chemical composition or shape.   Some allophanes which have been studied appear to have better organization than others (Collins, 1955).   In some instances the organization appears to approach halloysite in its general attributes, whereas in other cases it appears to resemble montmorillonite.   In such instances the physical properties of the allophane approach that of one or the other of these two clay minerals.   In general, the properties of allophanes vary tremendously.   Thus, the material may be dispersible into extremely small particles or may be essentially nondispersible in water.

Clay materials containing allophane frequently have substantial amounts (± 5 per cent) of phosphate and/or sulfate components.   Further, such material is characterized generally by relatively small amounts of alkalies and alkaline earths, except for those approaching montmorillonite which are likely to contain some magnesium.

Kaolinite Minerals

The structure of kaolinite was first suggested in general outlines by Pauling (1930).   It was worked out in some detail by Gruner (1932) and later revised by Brindley and his colleagues (1946 and 1951).   The structure is composed of a single tetrahedral sheet and a single alumina octahedral sheet combined in a unit so that the tips of the silica tetrahedrons and one of the layers of the octahedral sheet form a common layer (Fig. 2-4).   All the tips of the silica tetrahedrons point in the same direction and toward the center of the unit made of the silica and octahedral sheets.   The dimensions of the sheets of tetrahedral units and of the octahedral units are closely similar in their *a* and *b* dimensions, and consequently composite octahedral-tetrahedral layers are readily formed.

In the layer common to the octahedral and tetrahedral groups, two-thirds of the atoms are shared by the silicons and aluminums, and then they become oxygens instead of hydroxyls.   Only two-thirds of the possible positions for aluminum in the octahedral sheet are filled, and there are three possible plans of regular population of the octahedral layer with aluminums.   The aluminum atoms are considered to be so placed that two aluminums are separated by a hydroxyl above and below, thus making a hexagonal distribution in a single plane in the center of the octahedral sheet.   The hydroxyl groups are placed so that each hydroxyl is directly below the perforation of the hexagonal net of oxygens in the tetrahedral sheet.

The charges within the structure are balanced, i.e., there are no charges on the lattice due to substitutions within the lattice.   The structural formula is $(OH)_8Si_4Al_4O_{10}$, and the theoretical composition expressed in oxides is SiO_2, 46.54 per cent; Al_2O_3, 39.50 per cent; H_2O, 13.96 per cent. The analyses of many samples of kaolinite have shown that there is very little if any substitution within the lattice (Ross and Kerr, 1931).   In a few instances the evidence suggests a very small amount of substitution of

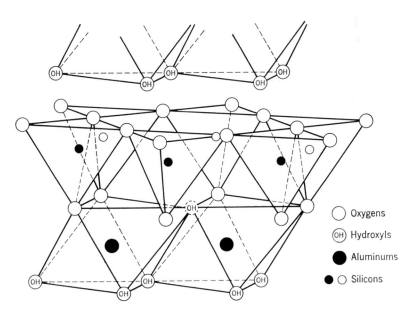

Fig. 2-4.   Diagrammatic sketch of the structure of the kaolinite layer, after Gruner (1932).

iron and/or titanium for aluminum in the relatively poor crystalline variety.

The minerals of the kaolinite group consist of sheet units of the type just described continuous in the *a* and *b* directions and stacked one above the other in the *c* direction.   The thickness of these units is about 7 A. The variation between members of the kaolinite group consists in the way in which the unit layers are stacked above each other and possibly also in the position of the aluminum atoms in the possible positions open to them in the octahedral layers.   Brindley (1951) has investigated the stacking of the unit layers in considerable detail, and his work should be consulted for information on this subject.

Because of the superposition of oxygen and hydroxyl planes in adjacent units, the units are held together fairly tightly by hydrogen bonding between the layers.   The plane between the unit layer is a cleavage plane. However, in kaolinite the cleavage is not so pronounced as in some other clay minerals where oxygen planes are adjacent at unit boundaries so that there is no hydrogen bonding.   Thus, the mineral is not readily dispersible in water into extremely small units.   Electron micrographs of kaolinite show well-formed six-sided flake-shaped units frequently with a prominent elongation (Fig. 2-5).   Often the edges of the particles are beveled instead of being at right angles to the flake surfaces.   The maximum lateral dimensions of flake surfaces range from about 0.3 to 4 μ and the thicknesses from 0.05 to about 2 μ.   When a kaolinite clay is dispersed in water, kaolinite particles of about this size are produced.

Numerous investigators (Brindley and Robinson, 1946; Grimshaw et al., 1945; Grim, 1947) have reported finding kaolinite minerals of lower crystallinity than that of the well-crystallized material just noted.   Brindley and his colleagues (1946 and 1951) have investigated in detail some examples of rather poorly crystallized kaolinite.   They state that in poorly organized kaolinite the structure is highly disordered along the *b* axis with unit layers randomly displaced by multiples of one third of the *b* dimension.   They suggest that there is some randomness in the distribution of aluminum atoms among octahedral positions.   The first-order spacings are slightly higher (7.15 to 7.20 A) and less sharply defined for the poorly crystalline than for the well-crystallized mineral, suggesting some occasional interlayer water between the silicate units.   Dehydration data tend to confirm the presence of such water.   Kaolinite in clay materials appears to vary from that in which about all unit layers show random *b*-axis shifts to that in which only occasional unit layers are shifted.   It seems, therefore, undesirable to apply a specific mineral name to poorly ordered kaolinite.   Available data also suggest that there may be some slight substitution of titanium or iron for aluminum in the poorly crystallized kaolinite. It may be that the presence of such re-placements is a cause of the lower degree of crystallinity.

In general, the poorly crystallized kaolinite occurs in less distinct hexagonal flake-shaped masses than the well-crystallized variety, and the particle size is generally smaller. It does not always follow, however, that the kaolinite with a very small particle size has a low degree of crystallinity. For example, the kaolinite component of some so-called flint clays is extremely fine grained and well crystallized. The poorly organized material tends to be somewhat more dispersible in water so that there is

FIG. 2-5.   Electron micrograph of kaolinite, Macon, Georgia, from Kerr (1950).

more cleavage between units and reduction in particle size as compared with the well-crystallized kaolinite.

Dickite and nacrite are composed of structure units similar to those making up kaolinite. They differ from the latter mineral, however, in the way in which the silicate units are stacked one above the other (Hendricks, 1938). Dickite and nacrite are usually listed as clay minerals although they are rarely found in clay materials. They are of substantially no commercial importance, and the almost complete absence of them in clay materials makes it unnecessary to consider their properties in detail.

Another mineral that has been described under the kaolinite group is anauxite, which was thought to be kaolinite with some excess silica in its structure. It is now quite well established that anauxite is not a valid mineral species as it is actually kaolinite with some extremely fine-grained excess silica as an impurity and not as part of its structure.

Halloysite Minerals

There are two forms of halloysite, one with a composition $(OH)_8Si_4Al_4O_{10}$ and the other with a composition $(OH)_8Si_4Al_4O_{10} \cdot 4H_2O$. The latter form dehydrates to the former irreversibly at relatively low temperatures ($\pm 60°C$). The basal spacing of the dehydrated form is about 7.2 A or about the thickness of the kaolinite layer, and the basal spacing of the hydrated form is about 10.1 A. The difference, 2.9 A, is about the thickness of the single molecular sheet of water.

Halloysite minerals are made up of successive layers with the same structural composition as those composing kaolinite. The layers are stacked one above the other in the *c*-axis direction and are displaced randomly in both the *a* and *b* directions. According to Brindley (1951) the probable displacements are simple fractions of the cell dimensions. He states that "the experimental results require only that the displacements along the *a* and *b* axes shall be random with respect to each other."

The highly hydrated form consists of kaolinite layers separated from each other by single molecular layers of water (Hendricks, 1938). The transition to the dehydrated form is due to the loss of the interlayer of water molecules. According to Brindley and his colleagues (1948) only partial dehydration takes place at low temperatures (60 to 75°C), and temperatures of the order of 400°C are necessary for complete removal of the interlayer water. At the lower temperatures a partially dehydrated form develops which tends to persist. Therefore, a natural occurrence of halloysite tends to be the partially dehydrated form which, if the deposit is massive, grades back from the outcrop to the hydrated form.

The interlayer water may be replaced by other polar molecules but not by more than a single layer of them. Wada (1959) has shown that the mineral may interact with various salts causing variations in the *c* dimension and, therefore, indicating implacement of salts in interlayer-water positions.

Bates et al. (1950) have shown that the mineral tends to occur in tubular units, as revealed by electron micrographs (Fig. 2-6). They have suggested that the $4H_2O$ form consists of tubes made up of overlapping, curved sheets of the kaolinite type with the *c* axis for any point of the tube nearly perpendicular to a plane tangent to the tube at that point. In the dehydration to the $2H_2O$ form the tubes frequently collapse, split, or unroll. It seems that the curvature develops in hydrated halloysite because of the irregular stacking of the layers and the interlayer of water molecules, which cause a weak bond between successive layers. Further, the tendency to curvature is the result of the slight difference in dimension of the silica part of the structure as compared with the alumina part of the structural unit.

According to Bates et al. (1950) the outside diameters of the tubular particles of halloysite range from 0.04 to 0.19 μ with a median value of 0.07 μ. The average wall thickness is about 0.02 μ. The tubes may range in length up to several microns.

It seems quite certain (Collins, 1955) that halloysite does not always occur in tubular form and that it is found sometimes in irregular or spherical units. The ease of dispersion of the mineral varies greatly depending on the state of hydration and perhaps on other characteristics.

Fig. 2-6. Electron micrograph of halloysite, Windover, Utah, courtesy of T. F. Bates.

In general, partially dehydrated forms break down more easily into individual units than do the fully hydrated or the completely dehydrated form.

In the case of halloysite, as of kaolinite, there are substantially no replacements within the lattice. There are, therefore, no unsatisfied charges on the surface of halloysite particles as a consequence of such replacements.

There is considerable variation in the names used to designate the forms of halloysite; thus, the low hydration form may be called halloysite or metahalloysite, and the higher hydration form may be called hydrated halloysite, endellite, or halloysite.

Montmorillonite Minerals

The montmorillonite minerals occur in extremely small particles so that single-crystal X-ray diffraction data cannot be obtained. Structural concepts, therefore, must be deduced from powder data and inferences made from better-known structures with the result that there is considerable uncertainty regarding details of the montmorillonite structure. Currently the generally accepted structure for montmorillonite minerals follows the original suggestion made in 1933 by Hofmann, Endell, and Wilm, modified by later suggestions of Marshall (1935), Maegdefrau and Hofmann (1937), and Hendricks (1942). According to this concept montmorillonite is composed of units made of two silica tetrahedral sheets with a central alumina octahedral sheet. All the tips of the tetrahedrons point in the same direction and toward the center of the unit. The tetrahedral and octahedral sheets are combined so that the tips of the tetrahedrons of each silica sheet and one of the hydroxyl layers of the octahedral sheet form a common layer. The atoms common to both the tetrahedral and octahedral layer become oxygens instead of hydroxyls. The layers are continuous in the *a* and *b* directions and are stacked one above the other in the *c* direction.

In the stacking of the silica-alumina-silica units, oxygen layers of each unit are adjacent to oxygens of the neighboring units with a consequence that there is a very weak bond and an excellent cleavage between them. The outstanding feature of the montmorillonite structure is that water and other polar molecules, such as certain organic molecules, can enter between the unit layers causing the lattice to expand in the *c* direction. Unlike halloysite, interlayer sheets of polar molecules many molecular layers thick may develop. The *c*-axis dimension of montmorillonite is not fixed but varies from 9.6 A, when no polar molecules are between the unit layers, to substantially complete separation in some cases. Figure 2-7 is a diagrammatic sketch of this structure of montmorillonite.

Exchangeable cations occur between the silicate layers, and the *c*-axis spacing of completely dehydrated montmorillonite depends somewhat on the size of the interlayer cations, being greater the larger the cation. The thickness of the water layers between the silicate units also depends on the nature of the exchangeable cations at a given water-vapor pressure. Under ordinary conditions, a montmorillonite with sodium as the exchangeable ion frequently has one molecular water layer and a c-axis spacing of about 12.5 A; with calcium there are frequently two molecular water layers and a c-axis spacing of about 15.5 A. The expansion prop-

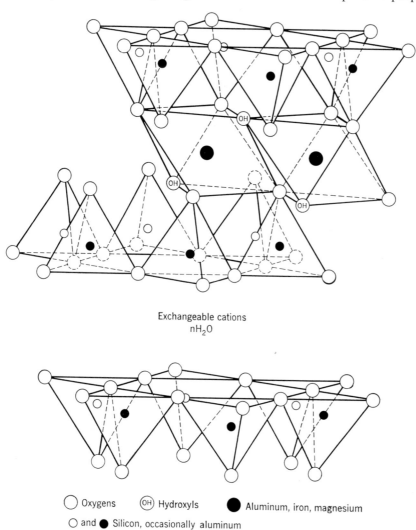

Exchangeable cations
nH₂O

○ Oxygens   ⊙ Hydroxyls   ● Aluminum, iron, magnesium

○ and ● Silicon, occasionally aluminum

Fig. 2-7. Diagrammatic sketch of the structure of montmorillonite, according to Hofmann, Endell, and Wilm (1933); Marshall (1935); and Hendricks (1942).

erties are reversible unless the structure is completely collapsed by the removal of all the interlayer polar molecules, in which case it may be difficult or impossible to expand the structure.

In some instances the unit layers are stacked one above the other without any fixed periodical arrangement in the a and b dimensions, whereas in other instances there seems to be some regularity in these directions. The theoretical formula for the structure given above is $(OH)_4Si_8Al_4O_{20}n$ (interlayer) H_2O, and the theoretical composition without the interlayer material is SiO_2, 66.7 per cent; Al_2O_3, 28.3 per cent; H_2O, 5 per cent. Montmorillonite *always* differs from the above theoretical formula because of substitutions within the lattice of aluminum and possibly phosphorus for silicon in tetrahedral coordination and/or magnesium, iron, zinc, nickel, lithium, etc., for aluminum in the octahedral sheet. In the tetrahedral sheet the substitution of aluminum for silicon appears to be limited to less than about 15 per cent. In the formula noted above only two-thirds of the possible positions in the octahedral sheet are filled. The substitution of magnesium for aluminum can be one for one or three magnesiums for two aluminums with all possible octahedral positions being filled in the latter case. Substitutions within the octahedral sheet may vary from few to complete. In cases where magnesium completely fills octahedral positions, the mineral is called saponite, and when the aluminum is completely replaced by iron the mineral is called nontronite. Layer minerals of this general type in which all possible octahedral positions are filled are called *trioctahedral,* and those in which only two-thirds of the possible positions are filled are called *dioctahedral.* Numerous analyses of montmorillonite have shown that the substitutions within the octahedral sheet are such that the mineral is either almost exactly trioctahedral or dioctahedral and not intermediate.

A further way in which montmorillonite always differs from the theoretical formula is that the lattice is *always* unbalanced by the substitutions noted above. This unbalancing may result from substitutions of ions of different valence in the tetrahedral or octahedral sheets or both. Unbalancing of one sheet may be compensated for in part, but only in part, by substitutions in the other sheet of the unit layer. Compensation also may be by substitution of hydroxyls for oxygens in the octahedral layer. It is significant that the substitutions in the montmorillonite lattice, with the internal compensating substitutions, always result in about the same net charge on the lattice. Many analyses have shown this to be about 0.66— per unit cell. This net positive charge deficiency is balanced by exchangeable cations adsorbed between the unit layers and around their edges. This charge deficiency corresponds to about two-thirds unit per unit cell. It would require the substitution of one magnesium for every sixth aluminum, or about one out of every six silicons by an aluminum in the tetrahedral sheet.

Edelman and Favejee (1940) have suggested an alternative structure which was claimed to explain more adequately the properties of the mineral. This structure differs from that described in that every other silica tetrahedron in both silica sheets is inverted, so that half of them point in the opposite direction. Those that point away from the silicate sheet would have the tip oxygens replaced by hydroxyls. Evidence from X-ray diffraction data, chemical data indicating lattice substitutions, and careful dehydration studies are all strongly against the original Edelman and Favejee structure. However, there is the distinct possibility that a small percentage of the silica tetrahedrons may be inverted. This would be extremely difficult to detect by any analytical procedure and may help to explain some of the properties of montmorillonite clays. Other structural modifications have been suggested. Thus McConnell (1950) suggested that $(OH)_4$ units occasionally replace silica tetrahedrons. In general, data are not at hand to determine the validity of such suggestions.

Montmorillonites tend to occur in equidimensional, extremely thin flake-shaped units. In some instances these units are elongate and are lath- or needle-shaped. Probably such elongate forms are due to substitutions within the lattice of ions of a size which does not easily fit into octahedral positions, thereby causing a directional strain on the lattice. Many forms in which there is substantial substitution of iron and/or magnesium for aluminum possess this elongate form.

The commonest montmorillonite forms found naturally are dioctahedral aluminous varieties in which there is a moderately small amount of substitution of magnesium and/or iron for aluminum; the substitution of aluminum for silicon is generally quite small. It has been shown recently in bentonite clays, which are composed largely of montmorillonite, that there is a mixing of montmorillonites with two or more different cation populations and consequent states of hydration (McAtee, 1958). Also it has been shown by Grim and Kulbicki (1959) that in many such clays there is a mixing of montmorillonites with different substitutions within the silicate structure. Significant variations with regard to lattice substitutions appear to be primarily in the population of octahedral positions, both as to the nature of the atoms and their spatial arrangements in possible octahedral positions.

The montmorillonites are relatively readily dispersible in water down to extremely small particle sizes. This seems to be particularly true when sodium is the exchangeable cation, in which case the particles may separate into units of about unit-cell thickness. Estimates based on electron micrographs of areal dimensions of the flakes are difficult to obtain because of their irregularity, but the dimensions are probably of the order of 10 to 100 times the thickness of the flakes.

Illite Minerals

The illite minerals are similar in their general structural characteristics to the micas (Grim et al., 1937; Grim et al., 1951). The basic structural unit is a layer composed of two silica tetrahedral sheets with a central octahedral sheet. The tips of all the tetrahedrons in each silica sheet point toward the center of the unit and are combined with the octahedral sheet in a single layer with a suitable replacement of hydroxyls by oxygens. The unit is the same as that for montmorillonite *except* that some of the silicons are always replaced by aluminums, and the resultant charge deficiency is balanced by potassium ions. In many of the well-crystallized micas one-fourth of the silicons are replaced by aluminums. The unit layers extend indefinitely in the *a* and *b* direction and are stacked in the *c* direction. The potassium ions occur between unit layers where they just fit into the hexagonal perforations in the surface of the oxygen layer. Adjacent layers are stacked in such a way that the potassium ion is equidistant from 12 oxygens, six of each layer (Fig. 2-8). The thickness of the silicate unit is approximately 10 A.

The micas may be dioctahedral or trioctahedral, and there is considerable possible variation in the population of octahedral positions and also possible variations in the manner of stacking of the silicate layers above each other. Thus, muscovite is dioctahedral with a structural formula $(OH)_4K_2(Si_6Al_2)Al_4O_{20}$, whereas biotite micas are trioctahedral with octahedral positions populated mostly by magnesium and iron. There are many polymorphic variations of biotite due to variations in the number of silicate layers per unit cell and the manner of stacking of the silicate layers (Hendricks and Jefferson, 1939).

Illite clay minerals appear to differ from the well-crystallized micas in having relatively less replacement of aluminum for silicon, less potassium, and some randomness in stacking of the silicate layers. Also, a small amount of water may be present between the silicate layers. Whether this apparent difference is a consequence of a difference in the composition of the silicate units or of interlayering of montmorillonite between the mica layers (see Mixed-layer Minerals, page 28) cannot in every instance be determined, but it appears very likely that both situations may prevail.

The illite clay minerals frequently occur in extremely small particles mixed with other clay mineral constituents so that the polymorphic form cannot be determined. In cases where the crystallinity is of a higher grade and the particle sizes are larger, the polymorphic form can be determined, and such determinations have indicated that most illites are dioctahedral, although trioctahedral forms have been identified. Glauconite commonly contains a dioctahedral illite with a fairly specific composition. Much material described as glauconite also contains an expandable component in a mixed-layer assemblage with the illite.

The structure of illite differs from that of montmorillonite in several important ways. The charge deficiency due to substitutions per unit layer is about 1.30 to 1.50 for illite as compared with about 0.65 for montmorillonite. The seat of this charge deficiency in illite is largely in the silica sheet and therefore close to the surface of the unit layers, whereas in montmorillonite it is frequently, perhaps chiefly, in the octahedral sheet at the center of the unit layer. Also in the case of illite the balancing cation between the unit layers is chiefly or entirely potassium.

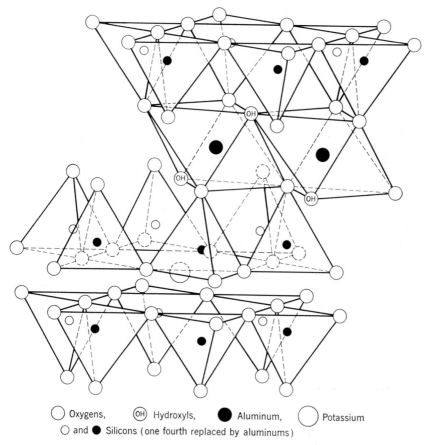

○ Oxygens,   ⓞₕ Hydroxyls,   ● Aluminum,   ○ Potassium
○ and ● Silicons (one fourth replaced by aluminums)

Fig. 2-8. Diagrammatic sketch of the structure of muscovite, after Jackson and West (1930).

Because of these differences the unit layers of the illite structure are relatively fixed in position, so that polar ions cannot enter between them and cause expansion. Also the interlayer balancing cations are not exchangeable except as they occur at the edges of the layers.

It is conceivable that all gradations can exist between illite and well-crystallized micas on the one hand and montmorillonite on the other hand. Data are not yet at hand to settle this point positively, but it is noteworthy that the illites so far studied in detail have shown similar and distinct attributes rather than complete gradational variations with muscovite or biotite.

It appears likely that complete gradational forms exist between illite and a clay mineral which expands as does montmorillonite. The substantially complete removal of potassium from illites would remove the bonding force holding the silicate layers together so that expansion might be possible. However, such material, which has been called *degraded illite*, would not be expected to possess all of the properties of montmorillonites in which the charge deficiency was less and the substitutions causing this charge deficiency were in the octahedral rather than the tetrahedral part of the structure. Such degraded illite, for example, would be expected to show less ready dispersion, higher adsorptive capacity for cations, and a greater tendency to fix any available potassium with the loss of the expanding property than would montmorillonite.

Electron micrographs of illite show generally small, poorly defined flakes commonly grouped in irregular aggregates without any distinct outline. Many of the flakes have a diameter of 0.1 to 0.3 μ, but larger particles up to several microns in diameter can occasionally be seen under the microscope in thin sections of illitic clays.

When placed in water the illite particles tend to disaggregate considerably in the poorly crystallized varieties and only slightly in the well-crystallized variety. The disaggregation is by cleavage between the silicate units. The range of the ease of cleavage varies from about that of montmorillonite in the degraded variety to about that of kaolinite in the fairly well-crystallized illite.

In a few instances, electron micrographs have revealed flakes of illite with a hexagonal outline, and Weaver (1953) has reported elongate lath-shaped units of the mineral.

Chlorite Minerals

The structure of the true chlorites consists of alternate mica-like and brucite-like layers (Pauling, 1930; McMurchy, 1934; Brindley and Robinson, 1951) (Fig. 2-9). The layers are continuous in the *a* and *b* dimensions and are stacked in the *c* direction with basal cleavage between the layers. The mica-like layers are trioctahedral with the general composition $(OH)_4(Si \cdot Al)_8(Mg \cdot Fe)_6O_{20}$. The brucite-like layer has the general composition $(Mg \cdot Al)_6(OH)_{12}$. The mica layers are unbalanced by the substitution of aluminum for silicon, and this deficiency of charge is balanced by an excess charge in the brucite sheet as a consequence of substitutions of aluminum for magnesium.

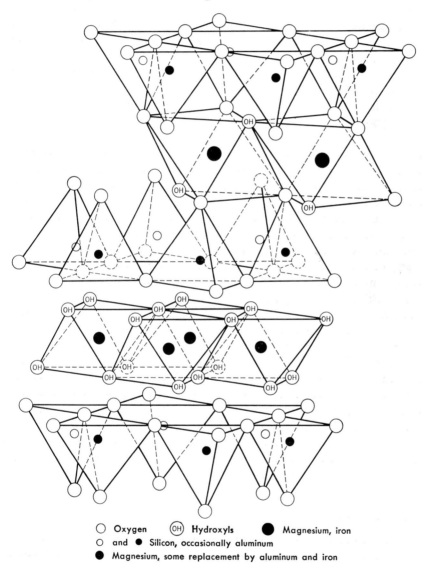

○ Oxygen   ⊙ Hydroxyls   ● Magnesium, iron
○ and ● Silicon, occasionally aluminum
● Magnesium, some replacement by aluminum and iron

Fig. 2-9. Diagrammatic sketch of the structure of chlorite, after McMurchy (1934).

Various members of the chlorite group differ from each other in the kind and amount of substitutions within the brucite layer and the tetrahedral and octahedral positions of the mica layer. They also differ in the detailed orientation of successive octahedral and tetrahedral layers, in the relation of the mica to the brucite layers, and in the stacking of successive chlorite units.

Clay mineral chlorites are relatively poorly organized and fine grained, with the consequence that the polymorphic form of the mineral frequently cannot be determined. Most clay mineral chlorites are trioctahedral, but some dioctahedral forms have been identified. Also in the clay mineral chlorites there frequently appears to be considerable substitution of iron for magnesium in the brucite layers. In general, in the clay mineral chlorites the organization of the brucite layer appears to be poorer and the stacking sequence appears to be less regular than in the well-crystallized forms. It is of importance to observe that the thickness of the layer consisting of a mica and brucite sheet is 14 A, which is just about twice that of kaolinite, with the consequence that it is often extremely difficult to differentiate between kaolinite and chlorite on the basis of X-ray diffraction data.

Clay mineral chlorite appears to occur always in mixtures with other clay minerals which has hampered the study of the attributes of the mineral. It has, for example, made it difficult to determine whether many of the attributes of clay mineral chlorite are a consequence of its being a mixed-layer assemblage or are characteristics of the mineral itself.

As in the case of illite, degraded chlorite has been reported in which the brucite part of the structure is disrupted and the cation removed (e.g., by weathering) to varying degrees. Also as in the case of degraded illite, such chlorite may develop some expanding characteristics. Whether such degraded chlorite is actually a mixed-layer structure or one in which there is random and partial destruction of the brucite layer cannot be determined in every case, but undoubtedly both conditions exist.

Since the mineral occurs in mixtures, little is known concerning its dispersibility or any customary size or shape of its particles. It appears likely, however, that the statements made concerning the dispersibility and size of the illite particles would also apply to clay mineral chlorite.

Nelson (1954) and Nelson and Roy (1958) have indicated the existence of a trioctahedral kaolin-type $MgO\text{-}Al_2O_3\text{-}SiO_2\text{-}H_2O$ structure with a 7-A series of basal reflections, which they call septechlorite. Moderate heating of the mineral causes the development of 14-A reflections. This mineral is reported in clays, but information concerning its occurrence is extremely scant.

Vermiculite

Analyses have shown the frequent presence in clay materials of the mineral with a *c*-axis dimension of 14 A which does not expand when treated with polar molecules but collapses to about 10 A on heating. The particle, thus, has some of the structural characteristics of chlorite and also some of montmorillonite. Its attributes are similar to those of large crystalline units of vermiculite; hence, it has been so designated.

The mineral is composed of silicate units of the type found in micas stacked one above the other in the *c*-axis direction and having a net negative charge deficiency similar to that found in the chlorite mineral. The charge deficiency is balanced by magnesium ions occurring between the silicate layers. The magnesium ions are hydrated; that is, they are surrounded by water molecules. The structure is, therefore, like that of chlorite except that the interlayer magnesium ions are hydrated rather than occurring in a brucite structure. The organization of the water around the magnesium ions and the relatively large charge on the lattice as compared with montmorillonite appear to prevent the expansion of the mineral when treated with polar molecules. The interlayer water is, however, easily driven off when heated to temperatures of the order of 100°C which permits the mineral to collapse to about 10 A like montmorillonite, but unlike chlorite (Gruner, 1934; Hendricks and Jefferson, 1938; Walker, 1951).

The magnesium between the silicate layers is replaceable, and the *c*-axis dimension can be varied by replacing the magnesium with some other cation. Also by proper selection of an interlayer cation the expandable character of the mineral can be enhanced (Barshad, 1949).

In clay materials vermiculite occurs in extremely small particles mixed with other clay minerals and frequently in a mixed-layer assemblage. Its specific characteristics are difficult or impossible to determine. The ease of dispersion and any general character of the shape and size of the vermiculite particles, therefore, are not known.

Attapulgite-Palygorskite-Sepiolite

The structure of attapulgite was first studied by DeLapparent (1938, 1941) and later in greater detail by Bradley (1940). According to Bradley, attapulgite consists of double silica chains running parallel to the *c* axis with the chains linked together through oxygens at their longitudinal edges. The apexes of the tetrahedrons in successive chains point in opposite directions. The linked chains, therefore, form a kind of double-ribbed sheet with two rows of tetrahedral apexes at alternate intervals in the top and bottom of the sheet. The ribbed sheets are arranged so that the apexes of successive sheets point together, and the sheets are held together by aluminums and/or magnesiums in octahedral coordination between the apex oxygens of successive sheets (Fig. 2-10). The octahedral layer is similar to that in the layer clay minerals but is continuous in only one direction. The octahedral layer is completed by central hydroxyls and by OH_2 groups at the open sides. The mineral has good cleavage parallel to (110) caused by the weak link through oxygens of the silica chains in the ribbed layer. Chains of water molecules running parallel to the c axis fill the interstices between the amphibole chains. The structure is balanced, and the composition of the ideal cell is $(OH_2)_4(OH)_2Mg_5Si_8O_{20} \cdot 4H_2O$. Bradley (1940) points out that substitution of aluminum for either magnesium, silicon, or both should weaken the structure, so that it appears doubtful that extensive replacement takes place and an aluminum end member would not be expected.

The structure can be visualized by considering it as a bundle of lath-shaped units tied together at their long edges in a regular fashion. The

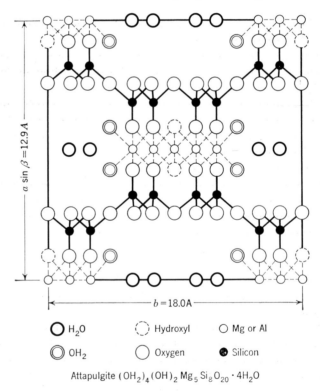

Attapulgite $(OH_2)_4(OH)_2Mg_5Si_8O_{20} \cdot 4H_2O$

Fig. 2-10. Schematic presentation of the structure of attapulgite, after Bradley (1940).

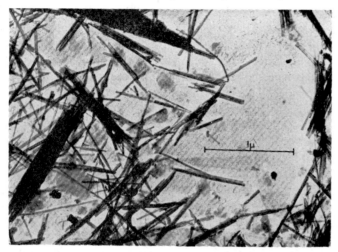

Fig. 2-11.   Electron micrograph of attapulgite, Attapulgus, Georgia, courtesy of T. F. Bates.

exterior of such a bundle of laths would have a plateau-and-channel or gutter appearance and the interior would be composed of an alternation of solid laths and elongate channels of rectangular cross section.

The structure of sepiolite has recently been described by Nagy and Bradley (1955). It is similar in its general attributes to that of attapulgite, differing essentially in the dimension of the laths and in the replacements within the structure. In sepiolite the laths are about 50 per cent wider than in attapulgite. Also in sepiolite there is very little replacement of either the magnesium or silicon ions.

The literature contains frequent descriptions of clays which appear to be composed of an elongate unit with the characters just described but which show substantial variations in their composition of aluminum, magnesium, and silica. Such materials have, in the older literature, been described as palygorskites (Caillere and Henin, 1951). The exact nature of such material is in many cases unknown.

Attapulgite frequently occurs associated with varying amounts of montmorillonite and possibly other clay minerals, so that there is the possibility that many of the materials described as palygorskites are mixtures of clay minerals.

Electron micrographs (Fig. 2-11) reveal that these clay minerals occur in bundles of lath-shaped units. When such clays are dispersed in water there is a tendency for the lath-shaped units to separate into smaller bundles by cleavage along the edges where the laths are joined together. The amount of such split-up of laths depends on the amount of work and the vigor of the work applied in the disaggregation. With considerable application of energy it is possible to disaggregate such clays into extremely small units. This is perhaps true to a greater extent for attapulgite-sepiolite than for any of the other clay minerals, so that for these clays to a greater extent than for any other clay minerals a particle-size analysis reveals only the degree of disaggregation and little concerning the size of the particles in the natural clay. Electron micrographs (Fig. 2-11) frequently reveal bundles with diameters of 50 to 100 A and lengths of 4 to 5 μ.

Mixed-layer Minerals

Many clay materials are composed of more than one clay mineral, and the minerals may be mixed in several ways. The mixture may be of discrete clay mineral particles in which there is no preferred geometric orientation of one particle with respect to its neighboring particles. Another common type of mixing is the interstratification of the layer clay minerals in which the individual layers are as thick as a single or a few silicate sheets. These "mixed-layer structures" are the consequence of the fact that the layers of the different clay minerals are similar, all being composed of silica tetrahedral layers and closely packed octahedral layers of oxygens and hydroxyl groups. Mixed-layer structures as stable as those composed of a single kind of layer are therefore possible.

Mixed-layer structures are of two different types. The interstratification may be regular, that is, the stacking along the c axis may be a regular repetition of the different layers. In such cases the resulting structure has distinctive characteristics unlike those of the component layers, and the assemblage is described as a distinctive species. An example of the regular mixed-layer mineral is chlorite composed of a regular alternation of mica and brucite layers. The other kind of mixed-layer structure is due to a random, irregular stratification of layers in which there is no uniform repetition of them. The mixing may be of two or more types of layer units with alternations of random numbers and consequently thicknesses of the different layer units (Gruner, 1934; Hendricks and Teller, 1942; Bradley, 1945).

Mixed-layers of illite and montmorillonite and of chlorite and vermiculite are particularly common. Clay mineral occurrences which are probably mixtures of illite and kaolinite have also been described (DeLapparent, 1934). Since random mixed-layers have an inherent variability, they cannot be given specific names; they can only be designated as mixtures of the layers involved.

The study of mixed layers is difficult, and in many cases, particularly in older analyses, their presence has not been recognized. The literature contains many references to questionable clay mineral species, and it is quite certain that in many instances such materials are mixed-layer assemblages. Careful X-ray diffraction studies will reveal the presence of mixed-layer structures and frequently indicate also the nature and relative abundance of the units that are mixed. Other analytical techniques in general do no more than hint sometimes at the presence of mixed-layer structures.

In general, the dispersibility of mixed-layer assemblages is probably relatively great in that the mixing would cause a certain reduction in the strength of the bond between particles so that they would be expected to be more cleavable into thinner units. This would be the case particularly when one of the components of such a mixed-layer assemblage was an expansible mineral. It seems obvious that a small amount of such expansible material interlayered with a nonexpansible component would greatly enhance the ease of splitting of the unit and its dispersion.

ION EXCHANGE

Clay minerals have the property of sorbing certain anions and cations and retaining these in an exchangeable state; i.e., they are exchangeable for other anions or cations by treatment with such ions in a water solution (the exchange reaction also takes place sometimes in a nonaqueous environment). The exchange reaction is stoichiometric. The exchangeable ions are held around the outside of the silica-alumina clay mineral structural units, and the exchange reaction generally does not affect the structure of the silica-alumina packet. A simple and well-known example of the ion-exchange reaction is the softening of water by the use of zeolites, permutites, or carbon exchangers. For a more detailed consideration of this property of the clay minerals see Kelley (1948), Marshall (1949), and Grim (1953).

The property of exchange capacity is measured in terms of milliequivalents per gram or more frequently per 100 grams. One equivalent of sodium expressed as Na_2O would be a combining weight of 31, and 1 meq per 100 g would be equal to 0.031 per cent Na_2O. Exchange capacities are determined at pH 7.

More information is available regarding cation exchange than anion exchange. In clay materials the common exchangeable cations are calcium, magnesium, hydrogen, potassium, ammonium, and sodium, frequently in about that order of general relative abundance. The common anions in clay materials are sulfate, chlorine, phosphate, and nitrate. The general relative abundance of the anions is not yet known.

The property of ion exchange is of great fundamental and practical importance in the investigation of the clay materials. In the application of clay mineralogy it is important because the nature of the exchangeable ion may influence substantially the physical properties of the material. Thus, a clay material carrying sodium frequently has very different plastic properties than material the same in every way except that calcium is the exchangeable cation.

Cation Exchange

The range of the cation-exchange capacity of the clay minerals is given in Table 2-1, after Grim (1953).

TABLE 2-1

CATION-EXCHANGE CAPACITY OF CLAY MINERALS
(in Milliequivalents per 100 Grams)

Kaolinite	3– 15
Halloysite $2H_2O$	5– 10
Halloysite $4H_2O$	10– 40
Montmorillonite	80–150
Illite	10– 40
Vermiculite	100–150
Chlorite	10– 40
Sepiolite-Attapulgite	20– 30

It follows from the consideration of the factors influencing cation-exchange capacity that there is no single capacity value that is characteristic of a given group of clay minerals. A range of capacity must be shown for each group.

The clay minerals are not the only components of clay materials that have cation-exchange capacity. All inorganic materials of extreme fineness have a small cation-exchange capacity as a result of broken bonds around their edges. This capacity increases as the particle size decreases, but even with the small size in which nonclay minerals occur in clays the exchange capacity is generally insignificant. An exception is the zeolite minerals, which are occasionally found in some clays and have cation-exchange capacities of the order of 100 to 300 meq per 100 g. Some organic materials having cation-exchange capacities ranging from 150 to 500 meq per 100 g are reported for some soils. In general, organic material with high exchange capacities is restricted to Recent sediments and soils.

There are three causes of cation-exchange capacity of the clay minerals:

1. Broken bonds around the edges of the silica-alumina units would give rise to unsatisfied charges which could be balanced by adsorbed cations. The number of broken bonds, hence the exchange capacity due to this cause, would increase as the particle size decreased. In

kaolinite and halloysite minerals broken bonds are the major cause of exchange capacity. In the illite, chlorite and sepiolite-attapulgite minerals broken bonds are an important cause of exchange capacity. In montmorillonites and vermiculites broken bonds are responsible for a relatively small portion (20 per cent) of the cation-exchange capacity.

2. Substitutions within the lattice of trivalent aluminum for quadrivalent silicon in the tetrahedral sheet and of ions of lower valence, particularly magnesium, for trivalent aluminum in the octahedral sheet result in unbalanced charges in the structural units of some of the clay minerals. In montmorillonite and vermiculite substitutions within the lattice cause about 80 per cent of the total cation-exchange capacity. In the illite, chlorite, and sepiolite-attapulgite minerals a small amount of the exchange capacity may result from lattice substitutions.

3. The hydrogen of exposed hydroxyls may be replaced by a cation which would be exchangeable. Some hydroxyl groups would be exposed around the broken edges of all the clay minerals, and cation exchange due to broken bonds would, in part at least, be replacement of the hydrogens of exposed hydroxyls. There is considerable doubt that this factor is a substantial cause of the cation-exchange reaction since it seems quite certain that the hydrogen of the hydroxyl would not normally be replaceable under the conditions of the exchange reaction.

In the clay minerals in which cation exchange results from broken bonds, the exchangeable cations are held around the edges of the flakes and elongate units. In the clay minerals in which the exchange reaction is due to lattice substitutions, the cations are held mostly on the basal-plane surfaces. In masses of clay with relatively small amounts of adsorbed water, i.e., with no more water than is required to develop plasticity, it is likely that the adsorbed cations are held directly in contact with, or at least very close to, the clay mineral surface. In clay-water systems in which the amount of water is at least greater than that required for the plastic state the exchangeable cations may be at greater distances from the clay mineral surfaces and separated from them by water molecules. In any given system of this kind the position of all the exchangeable cations with respect to the clay mineral surfaces is not the same, and even the relative positions of all of the same sort of cations probably will not be the same; some cations of a given type will be closer to the clay mineral surface than others. Only a portion of the adsorbed cations is likely to be ionized in a water system. Marshall (1949) has summarized available data on this subject showing that the percentage of the cation ionized depends on the particular clay mineral, the amount of water, the nature of the cations, and the relative concentration of the cations. The complete structural implications of ionization studies have not yet been worked out, but it seems clear that a single cation can be held by a given clay mineral with different bonding energies with the bonding energy depending in part on the position of the adsorbed cation on the clay mineral surface.

There is considerable difference of opinion as to whether or not the adsorbed cations are hydrated, i.e., surrounded by a definite envelope of water molecules. It seems likely that the matter of hydration depends on the nature of the cation, the clay mineral, and the abundance of water present.

The rate of the cation-exchange reaction varies with the clay mineral, with the concentration of the cations, and with the nature and concentration of the anions. In general, the reaction for kaolinite is most rapid, being almost instantaneous. It is slower for montmorillonites and attapulgite and requires even longer time, perhaps hours, to reach completion for the illites and chlorites.

Very early studies of cation exchange showed that under a given set of conditions various cations were not equally replaceable and did not have the same replacing power. Way (1850) in the earliest studies of this phenomena concluded that the replacing power of the common ions increased in the following order: sodium, potassium, calcium, magnesium, and ammonium. This means, for example, that in general calcium will more easily replace sodium than sodium will replace calcium. As the cation-exchange reaction was studied, it became obvious that there was no single, universal replaceability series. The series varies depending on the experimental conditions, on the anion involved, and on the clay mineral. Thus, there is a somewhat different replaceability series for each of the clay minerals.

The nature of the exchangeable cation in a clay material is indicated frequently by a pH determination. Thus a pH value of about 9 suggests sodium; of 7.5, calcium; of less than 7, hydrogen. It should be noted that all acid clays are likely also to carry iron and/or aluminum in exchange positions. Attempts to produce hydrogen clays in the laboratory result in clays also carrying aluminum and/or iron, which is very difficult to replace.

Some cations adsorbed by certain clay minerals in exchange reactions are very difficult to replace again. For example, potassium adsorbed by degraded illite may be fixed with consequent regeneration of the illite.

Anion Exchange

Investigation of anion-exchange reactions is very difficult, primarily because of the possibility that the clay minerals will decompose in the course of the reaction. Thus, in studies of the adsorption of phosphate by kaolinite there has been considerable argument as to whether many of the results observed are due to adsorption, to replacement of hydroxyl ions in the kaolinite by phosphate ions, or to reaction between the phosphate and alumina produced by some destruction of the kaolinite lattice taking place during the reaction.

There seem to be several possible explanations for the anion-exchange reactions on the clay minerals.

1. The reaction may be due to the presence of broken bonds around the edges of the clay mineral particles. It would be expected that broken bonds would provide as many negative as positive positions around the edges of the clay mineral particles so that anion-exchange capacity due to this cause would equal the cation-exchange capacity.

2. The hydroxyls on the surface of the clay mineral particles apparently can enter into exchange reactions as shown by McAuliffe et al. (1947) and Dickman and Bray (1941).

Hendricks (personal communication) has shown that another factor in anion exchange is the geometry of the anion in relation to the geometry of the clay mineral structural units. Anions such as phosphate, arsenate, and borate, which have about the same size and geometry as the silica tetrahedron, may be adsorbed by fitting on to the edge of the silica tetrahedral sheet and growing as extensions of these sheets. Other anions with a geometry which does not permit them to fit would not be expected to be adsorbed for this reason. Anion exchange due to this cause and also due to the replacement of hydroxyls would provide anion capacity unrelated to cation-exchange capacity and could be quite large. Table 2-2 gives anion-exchange capacities for some of the clay minerals.

TABLE 2-2

ANION-EXCHANGE CAPACITIES
(in Milliequivalents per 100 Grams)
(After Hofmann et al., 1956)

Montmorillonite, Geisenheim	31
Montmorillonite, Wyoming	23
Beidellite, Unterrupsroth	21
Nontronite, Untergriesbach	20
Nontronite, Pfreimdtal	12
Saponite, Groschlattengrun	21
Vermiculite, South Africa	4
Kaolinite (colloidal)	20.2
Kaolinite, Melos	13.3
Kaolinite, Schnaittenbach	6.6

Schoen (1953) has presented similar data indicating that an average ratio of cation- to anion-exchange capacity is about 0.5 for kaolinite, 2.3 for illite, and 6.7 for montmorillonite. The relatively larger anion capacity for kaolinite is attributed to the larger number of exposed hydroxyls, and the relatively larger cation capacity of illite and montmorillonite is attributed to the influence of lattice substitutions.

It has been suggested (Schofield, 1940 and 1949) that there may be anion-exchange positions on the surface of the clay minerals due to unbalanced charges resulting from replacements within the lattice. It is difficult to see how this could be since positive and negative deficiencies within the lattice would tend to balance each other, and there would be either a positive or negative deficiency but not both. Available data suggest that the charge deficiency is negative rather than positive.

Information is not at hand regarding the relative replaceability of various anions for the different clay minerals. It is known that some adsorbed anions are fixed by the clay minerals in an unexchangeable form, but it is difficult to distinguish simple fixation from reactions leading to the partial destruction of the lattice and the formation of a new compound, e.g., aluminum phosphate from kaolinite.

CLAY-WATER SYSTEMS

This subject is concerned with water which can be held by clay materials only at relatively low temperatures and which is driven off by heating to about 100 to 150°C. The water lost at such temperatures may be classed in three categories: (1) the water in pores, on the surfaces, and around the edges of discrete particles of the minerals composing clay materials; (2) in the case of vermiculite, montmorillonite, and the hydrated form of halloysite, the interlayer water between the unit silicate layers of these minerals which causes their swelling and expansion characteristics; and (3) in the case of the sepiolite-attapulgite minerals, the water which occurs within the tabular openings between the elongate structural units. Water of type 1 requires generally very little energy for its removal, and drying at temperatures only a little above ordinary room temperatures is adequate for its substantially complete elimination. Water of types 2 and 3 requires definite energy for its complete removal. In the case of the hydrated form of halloysite, drying at room temperature is adequate to remove most of the interlayer water, but higher temperatures are required for total removal. In the case of vermiculite and montmorillonite minerals, temperatures approaching at least 100°C are necessary for substantially complete elimination of interlayer water. The rate of removal of the interlayer water increases as the applied temperature increases. In the case of halloysite, the reaction is not reversible, and the hydrated mineral ordinarily cannot be formed again.

Vermiculites and montmorillonites rehydrate with difficulty if the dehydration is absolutely complete but with ease if only a trace of water is allowed to remain between the unit layers. The water in the channels of the sepiolite-attapulgite minerals is lost at about the same temperatures as the interlayer water of the layer clay minerals. The channel water is regained readily if removal is by drying only at low temperatures. The energy necessary for dehydration and the precise temperatures at which it occurs are shown for the various clay mineral groups by differential thermal analyses in Figs. 3-12 to 3-16.

Langmuir (1917), Goldschmidt (1926), and many others have presented evidence showing that the water held directly on the surface of the clay minerals is in a physical state different from that of liquid water. The specific characteristics of this water which delimit it from ordinary water would probably be restricted ordinarily to relatively short distances from the clay particle surfaces, generally of the order of 3 to 10 molecular layers of water, i.e., 8 to 28 A. However, in some cases it appears that considerably greater thicknesses can develop and that the possible thickness of the nonordinary water can vary a good deal even for a given clay mineral. Also, the transition from nonordinary water to ordinary water can be abrupt or gradual depending on the nature of the clay mineral and the character of the ions adsorbed on the clay mineral surfaces.

It appears certain that the possible thickness of the nonordinary water or "nonliquid" water is relatively small on irregular surfaces, such as those around the edges of clay mineral particles, and relatively large on the flat surfaces of the clay minerals. It follows that the water in pores would be substantially liquid water with nonliquid water forming only a thin film on the surface of the pores and where adjacent clay mineral particles come together.

There is no general agreement as to the precise nature of this nonliquid water. However, it is generally agreed that some form of organization of the water molecules exists in the water immediately adsorbed on clay mineral surfaces. Hendricks and Jefferson (1938) have suggested the configuration illustrated in Figs. 2-12 and 2-13; it is based on an orientation of water molecules with a structure tied to the configuration of the oxygens or hydroxyls in the basal surface layers of the unit cells of the clay minerals. A water layer is composed of water molecules joined into hexagonal groups of an extended hexagonal net. This arrangement is partly a result of a tetrahedral distribution of charge about a water molecule, two corners of the tetrahedron being occupied by hydrogen atoms and the other two corners by an excess of electrons. Each side of the hexagon must correspond to a hydrogen bond, with the hydrogen of one water molecule being directed toward the negative charge of the neighboring molecule. One-fourth of the hydrogen atoms, or a hydrogen atom of half of the water molecules, are not involved in bonding within the net. The net is tied to the surface of the clay minerals by the attraction between those hydrogen atoms not involved in bonding within the net and the surface oxygen layer of the clay mineral unit. When the surface of the clay mineral contains hydroxyl groups, part of the hydroxyls are free for bonding through hydrogen to oxygen atoms in the water layer. The net has just the *a* and *b* dimensions of the silicate-layer minerals, if the separation of the oxygen atoms of the water molecules is about 3 A in projection. It is assumed that the oxygen atoms are in one plane, and in this configuration there is relatively loose packing of the water molecules, there being four water molecules per molecular layer per unit cell of the clay minerals instead of six as would be the case in the close packing. The stability of such a layer of water molecules would arise from the geometrical relationship to the oxygen atoms or hydroxyl groups of the silicate framework.

The structure suggested by Hendricks and Jefferson gives the density of the adsorbed water as less than 1. Density values greater and less than 1 have been recorded in the literature (Grim, 1953), and precise

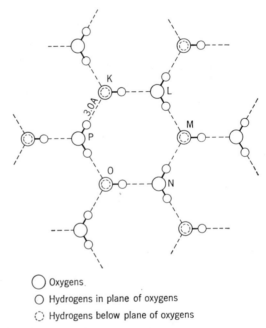

○ Oxygens.
○ Hydrogens in plane of oxygens
◌ Hydrogens below plane of oxygens

Fig. 2-12. Arrangement of oxygens and hydrogens in water net, after Hendricks and Jefferson (1938).

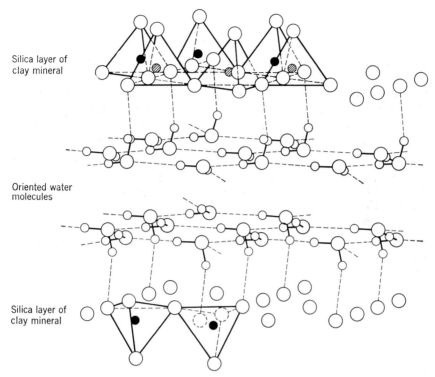

Silica layer of
clay mineral

Oriented water
molecules

Silica layer of
clay mineral

Fig. 2-13. Configuration of water net proposed by Hendricks and Jefferson (1938) showing the binding through hydrogens to the adjacent clay mineral surfaces.

density measurements, when they can be determined in the future, will provide strong evidence for or against the validity of this suggested structure of the adsorbed water.

The ions adsorbed on the surface of the clay minerals may affect the adsorbed water in several ways as follows: (1) they may serve as a bond to hold the clay mineral particles together or to limit the distance to which they can be separated; (2) the adsorbed cation may become hydrated, i.e., develop an envelope of water molecules which might interfere with or influence the configuration of adjacent adsorbed water molecules; (3) the size and geometry of the adsorbed ion would influence the manner in which it would fit into the configuration of adsorbed water molecules and thereby influence the nature of the configuration of the adsorbed water molecules and the extent to which the configuration could develop.

Additional information concerning the configuration of the water molecules in the adsorbed layers is given by Grim (1953), and the matter is further discussed in Chaps. 3 and 4 of this volume.

CHANGES ON HEATING

As indicated in the previous section, when the clay minerals are heated to just above room temperatures, they lose pore water and adsorbed water. Between 400 and 700°C the hydroxyl structural water is lost. Within this same temperature interval the structure of the clay minerals may be somewhat disrupted or altered. By heating to temperatures of the order of 900°C, the clay mineral structure is destroyed which is followed in some instances by the fusion of the material. More often, following the loss of the structure of the clay minerals, there is a considerable temperature interval in which new crystalline phases develop prior to the vitrification and fusion of the minerals.

The changes taking place on firing the clay minerals are vital in considering the fired ceramic properties of the clay minerals, and they are considered in detail in Chap. 3.

CLAY MINERAL—ORGANIC REACTIONS

It has been known for many years that clay mineral–organic complexes can be formed by ion-exchange reactions. Thus, in 1924 Smith reacted organic bases and their salts with montmorillonites and presented evidence that the reaction was one of ion exchange. Gieseking and Jenny (1936) and later Gieseking (1939) showed definitely that organic ions enter into cation-exchange reactions with the clay minerals, particularly with montmorillonite. Depending on the size and nature of the organic cation, the clay mineral particle may be completely clad with organic molecules 1 or more molecular layers in thickness. Such organic-clad clay mineral particles are hydrophobic and oleophilic. They may be polymerized with a variety of organic compounds.

It has also been known for many years that clay mineral–organic complexes can be formed by reactions of the clay minerals with polar organic compounds. Early work of Hofmann et al. (1934) and later work by Bradley (1945) and MacEwan (1944) showed definitely that nonionic organic molecules of polar character could be adsorbed by the clay minerals. The avidity of adsorption increases with the polarity and may be sufficient to replace adsorbed water. The polar molecules are thought to be held through hydrogen bonds. In the case of highly polar organic molecules, layers more than 1 molecule thick can be adsorbed on the basal planes of some clay minerals, for example montmorillonite.

Berger (1941) and later Deuel et al. (1950) have concluded that the exposed hydroxyls of clay mineral particles can enter into methylation reactions. Other investigators (Brown et al., 1952) have disputed this point, claiming that the reactions observed were not related to the clay mineral particles.

Clay mineral–organic reactions of ionic and polar compounds have been the subject of a vast amount of research in recent years. Grim (1953) has summarized much of these data and given references to the original work. Such reactions are of considerable importance in some utilizations of clay materials and are considered in later chapters of this volume.

There are other types of organic reactions with the clay minerals, such as take place in the decolorization of organic liquids, in the catalysis of organic compounds, in color reactions developing when some organic compounds and clay minerals are mixed (staining tests), and in the selective adsorption of certain organic molecules. These reactions may be of great practical importance. Unfortunately in many cases they are not well understood.

MISCELLANEOUS PROPERTIES

Grim (1953) has also summarized information on the miscellaneous properties of the clay minerals and given references to the original works supplying these data. Many properties, such as those concerned with optical and infrared characteristics, are particularly important for the identification of the clay minerals rather than for the commercial utilization of the materials. Other miscellaneous properties, such as solubility in acids and alkalies, which are pertinent to the utilization of clay materials, are considered in this volume under the appropriate heading of utilization.

ORIGIN AND OCCURRENCE

A vast literature exists concerning the origin and occurrence of the clay minerals. Grim (1953) has collected pertinent references and attempted to summarize them. His work should be consulted by anyone wishing to pursue the matter. In the following statements, only brief generalities will be presented as a background for later considerations.

Synthesis

All the clay minerals with the exception of attapulgite-sepiolite and possibly halloysite have been synthesized from mixtures of oxides at moderately low temperatures and pressures. Temperatures were of the order of a few hundred degrees centigrade and pressures were of the order of 100 atm or less. This work has shown in general that in alumina-silica systems without alkalies or alkaline earths and with silica to alumina ratios in the range of clay mineral compositions, kaolinite is formed. When potassium is added to such systems illite is formed, and when magnesium is added montmorillonite is formed at low concentrations; chlorite is formed when higher concentrations of the magnesium are added. In the presence of sodium a zeolite structure is formed. Calcium appears to have little influence on the direction of the synthesis; although possibly it favors the development of a montmorillonite-type structure.

Recently Henin and Robichet (1953) have shown that the clay minerals can be synthesized at ordinary temperatures and pressures if the oxides are mixed together very slowly and in great dilution.

Hydrothermal Origin

It has been recognized for a long time that argillaceous alteration products due to hydrothermal action are frequently to be found as an aureole around metalliferous deposits. Such alteration products are also found associated with hot springs and geysers. The size of the alteration envelope may vary from a few feet to as much as 100 ft or more. All types of clay minerals except attapulgite-sepiolite have been found in such alteration aureoles. Frequently there is a zonal arrangement of the clay minerals around the source of the alteration with mica and kaolinite being close to the source and chlorite and montmorillonite being more distant.

Weathering and Soils

All types of clay minerals with the possible exception of attapulgite have been identified in various types of soils. The clay minerals may be formed or their character may be substantially altered by soil-forming processes. The character of the clay mineral found in a given soil depends on the nature of the parent material and also on the climate, topography, vegetation, and time during which these factors have operated. A major way in which climate, topography, and vegetation influence weathering processes is by their control of the character and direction of movement of water through the alteration zone. The character of the parent material is relatively more important in earlier stages of weathering than where the weathering has continued for long periods of time.

Where climate and topography are such that the dominant movement of water is downward through the alteration zone, any alkalies or alkaline earths present in the parent material tend to be leached out. Primary minerals containing these components are broken down; in the case of the micas they are first degraded and then broken down. If leaching is intense following the removal of the alkalies and alkaline earths, the aluminum or silica may be removed from the alteration zone depending on the pH of the downward-seeping waters. The pH of such water is determined in turn by the climate and cover of vegetation. Under warm, humid conditions with long wet and dry periods, the surface organic material tends to be completely oxidized so that the downward-seeping waters are neutral or perhaps slightly on the alkaline side, with a consequence that silica is removed and alumina and iron left behind and concentrated. The result is a lateritic type of soil. Under more temperate conditions where the surface organic material is not completely oxidized, the downward-seeping water contains organic acids so that R_2O_3 components are leached with the silica being left behind and with the development of podsolic types of soils.

Under the leaching conditions in early stages, the weathering products are likely to be somewhat degraded illites and chlorites and expansible clay minerals with the later development of kaolinite and finally oxides and hydroxides as leaching becomes more complete.

In dry areas where the dominant movement of water is not downward so that leaching does not take place, the alkalies and alkaline earths remain close to the surface with the development of chernozem types of soils which contain illite, chlorite, and montmorillonite clay minerals. In extremely dry desert areas where the concentration of magnesium is particularly high, the formation of attapulgite has been reported (Millot, 1949), and it is believed to form under such an environment.

Weathering processes, especially where there is substantial vertical movement of moisture, tend to develop a sequence of horizons within the zone of alteration. The horizons frequently grade sharply into adjacent ones and have thicknesses measured in inches or a few feet; although where the weathering process has continued for long periods of time the horizons may develop to thicknesses of many feet. The horizons show differences in the degree of breakdown of the parent material, in the kind and relative abundance of secondary mineral components, in particle-size distribution, in organic material, and/or in pH and character of alkali and alkaline-earth content. The vertical movement of water causes a movement of soil constituents, thereby developing the sequence of varying horizons. Obviously the profile development must be taken into account in any investigation of the origin or properties of soils. It means, for example, that a soil or weathered material in general cannot be investigated by the collection of single samples of the weathered material and the parent material. Rather, a sequence of samples must be

investigated from the surface down in order to determine the true nature of the properties of the weathered material and the conditions of its formation.

Considerable experimentation has been carried out in the laboratory to duplicate the formation of clay minerals from feldspars, pyroxenes, etc., by weathering processes. In many cases the amount of alteration product formed was so small that its precise identification was difficult. In general, such studies substantiated the conclusions derived from soil studies noted above.

Recent Sediments

Illite and chlorite appear to be the dominant clay mineral constituents in sediments accumulating at the present time in the seas. Montmorillonite is also present and in some areas, such as the Gulf of Mexico, it is an important component. Kaolinite is also commonly present, but usually in very small amounts. Halloysite has been reported in Recent marine sediments (McAllister, 1959). Attapulgite-sepiolite has not been reported in Recent marine sediments. There is considerable difference of opinion as to whether or not there is any change in the character of the clay minerals as they are transported from a fresh-water to a marine environment. The bulk of the evidence seems to indicate that in such a transition there is a definite regrading of the micas and also that illite and chlorite develop from montmorillonite. Apparently other more drastic changes in the clay mineral composition do sometimes take place slowly; however, the conditions which lead to such substantial transformations are not known (Grim, 1958).

Recent sediments accumulating under conditions other than those in the sea may have any clay mineral composition, except that under highly saline conditions in desert areas illite, chlorite, and/or attapulgite are likely to develop depending on the nature of the cation that is present. For example, attapulgite or chlorite will develop in the presence of magnesium depending on the concentration of the magnesium, with the latter mineral forming at the higher concentrations.

Ancient Sediments

Analyses of many ancient sediments over many parts of the world appear to indicate that montmorillonite is much less abundant in sediments older than the Mesozoic than in younger sediments (Grim, 1953). There is also a suggestion from available data that kaolinite is less abundant in very ancient sediments than in those deposited after about the Devonian. Stated another way, the very old argillaceous sediments are largely composed of illite and chlorite. Attapulgite and sepiolite have not been reported in sediments older than the Tertiary.

Material which can be classed as clay has been described containing any clay mineral composition. In some instances, the component is a single clay mineral, but more often there is a mixture of clay minerals. Materials which are described as shales because they are relatively hard and/or have a laminated character frequently are composed of illite and chlorite. Montmorillonite is a common component of many shales of Mesozoic and younger age. Kaolinite is a common component of some shales but usually in minor amounts.

Slates appear to be dominantly composed of illites and chlorites. These clay minerals generally have a relatively higher degree of crystallinity than when found in clays. Kaolinite has been reported in some slates and Fairbairn (1943) reports that kaolinitic slates have relatively low schistosity.

The clay minerals found in carbonate rocks appear to be chiefly illite and chlorite. Kaolinite and montmorillonite are sometimes present in small amounts; however, montmorillonite may be an important constituent in the younger carbonate rocks.

Kaolinite and illite have been reported in various coals. Insufficient data are available to indicate whether there is any general relationship between the nature of the clay mineral component and the character and/or age of the coals.

Millot (1949) and DeLapparent (1937) have shown that sepiolite-attapulgite minerals frequently occur in argillaceous sediments associated with ancient saline deposits. Montmorillonite, illite, and chlorite are also common components of such sediments.

Bentonite

The term bentonite was first applied by Knight (1898) to a particularly highly colloidal plastic clay found in the Cretaceous beds of Wyoming. It has the unique characteristic of swelling to several times its original volume when placed in water and of forming thixotropic gels with water even when the amount of clay is relatively small. It was subsequently shown by Hewett (1917) that this clay was formed by the alteration of volcanic ash in situ. Later, Ross and Shannon (1926) studied a number of clays which had been formed by the alteration of ash and redefined bentonite to limit it to clays produced by the alteration of volcanic ash in situ. They pointed out that such clays are largely composed of montmorillonite clay minerals and that they are generally highly colloidal and plastic. The term as now used by many mineralogists and geologists has no reference to the physical properties of the clay.

It is now known that the alteration of volcanic ash in situ generally leads to the formation of a clay material that is composed of montmorillonite. In some instances other clay minerals, such as illite or kaolinite, may also be present. It is also known that the alteration of some ash may lead to clay material composed of halloysite and allophane, apparently depending largely on the composition of the original ash; such components form when the ash has an exceedingly low content of alkalies and alkaline earths. The physical properties of such altered ash are quite different if the component is montmorillonite rather than allophane and halloysite, and it may be desirable to restrict the term "bentonite" to such alteration products which are composed of montmorillonite.

In bentonites composed of montmorillonite, the structural characteristics and composition of the montmorillonite may vary, and also the character of the exchangeable cation may vary. The physical properties of the bentonite will accordingly vary depending on the nature of the montmorillonite and the exchangeable cation. In some instances such clays may have relatively moderate colloidal and thixotropic properties. In commercial usage there has been a tendency to restrict the term to the highly colloidal varieties characteristic of some of the original material found in Wyoming. The term "sub-bentonite" has in some cases been applied to montmorillonite materials which had relatively lower colloidal properties than the Wyoming material.

Also, it should be pointed out that in some commercial usage it has been customary to apply the adjective "bentonitic" to clay materials with relatively high colloidal properties without any consideration as to the origin or composition of the material. Also, in some instances bentonitic has been applied where it was thought that the alteration of ash played a role in the origin of an argillaceous material. It would seem desirable to avoid the use of bentonitic and to apply it as suggested by Ross and Shannon (1926). This creates the difficulty of determining the origin of the clay, but volcanic materials altered in situ to clays usually have characteristics which make such determination fairly simple and definite.

As will be shown in later pages of this volume, bentonites have very wide and important usages. In about the last thirty years deposits of bentonite have been eagerly sought all over the world, and they have been found and described in a great many areas. They seem to be particularly abundant in formations of Upper Cretaceous and Middle Tertiary ages.

CLAY MINERAL ANALYSES

The clay mineral composition of clay materials may be determined on the basis of X-ray diffraction, dehydration characteristics, thermal reactions on heating (differential thermal analyses), optical properties, infrared adsorption spectra, staining reactions, etc.

Chemical analyses may contribute to clay mineral identifications; for example, K_2O suggests the presence of illite. Determinations of cation-exchange capacity may be valuable; for example, a capacity of the order of 100 meq per 100 g for inorganic components indicates the presence of montmorillonite or vermiculite. Electron micrographs may provide pertinent data in showing the presence of elongate tubular particles which indicate the presence of halloysite.

If the clay material to be analyzed is composed of a single clay mineral, any of the above methods will usually permit a positive identification. If the clay material is composed of a mixture of clay minerals, possibly also with other components, the analysis becomes more difficult and several procedures may be necessary to obtain a complete analysis.

Quantitative evaluations of the clay mineral composition can be made with an accuracy depending on the complexity of the mixture. In materials composed of a mixture of poorly organized clay minerals together with some mixed-layer assemblages, probably the best quantitative determinations to be hoped for at present would have an accuracy of the order of about 5 per cent.

The most satisfactory single procedure for the identification of the clay minerals is by means of X-ray diffraction. It is the only procedure presently available that is adequate to evaluate complex mixtures containing mixed-layer assemblages.

The difficulty with using X-ray diffraction for quantitative determinations arises from the impossibility of obtaining standards of pure clay minerals corresponding to the clay minerals in the samples to be analyzed. In a mixture the diffraction intensity of a component varies with its abundance; the diffraction intensity also varies somewhat with the particle size and the crystallinity of the mineral. Because one does not know generally the crystallinity of the components of a mixture, one cannot determine the diffraction intensity of the pure components found in such a mixture. This difficulty can in part be surmounted by the use of one of the components as an internal standard (Johns, Grim, and Bradley, 1954.)

A further difficulty in clay mineral identifications with X-ray diffraction arises from the fact that the *c*-axis dimension of chlorite is approximately twice that of kaolinite. The difficulty is particularly severe for chlorites which contain considerable iron because the first order, which would normally permit the differentiation of chlorite and kaolinite, has very low intensity for iron-rich chlorites. Undoubtedly, much material identified as kaolinite in older clay mineral analyses is actually chlorite. Frequently this difficulty can be avoided by the use of higher orders of basal reflections where a slight difference in the *c*-axis dimensions of these minerals becomes apparent (Bradley, 1954).

It is common practice in clay mineral analyses to prepare so-called oriented aggregates, i.e., large aggregates in which the extremely small clay mineral particles all are arranged so that their basal planes are about parallel. This is done by slurrying the clay material and allowing the component particles to settle on a flat surface. Such oriented aggregates are tremendously helpful because diffraction data obtained from them preferentially emphasize diffraction lines from basal planes so that the *c*-axis dimension of the components can be measured. The most diagnostic character of the clay minerals for their identification is their *c*-axis dimension. Such aggregates of a single clay mineral or a mixture of discrete particles of several clay minerals produce a series of uniformly spaced diffraction lines which readily reveal the *c*-axis dimension of the components. Mixed-layer assemblages which are composed of random interlayerings do not show such an integral series of basal reflection, and this can be used as a basis for identifying such assemblages.

If a mixed-layer assemblage is the sole component of a clay material, the character and relative abundance of the units which are mixed can usually be determined (Brown and MacEwan, 1951). If the clay material contains other clay minerals in addition to the mixed-layer assemblages, it may be possible to determine only the approximate abundance of the mixed-layer assemblage and the probable nature of the components that are mixed.

In the author's laboratory the following procedure is used frequently in making clay mineral analyses. A powdered portion of the sample is examined with a petrographic microscope using magnifications of about 400 to 500 diam. If the examination reveals substantially no nonclay minerals and if the optical properties fit those of a pure clay mineral a good idea of the identity of the clay mineral is obtained from the optical data. This is checked, however, by obtaining an X-ray diffraction pattern of a powdered sample and also of an oriented aggregate. The powder pattern reveals prism reflection needed to get information on the dioctahedral or trioctahedral form of the mineral and also on its crystallinity. If the X-ray diffraction data also confirm the presence of a single clay mineral, no further analysis may be required.

If the above investigation reveals the presence of a complex mixture, additional analytical data are necessary. For example, the oriented slide will be treated with ethylene glycol which replaces the water of any highly expandable material and causes a change in the *c*-axis spacing to about 17 A. This change in spacing will reveal the presence of any such expandable mineral alone or possibly as a component of a mixed-layer assemblage. The oriented aggregate may be heated to about 100°C which causes the collapse of any expandable material with a consequent change in the *c*-axis spacing. An oriented aggregate may be heated to successively higher temperatures to selectively destroy certain of the clay minerals.

All the foregoing data may still not be adequate, and a DTA curve may be obtained. This may be of particular value in distinguishing between kaolinite and chlorite, since kaolinite shows a very intense exothermic reaction at about 950°C, and chlorite does not show such a reaction. The sample may be treated with a potassium salt, which would tend to regrade any illites. Such potassium treatment may be used to distinguish between expandable material which has developed from the complete degrading of an illite and that which has been derived from a bentonite source. Chemical analyses may be made to determine the amount of potassium and magnesium present. An electron micrograph may be obtained to inquire into the possible presence of tubular particles of halloysite.

In particularly complex mixtures, it may be desirable to fractionate the clay on a particle-size basis to endeavor to concentrate in a given particle size certain of the clay minerals in amounts which permit their positive identifications. The clay grade may be fractionated into portions of 2 to 1 μ, 1 to 0.1 μ, and less than 0.1 μ.

If a material has an abundance of nonclay minerals, the material is generally analyzed by X-ray diffraction as received, and in addition it is fractionated to concentrate the clay minerals. Frequently a split at about 2 μ is made which is commonly quite satisfactory in eliminating the nonclay minerals from the clay minerals in the finer-grade size.

On the basis of all the foregoing data a quantitative determination of the clay mineral composition is derived. It is obvious that a clay mineral analysis of a complex clay material is not a simple matter and that it is a matter where experience is of very definite value.

It is frequently desirable to have additional analytical data for clay materials, particularly in the study of the factors that determine their physical property. Thus, it may be desirable to determine the exchangeable cations or a study of the texture by thin-section analysis may be desired. Further data on the particle size as revealed by electron microscopy may be of interest. The amount of such additional data desired depends on the problem at hand.

REFERENCES

Barshad, I., The Nature of Lattice Expansion and Its Relation to Hydration in Montmorillonite and Vermiculite, *Am. Mineralogist,* **34,** 675–684 (1949).

Bates, T. F., F. A. Hildebrand, and A. Swineford, Morphology and Structure of Endellite and Halloysite, *Am. Mineralogist,* **35,** 463–484 (1950).

Berger, G., The Structure of Montmorillonite, *Chem. Weekblad,* **38,** 42–43 (1941).

Bradley, W. F., The Structural Scheme of Attapulgite, *Am. Mineralogist,* **25,** 405–410 (1940).

48   *Applied Clay Mineralogy*

———, Diagnostic Criteria for Clay Minerals, *Am. Mineralogist,* **30,** 704–713 (1945).

———, Molecular Association between Montmorillonite and Some Polyfunctional Organic Groups, *J. Am. Chem. Soc.,* **67,** 975–981 (1945).

———, X-ray Diffraction Criteria for the Characterization of Chloritic Material in Sediments, *Natl. Acad. Sci. Publ.* 327, pp. 324–334 (1954).

Brindley, G. W., The Kaolin Minerals, "X-ray Identification and Crystal Structures of Clay Minerals," chap. II, pp. 32–75, Mineralogical Society of Great Britain Monograph (1951).

———, et al., "X-ray Identification and Crystal Structures of Clay Minerals," Mineralogical Society of Great Britain Monograph (1951).

——— and K. Robinson, The Structure of Kaolinite, *Mineral. Mag.,* **27,** 242–253 (1946).

——— and ———, Randomness in the Structures of Kaolinitic Clay Minerals, *Trans. Faraday Soc.,* **42B,** 198–205 (1946).

——— and ———, The Chlorite Minerals, "X-ray Identification and Crystal Structures of the Clay Minerals," chap. VI, pp. 172–198, Mineralogical Society of Great Britain Monograph (1951).

———, ———, and J. Goodyear, X-ray Studies of Halloysite and Metahalloysite: III, Effect of Temperature and Pressure on the Transition from Halloysite to Metahalloysite, *Mineral. Mag.,* **28,** 423–428 (1948).

Brown, G., R. Greene-Kelley, and K. Norrish, Organic Derivatives of Montmorillonite, *Clay Minerals Bull.* 1, pp. 214–220 (1952).

——— and D. M. C. MacEwan, X-ray Diffraction by Structures with Random Interstratification, "X-ray Identification and Crystal Structures of Clay Minerals," chap. XI, pp. 266–284, Mineralogical Society of Great Britain Monograph (1951).

Caillere, S., and S. Henin, Palygorskite-Attapulgite, "X-ray Identification and Crystal Structures of Clay Minerals," chap. IX, pp. 234–243, Mineralogical Society of Great Britain Monograph (1957).

Collins, B. J. S., "Textural and Morphological Studies of Some Clay Minerals," Ph.D. thesis, University of Illinois (1955).

DeLapparent, J., Constitution et origine de la leverrierite, *Compt. rend.,* **198,** 669–671 (1934).

———, Structure et origine des terres naturelles susceptibles d'être utilisées pour décoloration des huiles minérale, *Compt. rend. congr. mondial pétrol.,* Paris (1937).

———, Défense de l'attapulgite, *Bull. soc. franç. minéral.,* **61,** 253–283 (1938).

———, Argile attapulgitique, *Compt. rend.,* **212,** 971–974 (1941).

Deuel, H., G. Huber, and R. Iberg, Organische Derivate von Tonmineralien, *Helv. Chim. Acta,* **33,** 1229–1232 (1950).

Dickman, S. R., and R. H. Bray, Replacement of Adsorbed Phosphate from Kaolinite by Fluoride, *Soil Sci.,* **52,** 263–275 (1941).

Edelman, C. H., and J. C. L. Favejee, On the Crystal Structure of Montmorillonite and Halloysite, *Z. Krist.,* **102,** 417–431 (1940).

Fairbairn, H. W., X-ray Petrology of Some Fine-grained Foliated Rocks, *Am. Mineralogist,* **28,** 246–256 (1943).

Gieseking, J. E., Mechanism of Cation Exchange in the Montmorillonite-Beidellite-Nontronite Type of Clay Minerals, *Soil Sci.,* **47,** 1–14 (1939).

——— and H. Jenny, Behavior of Polyvalent Cations in Base Exchange, *Soil Sci.,* **42,** 273–280 (1936).

Goldschmidt, V. M., Undersokeiser over lersedimenter, *Nord. Jordbrugsforskn.* nos. 4–7, pp. 434–445 (1926).

Grim, R. E., Differential Thermal Curves of Prepared Mixtures of Clay Minerals, *Am. Mineralogist,* **32**, 493–501 (1947).

———, "Clay Mineralogy," McGraw-Hill Book Company, Inc., New York (1953).

———, A Concept of Diagenesis in Argillaceous Sediments, *Bull. Am. Assoc. Petrol. Geologists,* **42**, 246–254 (1958).

———, W. F. Bradley, and G. Brown, The Mica Clay Minerals, "X-ray Identification and Crystal Structures of Clay Minerals," chap. V, pp. 138–172, Mineralogical Society of Great Britain Monograph (1951).

———, R. M. Bray, and W. F. Bradley, The Mica in Argillaceous Sediments, *Am. Mineralogist,* **22**, 813–829 (1937).

——— and G. Kulbicki, "Montmorillonite: High Temperature Reactions and Classification," *Am. Mineralogist* (In press).

Grimshaw, R. W., E. Heaton, and A. L. Roberts, Constitution of Refractory Clays, *Trans. Brit. Ceram. Soc.,* **44**, 69–92 (1945).

Gruner, J. W., The Crystal Structure of Kaolinite, *Z. Krist.,* **83**, 75–88 (1932).

———, Vermiculite and Hydrobiotite Structures, *Am. Mineralogist,* **19**, 557–575 (1934).

Hendricks, S. B., Crystal Structure of Nacrite and the Polymorphism of the Kaolin Minerals, *Z. Krist.,* **100**, 509–518 (1938).

———, On the Structure of the Clay Minerals: Dickite, Halloysite, and Hydrated Halloysite, *Am. Mineralogist,* **23**, 295–301 (1938).

———, Lattice Structure of Clay Minerals and Some Properties of Clays, *J. Geol.,* **50**, 276–290 (1942).

——— and M. E. Jefferson, Crystal Structure of Vermiculites and Mixed Vermiculite-Chlorites, *Am. Mineralogist,* **23**, 851–863 (1938).

——— and ———, Structure of Kaolin and Talc-Prophyllite Hydrates and Their Bearing on Water Sorption of Clays, *Am. Mineralogist,* **23**, 863–875 (1938).

——— and ———, Polymorphism of the Micas with Optical Measurements, *Am. Mineralogist,* **24**, 729–771 (1939).

——— and E. Teller, X-ray Interference in Partially Ordered Layer Lattices, *J. Chem. Phys.,* **10**, 147–167 (1942).

Henin, S., and O. Robichet, Sur les conditions de formation des minéraux argileux par voie expérimentale, a basse température, *Compt. rend.,* **236**, 517–519 (1953).

Hewett, D. F., The Origin of Bentonite, *J. Wash. Acad. Sci.,* **7**, 196–198 (1917).

Hofmann, U., K. Endell, and D. Wilm, Kristalstruktur und Quellung von Montmorillonit, *Z. Krist.,* **86**, 340–348 (1933).

———, ———, and ———, Röntgenographische und kolloidchemische Untersuchungen über Ton, *Angew. Chem.,* **47**, 539–547 (1934).

———, A. Weiss, G. Koch, A. Mehler, and A. Scholz, Intracrystalline Swelling, Cation Exchange and Anion Exchange of Minerals of the Montmorillonite Group and of Kaolinite, *Natl. Acad. Sci. Publ.* 456, pp. 273–287 (1956).

Jackson, W. W., and J. West, The Crystal Structure of Muscovite, *Z. Krist.,* **76**, 211–227 (1930).

Jasmund, K., "Die silicatischen Tonminerale," Angewandte Chemie, Monograph 60 (1955).

Johns, W. D., R. E. Grim, and W. F. Bradley, Quantitative Estimations of Clay Minerals by Diffractions Methods, *J. Sediment. Petrol.,* **24**, 242–251 (1954).

50 *Applied Clay Mineralogy*

Kelley, W. P., "Cation Exchange in Soils," Reinhold Publishing Corporation, New York (1948).

Kerr, P. F., P. K. Hamilton, D. W. Davis, T. G. Rochow, and M. L. Fuller, Electron Micrographs of Reference Clay Minerals, *Am. Petrol. Inst. Project 49 Prelim. Rept.* 6, New York (1950).

Knight, W. C., Bentonite, *Eng. Mining J.,* **66,** 491 (1898).

Langmuir, I., The Constitution and Fundamental Properties of Solids and Liquids, *J. Am. Chem. Soc.,* **39,** 1848–1906 (1917).

MacEwan, D. M. C., Identification of the Montmorillonite Group of Minerals by X-rays, *Nature,* **154,** 577–578 (1944).

McAllister, R. F., "Clay Minerals of Recent Marine Sediments to the West of the Mississippi Delta," Ph.D. thesis, Agriculture and Mechanical College, Texas (1958).

McAtee, J. L., Heterogeneity in Montmorillonite, *Natl. Acad. Sci. Publ.* 566, pp. 279–288 (1958).

McAuliffe, C. D., M. S. Hall, L. A. Dean, and S. B. Hendricks, Exchange Reactions between Phosphates and Soils, *Soil Sci. Soc. Am. Proc.,* **12,** 119–123 (1947).

McConnell, D., The Crystal Chemistry of Montmorillonite, *Am. Mineralogist* **35,** 166–172 (1950).

McMurchy, R. C., Structure of Chlorites, *Z. Krist.,* **88,** 420–432 (1934).

Maegdefrau, E., and U. Hofmann, Die Kristalstruktur des Montmorillonit, *Z. Krist.,* **98,** 299–323 (1937).

Marshall, C. E., Layer Lattices and Base-exchange Clays, *Z. Krist.,* **91,** 433–449 (1935).

———, "The Colloid Chemistry of the Silicate Minerals," Academic Press, Inc., New York (1949).

Millot, G., Relations entre la constitution et la genèse des roches sédimentaires argileuses, "Geol. appliq. et prosp. min.," vol. II, Nancy, France (1949).

Nagy, B., and W. F. Bradley, The Structural Scheme of Sepiolite, *Am. Mineralogist,* **40,** 885–892 (1955).

Nelson, B. W., New Data on the Composition and Identification of Chlorites, *Natl. Acad. Sci. Publ.* 327, pp. 335–348 (1954).

——— and R. Roy, Synthesis of Chlorites and Their Structural and Chemical Constitution, *Am. Mineralogist,* **43,** 707–725 (1958).

Pauling, L., The Structure of the Chlorites, *Proc. Natl. Acad. Sci.,* **16,** 578–582 (1930).

———, The Structure of Micas and Related Minerals, *Proc. Natl. Acad. Sci.,* **16,** 123–129 (1930).

Ross, C. S., and P. F. Kerr, The Kaolin Minerals, *U.S. Geol. Survey Profess. Paper* 165-E, pp. 151–176 (1931).

——— and E. V. Shannon, Minerals of Bentonite and Related Clays and Their Physical Properties, *J. Am. Ceram. Soc.,* **9,** 77–96 (1926).

Schoen, U., Identification of Clay by Phosphate Fixation and Cation Exchange, *Z. Pflanzenernähr. Düng. Bodenk.,* **63,** 1–17, 97–199 (1953).

Schofield, R. K., Clay Mineral Structures and Their Physical Significance, *Trans. Brit. Ceram. Soc.,* **39,** 147–158 (1940).

———, Calculation of Surface Area of Clays from Measurements of Negative Adsorption, *Trans. Brit. Ceram. Soc.,* **48,** 207–213 (1949).

Smith, C. R., Base Exchange Reactions of Bentonites and Salts of Organic Bases, *J. Am. Chem. Soc.,* **56,** 1561–1563 (1934).

Sudo, T., "Mineralogical Study on Clays of Japan," Maruzen Co., Ltd., Tokyo (1959).

Wada, K., Oriented Penetration of Ionic Compounds between the Silicate Layers of Halloysite, *Am. Mineralogist,* **44,** 153–165 (1959).

Walker, G. F., Vermiculite and Some Related Mixed-layer Minerals, "X-ray Identification and Crystal Structures of Clay Minerals," chap. VII, pp. 199–223, Mineralogical Society of Great Britain Monograph (1951).

Way, J. F., On the Power of Soils to Absorb Manure, *J. Roy. Agr. Soc. Engl.,* **11,** 313–379 (1850).

Weaver, C. E., A Lath-shaped Non-expanded 2:1 Clay Mineral, *Am. Mineralogist,* **38,** 279–289 (1953).

CHAPTER 3

Clays in Ceramic Products

INTRODUCTION

According to Webster's International Dictionary, ceramic is defined as "relating to the art of making earthenware or . . . to the manufacture of any or all products made from earth by the agency of fire, as glass, enamels, cements." To this list should be added brick, tile, and heat-resisting refractory materials. Ceramic, therefore, refers to the manufacture of products from earthen materials by the application of high temperatures. The ceramic properties of the earthen material are those characteristics which determine its suitability and manner of use in the production of ceramic products. Some natural materials other than clays, such as feldspar, limestone, and silica sand, are used in the production of some ceramic products, but the present work will be concerned only with clay materials.

The history of ceramics goes back to prehistoric times, when, about as soon as he learned to make and use fire, man apparently learned that heat would fix the shape of earthen materials and would tend to make them stable in water. Early producers of fired earthenware, or ceramists, learned their art by experience and apprenticeship without having any real knowledge of the processes that entered their art or factors that determined them. They soon learned that all earthen materials or clays did not have the same properties and only certain clays were usable for certain products.

With the development of modern science there began a widespread application of chemistry, physics, and geology to the ceramic art, so that at about the turn of the present century ceramics began developing into an engineering profession. More and more the ceramist understood what was going on when he produced a piece of ceramic ware and knew how to control the properties of the products that he wanted to make. Substantial difficulties stood in the way of his progress because the clay materials that he dealt with were composed of particles so small that

52

their exact nature could not be studied with the analytical tools available. Chemical analysis was about the only tool, and this was not completely satisfactory because it soon became obvious that clays of very different chemical compositions might have the same ceramic properties and clays of the same chemical composition might have very different properties. Chemical analyses are still important in ceramic researches, but their value is restricted. The development of X-ray diffraction techniques, electron microscopy and diffraction, infrared adsorption, etc., beginning in the early 1920s, gave the ceramist for the first time analytical tools adequate to determine the precise nature of his raw material and, also, of his final products. In the last few years the development of high-temperature X-ray diffraction techniques and rapid methods of analysis using spectrometers have made it possible to study many of the ceramic processes in detail while they are taking place. Ceramists have been quick to take advantage of these new tools with a consequent tremendous advance in their profession in the last 30 years.

The ceramic properties of clay materials are determined by their clay mineral composition and also, if they are present in substantial amounts, by their nonclay mineral composition, organic material, and soluble salts; the particle-size distribution of the components is also important. The clay mineral composition generally is the most important factor determining ceramic properties. The present work is restricted to an analysis of the relation of clay mineral composition to the ceramic properties of clay materials and to the products which can be made from them. To go beyond this point would lead to a full text on ceramics.

In general the production of ceramic ware involves the plasticizing of the clay by the addition of water so that it may be shaped or formed by some means into the desired object. After being shaped, the object is dried to increase its strength so that it may be handled, and then it is fired at elevated temperatures (frequently in the range of 2000°F) until there has been some vitrification, or fusion of the components to develop a glassy bond, which makes the shape permanent and strong so that it does not disintegrate in water. Various temperatures and types of kilns are used in making different products, and certain products may require additional processing; for example, the ware may be glazed, i.e., coated by a thin veneer of glass. Textbooks on ceramics and ceramic engineering describe such matters in detail, and they will not be considered herein. For an introduction to the literature, see Ries (1927) and Norton (1949 and 1952).

Particular properties are important in each one of the steps in the manufacture of a ceramic product, and they will be considered under the headings Plastic Properties, Drying Properties, Firing Properties, and

Miscellaneous Properties.   In the shaping of some ceramic products, the clay is mixed with enough water to develop a fluid suspension called a *slip* which is poured into a somewhat porous mold generally made of plaster of paris.   The characteristics of such clay-water suspensions are beyond the scope of this work, and there is abundant literature, primarily in the field of colloid chemistry, which goes into this matter.   For an introduction to the literature, see Eitel (1954) and Searle and Grimshaw (1959).

PLASTICITY

Plasticity may be defined as the property of a material which permits it to be deformed under stress without rupturing and to retain the shape produced after the stress is removed.   It is the property which permits the material to be shaped by the application of a force.   Clay materials in general develop plasticity when they are mixed with relatively small amounts of water.   Bloor (1957) has stated that there are three concepts inherent in the definition of plasticity: (1) a yield value, (2) deformation without rupture, and (3) retention of shape when deformation ceases. For clays two further factors must be considered: (1) the moisture content and (2) the length of time the stress is applied, because a certain amount of time is necessary for the clay to adjust so that the change in shape is produced without rupturing.   The rate of application of the stress is therefore very important.

When water is added to dry clay in successive increments, in general the clay tends to become readily workable, that is, readily shaped without rupturing.   The workability and retention of shape develop within a very narrow moisture range.   The addition of water beyond a definite amount tends to make the mass too soft to retain a shape and to develop the properties of a fluid; that is, it tends to flow.

The property of plasticity in clays is difficult to measure in such a way that the value obtained has any general significance.   Many procedures have been suggested; for a review of them see Bloor (1957), Hind (1930), Graham and Sullivan (1939), and Searle and Grimshaw (1959). Valuable results have been obtained, but their significance is often obscure because they do not reveal fundamental attributes of the material and they cannot be correlated with the practical utilization of the material.   Thus a clay which test measurements indicate to be very plastic may not be usable for making ceramic products because it may require too much water, may be too sticky, or for some other reason cannot be satisfactorily shaped.

In general, three ways to approach the measurement of plasticity have been followed.   One is to determine the amount of water necessary to develop optimum plasticity or the range of water content in which plasticity is demonstrated. Determinations of the water of plasticity and the Atterberg (1911 and 1912) values of plastic limit, liquid limit, and plasticity index would be placed in this category.

A second method is to determine the amount of penetration of an object, frequently a needle or some type of plunger, into a plastic mass of clay under a given load or rate of loading (Whittemore, 1935). The tests must be carried out with consideration given to the moisture content. Such procedures have been found valuable by construction engineers in evaluating the properties of undisturbed soil materials in place.

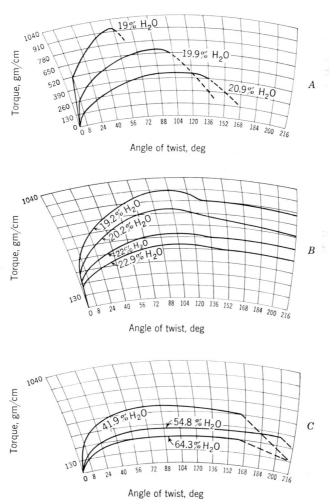

FIG. 3-1. Stress-strain curves for *A*, flint clay (kaolinite); *B*, plastic fireclay (kaolinite); and *C*, Wyoming bentonite (sodium montmorillonite), after Graham and Sullivan (1939).

Another way is to determine the stress necessary to deform the clay and the maximum deformation the clay will undergo before rupture. These determinations must, of course, be made with materials with different moisture contents and with varying rates of stress application. Figure 3-1, presenting curves for two kaolinite clays and for a sodium montmorillonite bentonite, illustrates the kind of data obtained by such a procedure. Bloor (1957) has presented a critical review of such methods. The fact that these data must be evaluated in terms of moisture contents increases the difficulty of using them. For comparative purposes, one must take arbitrary moisture contents or be satisfied with data showing differences in the variations of these values with changing amounts of moisture. It appears that such stress-strain determinations give little information of value on the practical utility of a clay, although they may indicate more fundamental attributes of the material.

Water of Plasticity

The water of plasticity of a clay is the per cent of water, determined on a dried-weight basis, usually at about 105°C, necessary to develop the optimum plasticity of a clay. The procedure followed in determining this value in general is to add increasing amounts of water to a dried clay until the optimum plasticity is reached. The determination of the optimum point is an arbitrary matter, but it is surprising to the inexperienced person that experienced persons making such measurements will usually agree closely on the amount of water required to develop optimum plasticity in a clay. Usually there is a definite amount of water at which the clay is easily moldable. With less moisture the mass cracks when molded; with more water the mass becomes sticky and deforms so easily that it tends to lose its shape after molding. Water of plasticity values are given in Table 3-1, showing the range characteristic of the various clay minerals. Each clay mineral group can be expected to show a range of values since particle size, exchangeable-cation composition, and crystallinity of the clay mineral itself also exert an influence. In natural clay materials, nonclay mineral components, soluble salts, organic compounds, and texture can also influence the water plasticity. Figure 3-2 shows the increase in the

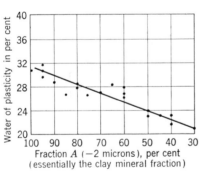

Fig. 3-2. Relation of water of plasticity to abundance of clay minerals in a series of illitic shales, after Grim (1941).

water of plasticity with the increase in the abundance of clay minerals in a series of illitic shales.

TABLE 3-1

WATER OF PLASTICITY
(in Per Cent by Weight)
(After White, 1947)

Kaolinite	8.9– 56.3
Illite	17 – 38.5
Halloysite	33 – 50
Attapulgite	93
Montmorillonite	83 –250

The single value for attapulgite means that the determination was made on a single sample and not that all samples of this mineral would have precisely this water of plasticity.   It would be expected that chlorite clay minerals would yield about the same values as the illites.   The maximum value given by White (1947) for illites is probably low because some illites no doubt can be found that yield values at least as high as the maximum values for kaolinite.   In general, the water of plasticity values are substantially the same for kaolinite, illite, chlorite, and halloysite clays.

The relation of the plastic properties to the nature of the exchangeable cation, particle size, and crystallinity of the clay minerals is illustrated best by the Atterberg limit values.   However, it can be stated that the values for kaolinite, illite, chlorite, and halloysite would be changed only slightly by variations in the exchangeable-cation composition, but the tendency would be for sodium to give lower values than other common cations, such as calcium, magnesium, potassium, and hydrogen.   In the case of the montmorillonites, the water of plasticity varies considerably with the nature of the exchangeable cation, with sodium giving high values, and calcium, magnesium, potassium, and hydrogen varieties giving values considerably lower.   Because of the pronounced thixotropic character of sodium montmorillonites, the water of plasticity is difficult to measure.   In fact, there is no definite value as there is no sharply defined moisture content for optimum plasticity.   It is interesting to note that the relative effect of sodium on the water of plasticity of montmorillonite is the opposite of its effect in the other clay minerals.

Information is not available for allophanes in general, but for some of them White (1953) indicates substantially no plasticity.   However, Atterberg limit data indicate that there are some allophane materials which would give water of plasticity values in the range of the montmorillonites.

In the making of ceramic products as low a value for water of plasticity is desired as is consistent with the formation of a good shape which will not crack on drying, has strength to permit handling, and does not require intense forming pressure. High water of plasticity means that relatively much water must be lost during drying, and the shrinkage, therefore, is likely to be high. The high values for attapulgite and montmorillonite are prime reasons why such clays are not favored for ceramic manufacture, although they may be added in small quantities to provide needed plasticity.

Atterberg Limits

Another method of evaluating plasticity is to determine the range of moisture contents from that value just adequate for ground clay to form a coherent mass to that value where an extremely small stress causes deformation. The difference between the lower value, called *plastic limit,* and the higher value, called *liquid limit,* is the *plasticity index.* This procedure of evaluating plasticity is little used by ceramists but very extensively used by construction engineers in soil-mechanics investigations. It is considered in detail in Chap. 5 where values are given for the various clay minerals of different particle size and carrying different exchangeable cations. In general, the water of plasticity is a slightly larger value than the Atterberg plastic limit. In other words, slightly more water than the minimum necessary to form a coherent mass is required for optimum plasticity for forming ceramic ware.

Rieke (1923) suggested an adaptation of the Atterberg values to increase their application to ceramic problems. He suggests the determination of a sticky limit, which is the moisture content at which the clay loses its stickiness. The sticky limit is intermediate between the plastic limit and the liquid limit, and he would use the difference between the sticky limit and the plastic limit as an index of plasticity. In general, a low Rieke index value is desirable because a high value would indicate a large water requirement for plasticity and probably a large moisture range in which the clays would be difficult to shape because of stickiness. The value for the sticky limit of a clay would be expected to be about equal to its water of plasticity. In Table 3-2, the sticky limit and Rieke index for kaolins and montmorillonites are given to show the kind of values obtained. In general, a Rieke index less than 10 is desirable for clays for ceramic use. A particularly significant matter shown in Table 3-2 is the very long moisture range through which the sodium montmorillonite clay exhibits stickiness.

TABLE 3-2

ATTERBERG LIMIT VALUES AND RIEKE INDICES
(After Fendius and Endell, 1935)

Clay	Plastic limit	Sticky limit	Liquid limit	Rieke index
Amberg kaolin............	37	41	52	4
Spergauer kaolin..........	42	50	71	8
Ca-Mont................	89	101	157	12
Na-Mont................	76	102	520	26

Stress-Strain Values

Sullivan (1939) and Sullivan and Graham (1940) subjected bars of kaolinite clays prepared with various exchangeable cations to torsion and plotted torque in grams per centimeter against the angle of twist. A typical curve for a plastic kaolinite clay is illustrated in Fig. 3-1B, from which were read yield point, maximum torque before rupture, angle of maximum torque, and angle of ultimate failure. Sullivan (1939) gives values for kaolins with different exchangeable cations, in each case making numerous runs at several different moisture contents. He showed, as would be expected, that the yield point decreases with increasing water content and that the angle of maximum torque varies with the nature of the exchangeable cation. According to Sullivan and Graham (1940), for kaolins the order of increasing yield point for a given water content is lithium, sodium, calcium, barium, magnesium, aluminum, potassium, iron, ammonium, and hydrogen; the order of increasing maximum torque for a given water content is lithium, sodium, calcium, barium, magnesium, aluminum, iron, potassium, hydrogen, and ammonium; and the order of increasing angle of maximum torque for a given water content is iron, hydrogen, aluminum, ammonium, calcium, potassium, magnesium, barium, sodium, and lithium. These data mean that lithium- and sodium-saturated kaolins require less force to yield at a given moisture content or, for a given force, less water is required to permit yield. Further, they mean that the maximum amount of force to continuously and easily deform a kaolinite clay is the least for lithium- and sodium-saturated kaolins. The data also show that lithium- and sodium-saturated kaolins experience the largest amount of deformation before they are deformed easily. In other words, less force is required to deform them than is required for kaolins with other cations at a given moisture content but that force must be applied through a larger amount of deformation. Henry and Siefert (1941) presented stress-strain data which suggest the same general conclusions.

Graham and Sullivan (1939) give stress-strain values (Table 3-3) for a well-crystallized kaolinite (flint clay), a poorly crystallized kaolinite (Ball clay), and Wyoming bentonite (sodium montmorillonite) obtained at different moisture contents. These data indicate that the poorly organized kaolinite clay requires more water than the well-crystallized kaolinite clay to develop plastic properties and also more force to yield and more force to give continuous easy deformation. The montmorillonite clay requires more water than the Ball clay to develop plastic properties but less force to yield and less force to yield continuously.

TABLE 3-3

STRESS-STRAIN VALUES FOR KAOLINS AND
A BENTONITE WITH VARYING WATER CONTENTS
(After Graham and Sullivan, 1939)

Clay	Water, % dry weight	Yield point, g/cm	Maximum torque, g/cm	Angle at maximum torque, deg	Angle of ultimate fracture, deg
Plastic kaolin	19.2	472	1,149	99	230
(Lawrence)	20.2	396	932	100	226
	22	297	681	101	312
	22.9	257	582	101	328
Kentucky Ball	34.4	358	743	90	178
clay	37.4	215	475	91	230
	38.9	772	389	92	248
Flint clay	19.0	358	820	73	77
(Pennsylvania)	21.8	182	508	107	129
	24.2	89	318	116	156
Flint clay	19.0	442	949	55	60
(Kentucky)	19.9	273	689	93	100
	20.9	136	445	115	130
Wyoming	41.9	254	582	87	164
bentonite	54.8	151	348	87	207
	64.3	102	262	87	160

Stress-strain values are not at hand for the other clay minerals, but it would be expected from other data, chiefly Atterberg limit values, that illite and chlorite clays would give results similar to those obtained for kaolinite and also that the effect of variations in the exchangeable-cation composition would be similar for these clays. It would be expected further that the effect of variations in the exchangeable-cation composition would be different for montmorillonite than for the other clay minerals, particularly for those with sodium and lithium.

Endell, Fendius, and Hofmann (1934), using a slightly different stress-strain apparatus, subjected clay specimens prepared at given moisture contents to compression between two disks with simultaneous torque. The amount of compression multiplied by the torque at the time of the appearance of the first rupture of the specimen is called the *work force of formation (verformungsarbeit)*. This value is measured at different moisture contents, and a curve of moisture contents versus *verformungsarbeit* is plotted as shown in Fig. 3-3. This procedure had been used earlier, and Zschokke (1902) had suggested that the maximum *verformungsarbeitkraft* be used as a plasticity index. Later Keppeler (1931) suggested that a more useful index would be obtained by multiplying Zschokke's value and the per cent of water at the maximum *verformungsarbeit*. Endell et al. (1934) were the first to apply this procedure to specific clay minerals, and data illustrating their results are given in Table 3-4. It is difficult to correlate such data with actual practice in forming clay bodies and to arrive at any notion of its fundamental significance. Thus, on the basis of Zschokke's number, sodium montmorillonite and calcium montmorillonite give about the same values, and in Keppeler's number there is not much difference between calcium montmorillonite and the kaolinite samples. It is known that these clays have quite different plastic properties.

Henry (1943), using an apparatus similar to that of Endell et al. (1934), suggested that the force applied at the time of rupture multiplied by the deformation resulting in rupture would give a number indicative of

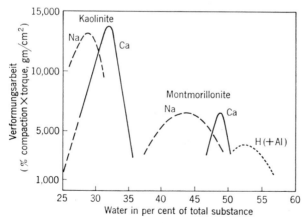

Fig. 3-3. Relation between *verformungsarbeit* and water content for kaolinites and montmorillonites, after Endell, Fendius, and Hofmann (1934).

TABLE 3-4
PLASTICITY NUMBERS ACCORDING TO ZSCHOKKE AND KEPPELER
(After Endell, Fendius, and Hofmann, 1934)

Clay	Zschokke plasticity value	Per cent water at maximum *verformungsarbeit*	Keppeler plasticity value
Na-Kaolinite	13,000	29	377,000
Ca-Kaolinite	14,000	32	384,000
Na-Mont.	6,500	44	286,000
Ca-Mont.	6,500	49	315,500
H-Mont.	3,500	52.5	183,750

the workability of the clay. Henry determined this workability number for a series of bodies which manufacturers believed to be at their optimum workability, i.e., at moisture contents giving their best workability characteristics. According to Henry "bodies which plant men classified as the most plastic are those which had the highest values of workability product in comparison with other bodies of the same softness." Data are not at hand for specific clay minerals.

Effect of Heating

Holderidge and Moore (1953) have shown that when kaolinite clays are heated to temperatures of the order of 250 to 270°C prior to the determination of their plasticity, the plasticity as represented by the Pfefferkorn (1924) number (based on deformation caused by the action of a piston on cylinders of clay at different moisture contents) is suddenly and substantially reduced. After heating to temperatures in excess of about 600°C where the kaolinite structure is greatly changed, one would expect that the material would be almost nonplastic. Data are not at hand for the other clay minerals, but it would be expected on structural grounds that illite and chlorite would show about the same changes as kaolinite.

In the case of halloysite, heating to temperatures of the order of 60 to 100°C, causing the irreversible dehydration to develop the $2H_2O$ form, is known to cause a substantial reduction in plasticity. At higher temperatures the mineral would be expected to act about the same as kaolinite.

Heating montmorillonites to temperatures of the order of 100 to 150°C until all of the interlayer water is lost generally is known to cause a substantial reduction in plasticity. At higher temperatures montmorillonite would be expected to react about the same as illite on the application of heat.

Discussion

Any satisfactory concept of plasticity must explain the following: the relationship between clay mineral composition, exchangeable-cation composition, and plasticity. It must explain the extremely high water of plasticity for montmorillonite clays and the fact that the presence of the sodium ion increases the water requirements for plasticity of montmorillonite but has the opposite effect for the other clay minerals. A satisfactory concept must explain the stickiness state, particularly as developed in some clays, and the fact that elongate and flake-shaped particles rather than equidimensional or granular particles favor the development of the plastic state. It must also account for the development of higher plasticity in disordered as compared with well-ordered kaolinite and illite and the fact that very small amounts of montmorillonite in clays composed of other clay minerals cause a relatively great increase in plasticity. The concept must explain the fact that a certain amount of time is required for the development of the plastic state after water is added to the clay and that plasticity in clays is developed only when the liquids added have certain definite properties. Finally, it must account for the changes in plasticity taking place when the clay minerals are heated before water is added to the clay.

There is a large amount of literature on the subject of plasticity, and much of it approaches the subject from the point of view of colloid chemistry. The theories developed are based almost entirely on the charge on the particles and the "double layer" believed to develop around the particles. In many instances experimental work was restricted to suspensions, that is, to clay-water systems with considerably larger amounts of water than in the plastic state, and the reasoning is frequently based on concepts arrived at primarily or entirely from investigations of clay-water suspensions, not plastic masses.

It is desired to present here a concept based on structural considerations as well as on the charges on the particles. It will be seen that the suggested concept attributes an important role to the physical state of the adsorbed water. In many of the older concepts the water was generally assigned an insignificant or at least a relatively unimportant role, although Goldschmidt in 1926 pointed out that the nature of the fluid added to clay was important in determining plasticity and further that the plastic property was not developed in all fluids but only in those with certain characteristics. Longchambon in 1938 arrived at the conclusion that the physical state of the water separating the clay particles in the plastic state was not that of liquid water and was a vital factor in determining plastic properties.

The author suggests that where there is a limited amount of water, as in the plastic condition, the physical state of the adsorbed water is a most important consideration, and where there is a large amount of water, as in the case of fluid suspensions, the physical state of the water is relatively much less important. The change in the physical state of the water must be restricted to a moderate distance from the particle surfaces. In suspensions this critical distance is exceeded so that there would be a substantial amount of fluid water between particles. The state of the water adsorbed directly on the particle surfaces, therefore, would be of relatively less significance.

Plasticity in a clay-water system in essence is a matter of some sort of bonding force between the particles to hold them together plus water, a lubricant, which permits some movement between the particles on the application of a deforming force. The bonding force is largely a result of the charges on the particles, and this matter has been discussed abundantly in the literature (Hauser, 1939; Kruyt, 1952). The bonding forces are Van der Waals and coulombic forces modified by the presence of compensating cations.

As noted above, Goldschmidt (1926), Longchambon (1938), Hendricks and Jefferson (1938), and many others indicated that the water immediately adsorbed on basal clay mineral surfaces is composed of water molecules in a definite orientation. For a more recent discussion of this matter and references to earlier literature, see Low and Lovell (1958). There is considerable difference of opinion as to the nature of this orientation (Grim, 1953) but very little as to the presence of some sort of orientation.

It is suggested that there is another binding force between the clay mineral particles in the plastic state, namely, a water bond produced by the union of layers of oriented water molecules developing outward from adjacent clay mineral surfaces. This bond would be relatively strong when the water layers were thin enough so that orientation of water molecules was complete, and it would be weak or nonexistent when the water layers were so thick that there was little or no orientation of water molecules at the junction of adjacent adsorbed layers. Hendricks and Jefferson (1938) have pointed out that the source of orienting force of the water molecules resides in the clay mineral surfaces and, therefore, that the degree or perfection of orientation would decrease outward from such surfaces.

It has been suggested (Grim and Cuthbert, 1945; Grim, 1948) that optimum plasticity develops when the adsorbed water is sufficiently oriented to provide a strong bond between particles and when this water is thick enough to prevent extreme rigidity at the junction of adjacent adsorbed water layers. The water thickness would be such that a small application of force would permit movement within the water layers.

Stated another way, optimum plasticity develops when all of the requirements of particle surfaces for rigid water are satisfied and there is a little
additional water, less rigidly fixed, which can act as a lubricant when
a deforming force is applied. It is further suggested that the effect of
adsorbed cations on plasticity is to a considerable degree the result of
their effect on the extent and perfection of the development of oriented
water rather than directly on the bonding force between the particles.

The comparatively large water-of-plasticity values for montmorillonites
are a consequence of their extremely small particle size with a tremendous
amount of adsorbing surface which in turn results from the weak bond
between the particles permitting the mineral to separate into flakes approaching unit-cell thicknesses. Also, both basal planes of the montmorillonite flakes present similar good water-orienting surfaces. In the
case of the two-layer clay mineral, such as kaolinite, the structure of only
one of the basal plane surfaces is like that of the montmorillonite; hence
the degree of orientation is likely to be different for the two clay minerals.
This is in addition to the much larger particle size of the kaolinite,
because the mineral does not cleave down to anything approaching unit-
cell dimensions. Illite, chlorite, and attapulgite would present surfaces
for water adsorption similar to those of montmorillonite, but at least
in the case of illite and chlorite, the particles are much larger than those
of montmorillonite. Illite and chlorite with comparable particle size
to a kaolinite clay would be expected to have a slightly higher water
of plasticity, and the data show that this is the case.

On the basis of the structure of the adsorbed water suggested by
Hendricks and Jefferson (1938), which has a density less than 1, it seems
likely that the thickness of adsorbed water on particles of sodium montmorillonite required to develop plasticity would be on the order of 9 to
10 molecular layers and for calcium montmorillonite on the order of 5 to
8 molecular layers (see discussion of bonding-clay properties in Chap. 4).
These values are derived on the assumption that all the basal planes
in the montmorillonites are available to water and that none of the
water is assigned to pore space between the particles. Neither of these
assumptions can be absolutely true, but they would tend to cancel each
other so that the values are probably of the right order of magnitude.
For the other clay minerals no satisfactory data are available, and such
values are difficult even to estimate because the amount of disaggregation of the clay mineral when mixed with water and, hence, the surface
area available for adsorption, cannot be determined. Also the relative
amount of pore water and adsorbed water cannot be evaluated. It seems
likely, however, that the thicknesses of adsorbed water layers required
on the surfaces of such clay mineral particles would be of the same
order as those for calcium-montmorillonite clays.

The water required for optimum plasticity is the sum of that adsorbed on mineral surfaces and free pore water. In the case of montmorillonites, the amount of free water would be relatively smaller than for the other clay minerals.

The effect of the adsorbed cation is essentially a matter of its position on the clay particle; its size determines whether or not it interferes with the growth of water orientation and also whether or not it tends to hydrate, that is, to surround itself with a net of water molecules which might enhance or interfere with the growth of the adsorbed water layers.

In the case of montmorillonite, the adsorbed cations neutralize the charge on the clay because of substitution within the lattice. As Mering and Glaesser (1954) have shown, when sodium is the adsorbed cation, it will be held down in the hexagonal holes on the basal surface in order to be at the closest point to the seat of the charge it is neutralizing. In this case there is no cation on the surface to interfere with the growth of thick water layers, and the charges on the particles are neutralized. As a consequence, the sodium montmorillonite is easily dispersed into extremely thin particles, and water layers can grow to a great thickness with the result of a very high water-of-plasticity value.

In the case of montmorillonite with a divalent cation like calcium, the cation satisfies two charges within the lattice, but it can only get close to one of them. The montmorillonite surface, therefore, would be in a relatively high energy state as Mering and Glaesser (1954) have pointed out. Further, the cation tends to hydrate. The result is less complete separation of the montmorillonite particles with well-oriented water developing to a lesser thickness than that in the sodium montmorillonite. Consequently, the calcium montmorillonite has a lower water requirement for optimum plasticity.

White and Pichler (1959) have shown that the water requirement for the development of plasticity in montmorillonites varies with the composition of the montmorillonite as well as with the nature of the adsorbed cation. This would be expected because such a variation in composition is essentially a matter of variation of substitution within the lattice and the consequent position and intensity of the charge holding the adsorbed cation. For example, the seat of the charge in some montmorillonites is in the central octahedral layer, whereas in others it is in the outer tetrahedral layer or in both these parts of the structure. As a consequence of the seat of the charge and possibly of the character of the particular atom substituted, it would be expected that the adsorbed cations might take up different positions, the energy of the surface would be different, and the amount of development of oriented water on the surface would be different.

Recently, Grim and Kulbicki (1959) presented data to indicate that in some montmorillonites there is probably some relatively slight inversion of the tetrahedrons in the silica surfaces. Such inversion would be expected to provide some interference to the development of oriented water; montmorillonites with substantial amounts of such inversion would be expected to have relatively poor water-orienting power. These authors indicate that the montmorillonites from the Wyoming area which have extremely high water requirements for the development of plasticity are composed of units in which there is substantially no inversion of the silica tetrahedrons. Hence, they have a surface with unusually great potential for the orientation and adsorption of water.

In the case of other clay minerals, the seat of the charge holding the adsorbed cations is largely a broken bond on the surface, and the adsorbed cation, therefore, is likely to be on the surface. When sodium is adsorbed on the surface, it does not tend to hydrate (Hendricks et al., 1940; Mering, 1946), and, therefore, its sole effect would be to interfere with the development of oriented water layers. Calcium would also be held on the surface, but because it tends to hydrate, it can be concluded that there would be a tendency for an enhancement of the growth of water layers when this cation is present. As a consequence, the presence of sodium would reduce the water of plasticity as compared with calcium. In summary, the difference between the effect of sodium on the water of plasticity of montmorillonite and its effect in other clay minerals is caused by the position of the sodium ion in the clay mineral particle, which in turn is the consequence of the difference in the seat and the nature of the charge holding the adsorbed cation.

It is suggested that stickiness develops when the adsorbed water has only a moderate amount of organization. Layers of well-oriented water, such as result from an organization enhanced by hydration of the adsorbed cation, are likely to give little stickiness. Also, when the water organization is good to a definite thickness and then abruptly passes to no orientation, that is, liquid water, there is little stickiness. On the other hand, when the cation does not hydrate and the oriented water gradually changes from oriented to nonoriented, there is likely to be pronounced stickiness. Sodium-montmorillonite clays are notoriously sticky, and, in general, when sodium is the adsorbed cation, stickiness is apt to be more pronounced than when calcium is the adsorbed ion.

Granular particles, such as quartz and calcite, in a clay tend to reduce plasticity and are merely diluents. Even though such particles may be very small, of the order of $1\ \mu$ or less, it is difficult or impossible to render them plastic by the addition of water so they can be shaped without cracking under a forming force and so that the shape will be retained. Plasticity is not, therefore, solely a matter of surface, but also a matter of the kind of surface and the proper shape of the particles.

Granular particles of such minerals probably do not present any substantial plane surfaces of the proper structure for the adequate adsorption of oriented water. Further, their shape is such that adjacent particles would meet at edges and corners rather than on plane surfaces. As a consequence, the binding forces between particles would hold them together less tightly, and the ease of lubrication and slippage between such particles would be very much less than in flake-shaped units. In the case of the clay minerals, the smaller the particle size the higher the water of plasticity and the plasticity index. This is to be expected since the smaller particles would have a larger amount of adsorbing surface.

Platen and Winkler (1958) have presented curves (Fig. 3-4) to show the relation of the Atterberg plasticity index to the amount of surface area for different clay minerals. These data show quite clearly the relationship between the surface area and plasticity index and also point out that the relationship is somewhat different for the different clay minerals. Thus, two samples of clay with the same surface area but composed of different clay minerals have different plasticity indices. This means that the amount of surface is important and that the nature of the surface as determined by the character of the clay mineral is also important in determining the plasticity.

Holderidge (1956) has shown that the plastic properties of Ball clays are enhanced as the constituent kaolinite is increasingly disordered. This is easily understood since the disordering would tend to permit the kaolinite units to be more easily dispersed with the development of a larger amount of surface. Other factors, such as the nature of the surface, might also be important. There would, for example, be more broken bonds with somewhat higher adsorption capacity in the disordered kaolinite, but it seems doubtful if such factors would be of sufficient magnitude to cause a significant difference as compared with a well-organized kaolinite. In the case of the other clay minerals, relatively poor ordering would be expected to have the

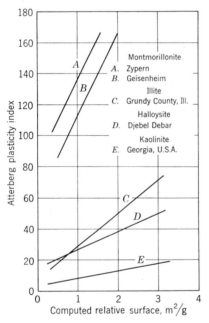

FIG. 3-4. The relation of plasticity index to surface area, after Platen and Winkler (1958).

same effect, that is, to increase the amount of surface area and enhance the plasticity.

Many clay materials are composed of units which are mixed-layer assemblages of two or more clay minerals. It would be expected that in many cases such clays would have relatively higher plastic properties than those in which the constituent minerals were composed of discrete particles, because the mixed layering would probably provide planes of weakness within the aggregate particles causing relatively easy dispersion in water with the attendant development of a large amount of surface. This would be particularly true if one of the components of the mixed-layer units was a montmorillonite-type material, as this mineral would definitely provide planes of weakness.

The matter of whether the constituent particles are elongate lath-shaped units or equidimensional flakes seems to be of little consequence in developing plasticity. This is shown by the high water of plasticity for attapulgite clays. Some illites and montmorillonites occur in elongate units rather than in equidimensional flakes, and adequate data to evaluate precisely the influence of shape are not at hand for these minerals. However, in general it seems that the elongate units tend to provide rather lower plasticity than equidimensional units, but it may be that this difference, in part at least, is contingent upon a variation in some other factor, such as the nature of the exchangeable cation or the charge on the surface. In the case of the tubular halloysite as compared with the flake-shaped kaolinite, both minerals exhibit rather low plastic properties, and there seems to be no great difference between them. Visconti (1956) has stated that the presence of halloysite in a kaolinitic clay tends to reduce its plasticity. In this connection it must be remembered that the plastic characteristics of halloysite vary greatly depending on the state of its hydration—the mineral in an intermediate stage of hydration provides much higher plasticity than it does in either the $2H_2O$ or the $4H_2O$ form.

It is a well-known fact that clays do not develop plasticity with the addition of all types of fluids. Goldschmidt (1926) pointed out that plastic properties developed only with liquids that had a polar character. In liquids which were nonpolar (e.g., carbon tetrachloride), he found that the mixtures were without plasticity and not analogous to those obtained in mixtures of clay and water. Goldschmidt concluded that the plasticity of clays was dependent both upon the chemistry of the mineral phase and the atomic structure of the liquid phase. He concluded that the water molecules stick to each other and to the minerals because of their dipole moment. Apparently a type of fluid is required in which the molecules are tied to the surface and to each other. The fact that the nature of the fluid is important in determining plasticity indicates that the function of the fluid is not only to separate the clay mineral particles and that the charge on the particles is not the sole factor in determining the plastic properties of clays. In other words, the fluid itself must be considered as a positive factor and not a passive element.

It is well known that the weathering of clays and shales generally tends to increase their plastic properties. It may tend to develop plasticity in clay materials which otherwise are substantially nonplastic, or it may simply increase the water of plasticity and the ease of developing this property. This can be explained by the fact that in weathering there would be a tendency for materials to be alternately wetted and dried; that is, water would penetrate between particles and to some extent along cleavage planes within particles. This would inevitably tend to weaken the bond between the particles, thereby increasing their ease of dispersion and the amount of surface developed. In the weathering process there may also be some movement of water through the particles with attendant leaching and consequent removal of potassium and magnesium ions between the silicate sheets of illite and chlorite respectively. Such degrading of micas would also increase dispersibility and the amount of surface. The effect of the leaching may be only to cause a cation-exchange reaction rather than a degrading of the micas, but this might well have an effect on plastic properties.

When dry clays are mixed with water, the plastic state is not developed immediately but only after a certain amount of working and frequently after the moistened clay has been allowed to stand; the clay-water mass is said to require tempering. This can be explained in part by the fact that a certain amount of time is necessary for the water to penetrate to all of the adsorbing surfaces. It is also, in part at least, to be explained by the fact that a certain amount of time is required for the water molecules to develop their oriented character after they reach the adsorbing surfaces. This can be likened to the amount of time required for the crystallization of water into ice.

When clays are heated to increasingly high temperatures, they first lose their pore water and then their adsorbed water. As the adsorbed water is lost, the flat plane surfaces tend to come together. Apparently the complete collapse of the particles makes it extremely difficult for water to again penetrate to the adsorbing surfaces. As a consequence, heating clays to temperatures of the order of 100 to 300°C, as indicated previously, tends to substantially reduce their plastic character when they are again mixed with water. It is interesting that the addition of fluids with higher polarity than water to such dried clays will sometimes develop a plastic state, whereas it will not be developed with water. Apparently the higher polarity causes the fluid to penetrate to surfaces unavailable to water. When the clay minerals are heated to temperatures of the order of 500°C and above (see pages 86–97), they lose their hydroxyl water with a consequent change in the crystalline structure, and, as a further consequence, the shape of the particles and the character of the surface change. The result is likely to be the development of a substantially nonplastic material.

One of the interesting points regarding plasticity is that some types of organic material apparently enhance this property, whereas others tend to destroy it. In the instances in which the plastic characteristic is destroyed, the organic molecules probably tend to be adsorbed and to develop a hydrophobic surface. Such clays might well develop plasticity with some organic fluids but not with water. Little is known concerning the character of the organic materials which tend to enhance plasticity, as in the case of the Ball clays. The explanation probably resides in the nature of the organic material, and one would suspect that such organic materials would provide particularly hydrophilic surfaces.

GREEN PROPERTIES

Green properties refer to those properties developed by a clay body after it has been rendered plastic by the addition of water and shaped into a definite form but has not been dried. The properties are those, therefore, that prevail while the plasticizing water is still present in the clay bodies.

Green Strength

Green strength is usually measured as a transverse breaking strength of a test bar suspended on two narrow supports; it is measured in pounds per square inch or kilograms per square centimeter. Usually in ceramic ware, green strength is adequate to permit the ware to be handled, and this is all that is required. As a consequence, it is usually not measured, and the literature contains little data for specific clay minerals.

Green strength varies tremendously with small variations in the water content (this is perhaps best illustrated by the data for clay-bonded molding sands given in Chap. 4), and consequently results must always be presented and compared at specific moisture contents. Customarily, values are obtained either at a moisture content providing the maximum green strength or at a moisture content equal to the water of plasticity. As water is continuously added to a dry clay, the green strength increases up to a maximum amount and then decreases. The strength at water of plasticity is in general lower than the maximum value. The water of plasticity of a clay provides water in excess of that required for maximum green strength.

The values in Table 3-5 (Hofmann, 1954) were obtained at moisture contents giving maximum strength. In the case of kaolinite, several samples were measured, and the range of values represents variations due to particle size and perhaps other factors, such as crystallinity. In the case of the other clay minerals, single samples were measured; additional samples would, for the same reasons, undoubtedly also show a range of values. Hofmann's data together with conclusions based on molding sand studies (Chap. 4) indicate that the maximum green strength of kaolinite and illite clays would be much the same; it might frequently be slightly greater for illite. Chlorite would be similar to these clay minerals in its green strength. Holderidge (1956) has shown that Ball clays composed of poorly ordered kaolinite have greater strengths than similar clays with better-organized kaolinite. Similarly, it would be expected that relatively poorly ordered chlorite and illite would have higher strengths than well-ordered varieties. Clays composed of mixed-layered assemblages of these clay minerals would probably show greater strength than clays of similar composition in which the mixing was of aggregate particles. The green strengths of montmorillonites appear to be greater by a factor of about 2 or more than that of the aforesaid clay minerals. The calcium varieties of montmorillonite would be expected to have greater green strength than those carrying sodium. Attapulgite probably would have green strength about equal to the calcium montmorillonite. The halloysite tested by Hofmann (1954) had quite a high green strength as shown in Table 3-5, and this sample was probably in an intermediate state of hydration. Samples of halloysite with water contents about equal to the $2H_2O$ and $4H_2O$ form and not in an intermediate state of hydration would probably have little strength. The strength of allophane samples would be expected to range from high to low. Except for the montmorillonite clay minerals the character of the exchangeable cation would be expected to cause little variation in the green strength.

The presence of considerable quantities of nonclay minerals reduces

TABLE 3-5

GREEN STRENGTH

(in Kilograms per Square Centimeter)

(After Hofmann, 1954)

Kaolinite........................ 0.34–3.2
Illite............................. 3.2
Calcium montmorillonite........... Greater than 5
Halloysite....................... Greater than 5

the green strength. Small amounts of such minerals may actually increase the green strength, because they permit the development of a more uniform clay body.   There are no precise data on this matter, but, again reasoning from molding-sand information, kaolinite, illite, and chlorite clays could probably stand about 25 per cent nonclay before there would be a significant reduction in strength, whereas, for montmorillonites the amount might well be over 50 per cent.

In ceramic use difficulties are sometimes encountered with materials having a high content of well-sorted fine silt, because their green strengths are so low that they are difficult to handle in the green state without being deformed.   Such materials may appear to be quite plastic, but the amount of material with low water-adsorbing power may be so great and the amount of the clay mineral components so small that the green strength is extremely low.

At water contents equal to the water of plasticity little precise data are available, but, reasoning from various plasticity studies using deformation techniques, the green strengths of kaolinite, illite, and chlorite clays are likely to be greater than that of montmorillonite clays by a factor of about 2.   In montmorillonite clays, maximum green strength develops at moisture contents considerably lower than the water-of-plasticity value.   In kaolinite, illite, and probably also chlorite clays when nonclay minerals are abundant, maximum green strength appears to develop at moisture contents higher than the water-of-plasticity values, and when nonclay minerals are scant it develops at water contents equal to, or lower than, the water-of-plasticity values.   It must be remembered that water-of-plasticity values are considerably higher for montmorillonites than for kaolinites, illites, and chlorites, thereby accounting for the lower strength values for the montmorillonites.

It is suggested that the most important controlling factor in determining green strength is the state of the water adsorbed on the surface of the mineral particles.   Maximum strength prevails when the moisture content is substantially equal to that which can be held in a well-oriented condition.   Since a water-of-plasticity value represents additional water to that held in a well-oriented condition (except in clays with large amounts of nonclay minerals), the higher this value is, the lower the green strength.   Green strength is also related to the particle size of the clay minerals and to their texture.   By texture is meant their orientation with respect to each other in space and with respect to nonclay minerals which may be present.   Smaller particles would be expected to give relatively greater strength because of the increase in surface area for the adsorption of water and also perhaps because they could provide a more uniform structure.   The green strength is related to the arrangement of the mineral components in the test piece.   Thus, if the flake-shaped clay mineral particles develop preferred orientation in certain directions, the breaking strength would be expected to be somewhat greater in a direction transverse to such orientation. This must be kept in mind in comparing data and may be put to use in actual practice by arranging shaping procedures to get preferred orientation to attain certain desired strengths.

On the basis of the above concept, montmorillonites, with their small particle size and pronounced water-orienting power, would be expected to have a higher maximum green strength than that of other clay minerals, thereby yielding a dense, uniform, strong test piece. Since other clay minerals tend to occur in larger particles with perhaps less water-orienting power, the particles are not knit together into a uniform test body—there would be voids and less complete contact between individual particles. However, at the water-of-plasticity value, the much larger moisture contents of the montmorillonites, with some of this water being poorly oriented, would provide many zones of weakness and hence lower strength than that developed by the other clay minerals at the water of plasticity. The very high orienting power of the calcium ion at low moisture contents as compared with the sodium ion would cause a greater maximum green strength for clays carrying the calcium ion, especially for montmorillonite clays. In the case of clays composed of the other clay minerals, sodium may provide higher green strengths as the clays are used because this ion reduces the water-of-plasticity values for such clays.

Grim and Cuthbert (1946) have shown that the green strength of clay-sand mixtures may increase if the test piece is allowed to stand before testing under conditions which prevent the loss of plasticizing water. A time factor, therefore, may be involved with the development of green strength. These investigators have shown that the increase in strength for halloysite clays on standing may be several-fold, and that it is considerably less for kaolinite and illite clays. For montmorillonite clays there seems to be no such increase in strength. These authors concluded that this factor is a consequence of the time required for water to penetrate to all the potential surfaces of the clay minerals and for the orientation to develop in the adsorbed water. The great ease with which water penetrates between the units of the montmorillonite would make this factor of comparatively little importance for clays composed of this type of clay mineral.

Lamination

In the processes of forming ceramic ware, a preferred aggregate orientation of the clay mineral particles sometimes develops (Williamson, 1955). Thus, in extruding plastic clay through a die, the friction of the clay column against the die causes the center of the extruded column to move faster than the sides with consequent shearing stresses set up in the clay mass. The flake-shaped clay minerals tend to align themselves parallel to each other in relation to this shearing stress. As indicated above, such parallel aggregate orientation may cause greater green strength in certain directions through the clay body than in other directions.

The parallel aggregate orientation also may provide potential planes of weakness which may develop when the clay is dried and fired. This so-called lamination is favored by relatively large clay mineral particles. It seems to be particularly developed in illite and chlorite clays. The presence of granular nonclay mineral components in the clay would tend to reduce it.

The same phenomenon of aggregate orientation may develop in ware produced by casting a slip in a porous mold with the orientation developing so that the large dimensions of the clay flake-shaped particles are parallel to the surface of the mold.

DRYING PROPERTIES

After forming ceramic ware in the presence of water, it must be dried before it can be fired. This involves removal of the water in pores and adsorbed on the surfaces of the clay mineral particles, that is, all the water which is not a part of the crystal structure of the minerals. Drying is carried out normally at temperatures somewhat in excess of the boiling temperature of water. The actual temperature used varies. In general as high a temperature as possible is used which does not crack the ware in order to obtain the fastest possible drying rate. In the actual drying operation several attributes of the clay are important, namely, the amount of shrinkage accompanying drying, the strength after the loss of the water, and the ease of drying. The latter is of greatest importance and involves the rate of drying and the degree of temperature control, humidity, air velocity, etc., required in the dryer during the drying operation in order not to distort the ware or develop imperfections, such as cracks.

Drying Shrinkage

Drying shrinkage is the reduction in size, measured either in length or volume, of a mass of shaped clay that takes place when the mass is dried so as to drive off the pore water and adsorbed water. The measurement is made on pieces which have been prepared normally at water-of-plasticity values. The drying shrinkage is frequently expressed in per cent reduction in size based on the size after drying. In practice the measurement is made on a test piece after drying at 105°C for at least 5 hr.

Values showing the range of linear drying shrinkage for some of the clay minerals are given in Table 3-6. The chloritic clay minerals would

TABLE 3-6

LINEAR DRYING SHRINKAGE OF CLAY MINERALS[a]

(in Per Cent)

(After White, 1947)

Kaolinite................. 3–10
Illite..................... 4–11
Montmorillonite........... 12–23
Attapulgite...............   15
Halloysite................ 7–15

[a] Values computed as per cent of dry length
after drying test pieces of 1 sq in. cross section in an
oven at 105°C for 5 hr.

have values similar to those for illite.   Data are not at hand for allophane, but its shrinkage would be variable with maximum values probably in the range of those for the montmorillonites.

In general, the drying shrinkage is directly related to the water of plasticity.   It increases as the water of plasticity increases, and for a particular clay mineral it increases as the particle size decreases.   The data given in Table 3-7 show the amount of increase in shrinkage with the decrease in particle size of kaolinite.   The amount of drying shrinkage would be expected to vary with the degree of crystallinity of the clay mineral.   Thus, Ball clay (Holderidge, 1956), which contains relatively poorly ordered kaolinite, shows values in the high end of the range shown in Table 3-6.   Similar variations would be expected for illites and chlorites.   Under a similar line of reasoning, clays composed of mixed-layer assemblages of clay minerals would be expected to have relatively higher drying shrinkage than clays of similar composition, but with the clay mineral mixing being that of discrete particles.

The elongate and fibrous clay minerals tend to have relatively large shrinkage values because of the relatively loose packing of such particles in the specimens.   This is shown in the relatively high shrinkage of halloysite as compared to kaolinite.   In the case of halloysite, the high shrinkage is also due to the collapse of the tubular particles (Hampel and Cutler, 1953).

So far as the amount of drying shrinkage is concerned, the nature of the adsorbed cation causes variations only as it influences the water of plasticity.   Thus, Henry and Siefert (1941) and later Hofmann et al. (1958) have shown that for kaolin clays the amount of shrinkage decreases in the order of hydrogen, calcium, potassium, and sodium.   The same order would be expected for the other clay minerals except montmorillonite.   In clays composed of montmorillonite, those carrying sodium have the highest drying shrinkage just as they have the highest water-of-plasticity values.

TABLE 3-7

LINEAR DRYING SHRINKAGE OF KAOLINITE
(in Relation to Particle Size)
(After Harman and Fraulini, 1940)

Particle size, μ	Linear drying shrinkage, % of dry length
10 –20	1.45
5 –10	1.89
2 – 4	2.19
1 – 0.5	2.35
0.5 – 0.25	2.69
0.25– 0.10	3.70

The presence of nonclay minerals tends to reduce drying shrinkage in amounts varying with their shape, particle-size distribution, and of course their abundance.   Granular particles with a considerable particle-size range are most effective.   The presence of some (±25 per cent) nonclay mineral component is generally desirable in a ceramic body to improve its shrinkage characteristics; the presence of this amount is not likely to affect adversely the other ceramic properties.

Figure 3-5 illustrates the reduction of volume drying shrinkage in a series of illitic shales as the amount of minus 2 μ fraction, fraction A (clay mineral fraction), is reduced.   It is interesting that sample A of Fig. 3-5, which has unusually high drying shrinkage, contains a small

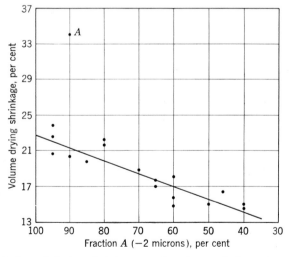

FIG. 3-5.   Relation of drying shrinkage to abundance of clay minerals in a series of illitic shales, after Grim (1941).

amount of montmorillonite in addition to the illite, which explains the relatively high value.

Williamson (1941) has shown that drying shrinkage is not uniform through a clay mass if there is preferred orientation of the clay particles. Thus, if the clay mass shows parallel orientation of the basal-plane surfaces of the clay minerals, the shrinkage in the direction at right angles to the basal planes will be substantially greater than that in the direction parallel to them. This is to be expected since the flake-shaped character of the clay minerals provides much more water-adsorbing surface on the basal-plane surfaces than at their edges. This is a matter of considerable importance because in the shaping of ceramic ware it may be difficult to avoid or control the development of preferred orientation (see Lamination, Chap. 3). Williamson (1955) has shown that a further consequence of the development of preferred orientation is that a piece of ware accidentally deformed in the plastic state and then forcibly restored to shape may inconveniently "remember" the accidental deformation and show distortion when dry. Williamson explains this phenomenon as follows:

> The clay particles are separated by water and tend to take up position within a force-network such that potential energy is a minimum. Thus, they resemble ions or molecules in a crystal lattice. A particle that has moved to a new stable position must have surmounted a potential barrier; such a movement accompanies plastic deformation. If, however, the particle is affected by a force adequate to displace it, but insufficient for this barrier to be surmounted, it tends to fall back into its original position. The associated deformation is elastic. The "memory" phenomena depend on such failures of particles to secure new stable positions.

As Norton (1952) has shown, the mechanism of drying is a simple one. If volume shrinkage is plotted against the volume of water in a clay during drying, a curve similar to that in Fig. 3-6 is obtained. The curve shows that in the initial part of the drying the volume shrinkage is about equal to the volume of water lost. Beyond a given moisture content there is either no further shrinkage or only a very small amount as the water is lost. The water lost during the shrinkage interval is called *shrinkage water* and it is believed to be that which separates the component particles. The

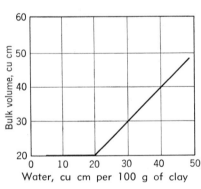

FIG. 3-6. Drying shrinkage in relation to loss of water, after Norton (1952).

critical point at which shrinkage stops is reached when the moisture film around the particles becomes so thin that the particles touch one another sufficiently so that shrinkage can go no farther.   The water lost following the shrinkage period is called *pore water*.

Norton (1949) has pointed out "the critical point is not usually so sharply defined [as shown in Fig. 3-6], nor does the lower end of the shrinkage curve always lie along the axis.   When the clays of the swelling type, such as bentonite (montmorillonite), are present, the curve is above the axis and only shrinks the final amount just before dryness, because of the fact that the last of the water is more firmly held between the crystal layers than on the surface of the particles."   The author would prefer to state this slightly differently as follows: The water adsorbed directly on the surface is fairly tightly held so that it is more difficult to drive off than the pore water; consequently, considerable adsorbed water may remain after the free pore water is evaporated.   In the case of montmorillonite, the relative amount of such tightly held water is large so that a pronounced departure from the curve in Fig. 3-6 would be expected.

In some instances a slight expansion has been recorded at the end of the drying period.   Data are not at hand to indicate whether this is the characteristic of a particular clay mineral, but it appears not to be. No satisfactory complete explanation has been advanced for the phenomena.   Henry and Siefert (1941) suggest that when the last thin film of water is driven off, the force pulling particles together is removed with a consequence that the clay flakes undergo relaxation permitting some expansion.

Williamson (1941) has stated that in some clays there is a small amount of secondary shrinkage after the primary shrinkage ceases.   He has attributed this to the desiccation of a small amount of gel that apparently holds some shrinkage water requiring more energy for its removal.

Koenig and Lyons (1955) have presented data illustrating a reduction in the amount of drying shrinkage of specimens prepared from kaolinite clays that have been precalcined.   This can be explained by the tendency of the particles to aggregate into larger-sized units on calcination and possibly also by changes in surface characteristics which would tend to reduce their water adsorbing capacity.

Ease of Drying

In the production of ceramic ware, it is obviously necessary that the shape of the ware be retained after drying and that it be free from cracks and other defects.   It is also important that such results be obtained without a need for excessively slow drying and excessive control of humidity, air flow, etc., in the dryer.

Clays vary greatly in the ease with which satisfactory drying results are obtained. Stone (1957) has analyzed in detail the variations between drying characteristics of a clay composed of poorly crystallized kaolinite with a small amount of illite, and drying characteristics of an illitic shale. The following statements are quoted from his work:

> The drying shrinkage curve [shown in Fig. 3-7A] for the kaolinitic clay shows an initial water content of 15.5 per-cent and a total drying shrinkage of 4.5 per-cent. The water content versus shrinkage curve breaks rather smoothly at a point between shrinkage water and pore water and continues to show shrinkage after the shrinkage water has been removed. Both of these features are characteristic of the illitic and finely crystalline kaolinite nature of this clay. Such clays characteristically show considerable warpage. This clay shows approximately 1/10 inch warpage during the first two hours of drying which is rather high. Hence a considerable degree of care would be necessary in drying. The pore water to shrinkage water ratio is exceptionally high, being 3 to 1. Concurrent with this high pore water to shrinkage water ratio, is a high rate of shrinkage which in this case is approximately one per-cent shrinkage per one per-cent of water. The drying shrinkage curve [in Fig. 3-7B] shows typical illite behavior. The water of workability is 26 per-cent and linear drying shrinkage is 7.3 per-cent. These figures are both somewhat higher than for the kaolinitic type material. The rate of shrinkage is 0.6 per-cent per one per-cent water as compared with the much higher rate for the kaolinitic material. The rate of water loss of shales of the illitic type is frequently in the order of 0.5 to 0.6 per-cent per hour during the early stages of drying. This figure is to be compared with values as high as one to 1.2 per-cent per hour for very short non-plastic clays of the kaolinitic type. Therefore, the relatively low rate of shrinkage in terms of per-cent shrinkage per per-cent water is partially overcome by the relatively slow rate at which the illitic shale loses its water. These two factors tend to counteract each other with reference to warpage. However, if the shale type clay is placed in very

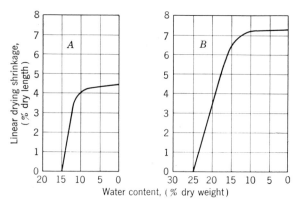

Fig. 3-7.   Drying shrinkage and water content of *A*, a poorly crystallized kaolinitic clay with some illite, and *B*, an illitic shale, after Stone (1957).

severe drying environment, which causes the rate of water loss to be excessive, then warpage will become pronounced. The low rate of water removal signifies that relatively long drying period is necessary, that is, relatively long compared to that required for sandy clays.

In general, kaolinitic and illitic clays are not particularly difficult to dry, and their over-all drying properties are much the same. However, as Stone has shown, the detailed drying characteristics may be different and must be taken into account in planning a satisfactory drying program.

Henry and Siefert (1941) have shown that, on drying, hydrogen kaolins lose water and shrink faster than sodium kaolins. Sullivan and Graham (1940) have shown that for kaolins the amount of shrinkage in relation to exchangeable cation is, in decreasing order, hydrogen, calcium, sodium; the difficulty of drying is in the reverse order. It seems generally to be true that all types of clay carrying sodium are more difficult to dry than those carrying hydrogen, potassium, and multivalent cations, even though the amount of water to be lost in drying may be smaller in the sodium clays. Sullivan and Graham (1940) have shown also that the presence of sodium tends to reduce the rate of the loss of the nonshrinkage water.

In general, drying becomes more difficult as the particle size decreases and the amount of nonclay minerals decreases. This is easily understood since drying involves the escape of moisture from the interior of the ware, and the extremely small particles and pore spaces would not permit easy escape of the water. Further, an increase in amount of adsorbing surface would accompany a decrease in particle size, which in turn would cause an increase in the relative amount of water tightly adsorbed. The presence of granular nonclay minerals, such as quartz, would tend to open up the structure for more easy escape of the water, reduce the amount of water-adsorbing surfaces, and provide a skeletal structure reducing amount of shrinkage and thereby aid in drying.

In clays carrying cations other than sodium, the ease of drying is increased as the water of plasticity is reduced. The detrimental effect of the sodium ion is probably due to its dispersing action; that is, it causes the clay particles to be separated into relatively small units thereby increasing the water-adsorbing surface area and decreasing the size of the pores. In the sodium clay, a comparatively very large portion of the water would be adsorbed on the clay mineral surfaces, and there would be relatively little pore water that would be free to escape easily. It follows from their water-adsorption and dispersion properties that montmorillonite clays would be more difficult to dry than clays composed of the other clay minerals. Although there is little confirmatory evidence, one would expect that the clays composed of elongate units, such as attapulgite, would be relatively easy to dry since the shape of the units would provide an open texture.

Satisfactory drying is a matter of uniform drying from all surfaces of the ware and uniform shrinkage in all directions. Obviously, therefore, aggregate preferred orientation in the formed ware (Williamson, 1955), a nonuniform texture throughout the ware, or a nonuniform distribution of moisture content would cause drying difficulties. It is a fact recognized by ceramists that drying problems often have their roots in the forming process. However, the need for uniform composition throughout the ware is not always recognized. Thus, a white-ware body containing an appreciable amount of montmorillonite and some Ball clays, which are the components of such bodies contain 5 to 10 per cent montmorillonite, would not be expected to show any detrimental effect on drying if this clay mineral were uniformly distributed throughout the ware. On the other hand, if it were concentrated in some ware because of different settling rates in storage tanks or for some other reason it could cause a very significant drying problem.

Dry Strength

Dry strength is measured as the transverse breaking strength of a test piece after drying long enough to remove about all the pore and adsorbed water, usually at 105°C for about 5 hr. The measurement is made using suitable precautions to prevent the readsorption of water. In some clays, particularly montmorillonite, the last small part of the adsorbed water is very difficult to remove, so that much test data reported for such clays probably do not represent specimens free of all adsorbed water.

Values for the dry strength of the individual clay minerals (Table 3-8) show a tremendous range because of variations in particle-size distribution, perfection of crystallinity, and, especially for montmorillonite, the nature of the exchangeable ions. The single values for attapulgite and halloysite are for single specimens. Chlorite would probably have values similar to those for illite.

TABLE 3-8

DRY STRENGTH OF CLAY MINERALS
(in Pounds per Square Inch)
(After White, 1947)

Kaolinite	10– 702
Illite	216–1,076
Montmorillonite	275– 830
Attapulgite	650
Halloysite	285

Perhaps the most significant factor shown in Table 3-8 is that the range of dry strength is about the same for kaolinite, illite, montmorillonite, chlorite, and attapulgite. In most cases, kaolinites, illites, and chlorites would have lower strength values than montmorillonite and attapulgite, but the maximum values attainable for these clay minerals are all about the same. It seems, therefore, that in these cases the clay mineral itself is not the major factor in determining dry strength.

The dry strength of the clay minerals is much greater than their green strength. Hofmann (1954) has pointed out that the difference between green and dry strength is less for halloysite than for the other clay minerals. He attributes the relatively low dry strength of halloysite to the textural changes that take place in the tubular units of the mineral on the loss of adsorbed water. The scant data (White, 1953) available for allophane suggest that the dry strength would be relatively low.

It should be mentioned that the dry strength of clays with high shrinkage is difficult to measure because of their tendency to develop cracks, or at least planes of weakness, on drying. Actually, if measurements are made on test pieces containing considerable nonclay granular minerals, somewhat different test results are obtained than those presented in Table 3-8. In the presence of such nonclay material, the montmorillonites have a far higher dry strength than the other clay minerals. Thus, a comparison of the dry strength for pure clay mineral materials may be misleading because it does not show the potential dry-strength-producing ability of montmorillonite when it is in the presence of considerable nonclay mineral material and when it is mixed in small amounts with other clay minerals (Endell and Wens, 1934). This latter point is shown by the data in Table 3-9.

TABLE 3-9

EFFECT OF MONTMORILLONITE ADDITIONS
ON THE DRY STRENGTH OF KAOLINITE
(After Anon., 1955)

Per cent montmorillonite added	Modulus of rupture, psi
0	283
1	391
3	536
5	732

The montmorillonite added was of the sodium variety, and the data show that a 5 per cent addition increased the dry strength threefold.

Nonclay components, if present in large amounts and particularly if the particles are well sorted, tend to reduce the dry strength. Figure 3-8 shows the decrease in dry strength with an increase in the amount of material coarser than 2 μ in a series of illitic shales. It is interesting that

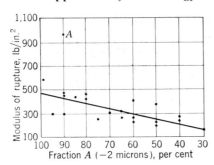

Fig. 3-8. Relation of dry strength to clay mineral content in a series of illitic shales, after Grim (1941).

sample *A* showing the relatively high dry strength contains some montmorillonite in addition to the illite. Small amounts (less than 20 per cent) of poorly sorted nonclay mineral components may actually increase dry strength by causing more uniform test pieces.

Dry strength is closely related to particle size, and in fact this seems to be a major controlling factor. Data presented in Table 3-10 for kaolinite show that the fraction finer than 0.25 μ has about 30 times the dry strength of a fraction coarser than 1 μ. On the basis of comparable particle size, there is little difference in the dry strength of clay minerals. Consistent high values obtained for some montmorillonites are a consequence of their ability to break down into extremely small particle sizes.

TABLE 3-10

DRY STRENGTH OF KAOLINITE
IN RELATION TO PARTICLE SIZE
(in Pounds per Square Inch)
(After Anon., 1955)

Whole clay	243
Coarser than 1 μ	26
1–0.25 μ	88
Finer than 0.25 μ	750

It follows from the foregoing consideration that clays composed of poorly organized clay mineral particles would have higher dry strengths than those composed of well-organized minerals. This is illustrated by the relatively high strength of Ball clays in which the kaolinite is rather poorly organized. Similarly, clays composed of mixed-layer assemblages would be expected to show higher strength than clays of similar composition, but with the components present in discrete units.

Considerable data (Endell et al., 1934; Speil, 1940; Graham and Sullivan, 1940) indicate that the presence of adsorbed sodium causes higher dry-strength values than do the other common cations, all other factors being equal. Dry strength sometimes may be increased several-fold with a substitution of sodium for the other cations, but at the same time the ware becomes much more difficult to dry without warping or cracking.

The influence of sodium is much greater on clays carrying montmoril-lonite than on those composed of the other clay minerals.   In the case of cations other than sodium there seems to be little difference in the dry strength developed because of them.   Speil (1940) has shown that an excess of sodium over that necessary to satisfy the cation-exchange capacity causes a further increase in the dry strength of kaolinite clays.   This may also apply to other clays.

The presence of organic material in some clays increases their dry strength.   This appears to be a part of the explanation for the high dry strength of some Ball clays.   In practice organic compounds are some-times added to clays to enhance their strength as well as other properties.

Maximum dry strength develops in clays composed of extremely fine particles so that the mass has a dense and uniform texture with a max-imum amount of close contact between the particles.   Moderate amounts of fine nonclay mineral material with a wide range in particle-size distribu-tion may enhance the development of uniform texture and, hence, the dry strength.   The forces holding the particles together may be classed as Van der Waals, molecular, and coulombic, with the first two probably being the most important.   The strength of these forces decreases rapidly with the distance separating the particles, so that a dense texture would enhance them.   The effect of the sodium cation is probably largely a dispersing one; that is, it increases the fineness of the clay mineral parti-cles and thereby increases the density and uniformity of the texture of the clay mass.   The effect of the organic compounds is probably a gluing action produced on drying by the development of a cementing material between particles.

Another factor adding to the dry strength is the texture of the body. It has been pointed out that the texture need be dense and uniform, but it is likely that certain arrangements of flake-shaped or elongate particles might provide some interlocking particles that would increase strength. It seems likely that the possible effect of such textural characteristics would be greater for compressive strength than for transverse strength. Recently, Hofmann, Czerch, and Scharrer (1958) have shown that, in forming clay bodies by the extrusion process, the presence of the sodium ion as compared with the presence of potassium, magnesium, or calcium tends to develop preferred aggregate orientation.   These authors suggest that the relatively higher dry strength of the sodium clays is a consequence of this preferred orientation. These authors worked with a kaolinite clay, but it is likely that their conclusions would be applicable to clays com-posed of the other clay minerals.

Koenig and Lyons (1955) have shown that the dry strength of kaolinite clays decreases when precalcined to dehydration temperatures ($\pm 600°C$).

As indicated in discussing drying shrinkage earlier in this chapter, such decreases can be explained by the changes taking place in the kaolinite particles when subjected to elevated temperatures.

The literature contains many references to a wide variety of chemical additives which are claimed to increase the dry strength of ceramic ware. West and Veale (1953) have shown, for example, that very great increases in dry strength are attained in a fireclay composed of kaolinite and illite following the addition of very small amounts of sulfuric and phosphoric acids. In this case the explanation probably resides in reaction products formed by the attack of the acids on the clay minerals which serve to cement or bind the clay particles together. This probably explains the effect of many such additives. In other cases the reaction of the additive with water to form a cementitious product, or the simple drying of the additive as in the case of some organic material, probably serves to produce a cementing material which would act as a bond.

Drying Scum

On drying, soluble salts contained by the clay tend to be carried to the surface where the evaporation of the water deposits them as a scum. Such salts are frequently sulfates, and the usual corrective procedure is to render them insoluble by the addition of a barium compound. In general, scumming may develop on ware of any clay mineral composition. Other things being equal, clay minerals other than kaolinite would probably have the greatest tendency to cause scumming because of their content of alkalies and alkaline earths, either as fixed components or as exchangeable ions. The amount of such components which can be dissolved would probably be small but still larger than for kaolinites which contain no alkalies or alkaline earths and have low adsorptive capacities.

FIRING PROPERTIES

General Statement

In considering this subject, a brief general statement of the events taking place when a clay material is heated to the temperature causing its fusion will be given and then the specific effects of the various clay minerals on the diverse aspects of firing will be discussed. It should be stated at the outset that the components of clay materials other than the clay minerals may play a dominant role in determining the characteristics developed on firing. Indeed, small amounts of certain elements, such as the alkalies, may largely determine what high-temperature phases may develop and the temperature of fusion.

As the temperature is raised to about 100 to 150°C, the shrinkage and pore waters are lost with attendant dimensional changes as indicated in the discussion of drying shrinkage. In the case of the expanding clay minerals, temperatures of the order of 100 to 300°C cause the loss of the ability to swell again. The loss of swelling potential is related to the complete loss of interlayer water; hence, heating must be continued at the indicated temperature for a considerable time. As Hofmann and Endell (1939) and others later (Greene-Kelley, 1953; Hoyos and Rodriguez, 1954) have shown, the precise temperature for the permanent loss of swelling is dependent on the nature of the adsorbed cation with the loss taking place in montmorillonites at 105 to 225°C, 300 to 390°C, and 390 to 490°C when lithium, calcium, and sodium, respectively, are the adsorbed cations. The very low temperature required by lithium for the loss of swelling potential is explained by the ease of penetration of this small ion into vacant octahedral positions in the dioctahedral lattice and the consequent reduction of charge on the lattice.

At temperatures of the order of 200 to 300°C, the oxidation of any organic material begins. The rate of oxidation depends on the nature of the organic material, the amount of oxygen available, the ease of its access through the mass of clay to the organic material, and the temperature. The nature of the organic material depends on its composition, its particle size if in discrete particles, and whether or not it is adsorbed on the clay mineral surfaces. The second factor is concerned with the texture of the clay, whether it permits the oxygen to enter and the re-action products to leave the clay body. In general, the rate of oxidation increases as the temperature increases. As is well known, it takes time to eliminate the organic material in firing a clay body, and these components must be eliminated before the ware is vitrified; otherwise the gases produced may expand and disrupt the body. Actually, the vital factor in firing many clays is the elimination of any gas-forming components before vitrification. The objective is to raise the temperature as high as possible short of vitrification in order to get the most rapid and safe rate of oxidation of the organic material and other oxidizable components.

The oxidation of sulfides, which are present in many clays, frequently in the form of pyrite, begins between 400 and 500°C. Fine-grained pyrite in the presence of abundant oxygen loses its sulfur and oxidizes with an abrupt exothermic reaction in this temperature range (Grim, 1951). In the actual firing process, the lack of sufficient oxygen may greatly retard the oxidation of the sulfides. Further, the sulfur liberated from the sulfides may react with aluminum and/or iron, made available by the partial disruption of the lattice structures of some of the clay minerals at about the same temperature, to form compounds which are resistant to oxidation; the lattice disruption is that accompanying the loss of hydroxyls from the structure of the clay minerals. The nature of these compounds is not well understood, but their presence is often indicated by a black core showing up in the center of fired bricks. Unoxidized organic material was in the past offered as the explanation for such cores and undoubtedly is the true explanation in many cases, but the presence of sulfur compounds is now known to be the explanation in some instances. So far as the clay minerals are concerned, those showing considerable lattice alteration accompanying the loss of hydroxyls, for example, the kaolinites, would be expected to provide relatively more accessible metals to react with any sulfur. In fact, black coring is a particular problem in the burning of refractory kaolinitic clays.

Beginning somewhat below 500°C and in some cases continuing to 900°C, the hydroxyl water is driven from the clay minerals. The exact temperature, rate, and abruptness of loss of hydroxyls depends on the nature of the clay minerals and their particle size. A reduction of

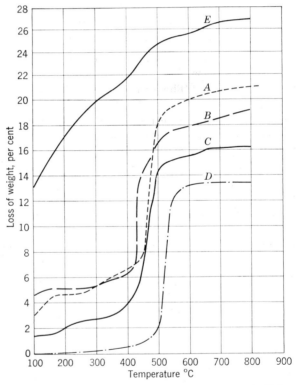

Fig. 3-9. Dehydration curves, after Ross and Kerr (1931 and 1934): *A*, halloysite, Liege, Belgium; *B*, halloysite, Adams County, Ohio; *C*, halloysite, Hickory, North Carolina; *D*, kaolinite, Ione, California; *E*, allophane, Moorefield, Kentucky.

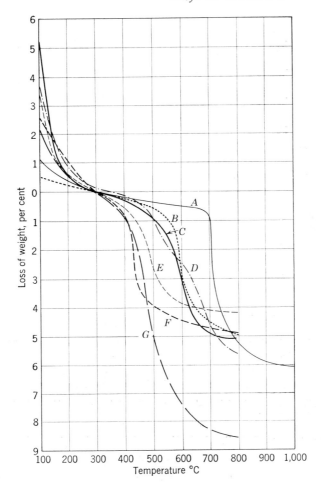

FIG. 3-10. Dehydration curves, after Ross and Hendricks (1945): *A*, hectorite, Hector, California; *B*, montmorillonite, Belle Fourche, South Dakota; *C*, montmorillonite, Tatatilla, Mexico; *D*, montmorillonite, Montmorillon, France; *E*, nontronite, Spokane, Washington; *F*, nontronite, Sandy Ridge, South Carolina; *G*, montmorillonite, Pontotoc, Mississippi.

particle size, particularly if it is accompanied by poorer crystallinity, tends to reduce the temperature required for the loss of hydroxyls and causes them to be lost more gradually over a longer temperature interval. The exact temperature of hydroxyl loss and the relation to particle size is abundantly shown in the literature through differential thermal analyses and dehydration data. Figures 3-9 to 3-16 illustrate characteristic DTA and dehydration data for the various clay minerals.

In general, the kaolinite and halloysite minerals lose their hydroxyls

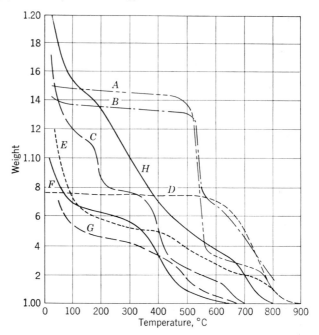

FIG. 3-11.   Dehydration curves, after Nutting (1943). The weight at 700 to 900°C is taken as the base weight in plotting the curves: *A*, penninite, Paradise Range, Nevada; *B*, chlorite, Danville, Virginia; *C*, palygorskite (mountain leather), Montana; *D*, sericite, Prince Rupert, British Columbia; *E*, vermiculite, North Carolina; *F*, illite, Fithian, Illinois; *G*, glauconite, Lyons Wharf, Virginia; *H*, sepiolite, Asia Minor.

abruptly at 450 to 600°C.   Brindley and Nakahira (1957) have deduced activation energies of 65 and 55 kcal per mole for the dehydroxylation of kaolinite and halloysite, respectively.   These authors show that the reaction rate is markedly dependent on size and shape factors of the specimens, and this is attributed to entrapped water vapor.   Vaughan (1955) has given activation energies of 25 to 40 kcal per mole for various kaolins.

The loss of hydroxyls from illites and montmorillonites varies greatly with structure and composition, but it is in the range of 450 to 650°C for dioctahedral forms of these minerals.   The presence of iron in the lattice tends to reduce the dehydroxylation temperature, whereas magnesium increases it.   In the case of dioctahedral minerals, the loss is rather abrupt, although less so than for the kaolinites and halloysites. For trioctahedral forms of these minerals it is more gradual and may persist continuously to temperatures of the order of 850°C when the original structure is lost.

In the case of chlorites, there are generally two distinct intervals of hydroxyl loss: an abrupt lower-temperature one for the loss of hydroxyls from the brucite layer at temperatures between about 450 and 650°C and a second one, for the loss of hydroxyls, from the mica part of the structure, which varies in temperature and abruptness, depending on whether the structure is dioctahedral or trioctahedral. In the case of trioctahedral forms, the water loss is more gradual and may continue up to temperatures of the order of 900°C.

In the case of attapulgite, adsorbed water is lost at about 100°C, water in the channels attached to the sides of the silicate units is lost between about 250 and 350°C, and hydroxyl water is lost from 400 to 700°C with most of it in the lower-temperature portion of this interval.

Sepiolite shows a loss of adsorbed water at about 100°C with further dehydration taking place gradually at about 300°C and continuing to 700°C.

The dehydration characteristics of the allophanes are variable. In examples in which there is little or no structural organization, the dehydration begins at temperatures of the order of 100°C and continues more or less gradually up to temperatures of about 900°C. In other examples in which there is some organization, there is superimposed on such gradual dehydration an interval of relatively more rapid loss of hydroxyls in the temperature range 400 to 600°C.

The reaction for the loss of hy-

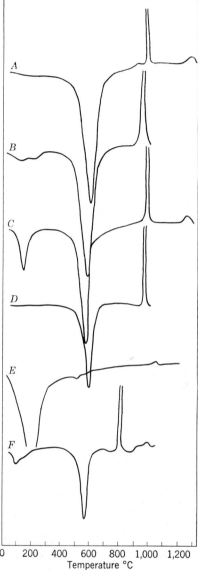

Fig. 3-12. Differential thermal curves, after Grim (1953): *A*, kaolinite, Macon, Georgia, well crystallized; *B*, kaolinite, Anna, Illinois, poorly crystallized; *C*, hydrated halloysite, Bedford, Indiana; *D*, anauxite, Ione, California; *E*, allophane, Bedford, Indiana; *F*, allophane, Iyo, Japan.

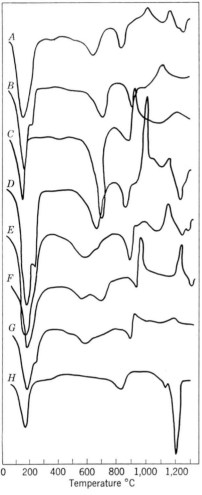

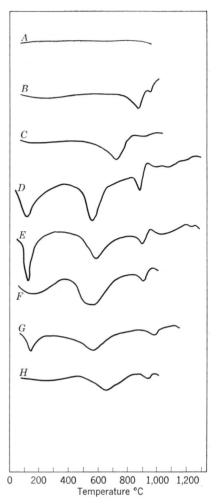

FIG. 3-13.   Differential thermal curves, after Grim (1953): *A*, montmorillonite, Otay, California; *B*, montmorillonite, Tatatilla, Mexico; *C*, montmorillonite, Upton, Wyoming; *D*, montmorillonite, Cheto, Arizona; *E*, montmorillonite, Pontotoc, Mississippi; *F*, montmorillonite, Palmer, Arkansas; *G*, nontronite, Howard County, Arkansas; *H*, hectorite, Hector, California.

FIG. 3-14.   Differential thermal curves, after Grim (1953): *A*, biotite, University of Illinois collections; *B*, muscovite, University of Illinois collections; *C*, muscovite, Bryman, California (minus 1 μ fraction); *D*, illite, Fithian, Illinois; *E*, illite, Grundy County, Illinois; *F*, illite, Thebes, Illinois; *G*, glauconite, New Jersey; *H*, glauconite, Washington.

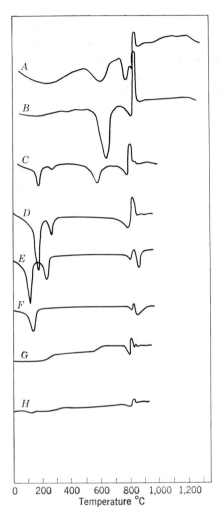

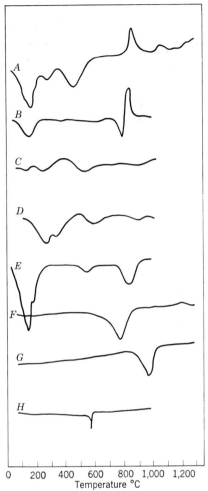

Fig. 3-15. Differential thermal curves: *A*, prochlorite, Chester, New York; *B*, clinochlore, Brewster, New York; *C*, vermiculite and chlorite, Lenni, Pennsylvania; *D–H*, vermiculite, North Carolina (*D*, natural, *E*, *F*, *G*, and *H*, with Ca^{++}, Na^+, NH_4^+, and K^+, respectively) *A–C*, after Grim (1953); *D–H*, after Barshad (1948).

Fig. 3-16. Differential thermal curves, after Grim (1953): *A*, attapulgite, Attapulgus, Georgia; *B*, sepiolite, Salinelles, France; *C*, palygorskite, North Africa; *D*, palygorskite, from Caillere (1936); *E*, vermiculite, Arizona; *F*, pyrophyllite, North Carolina; *G*, talc, Vermont; *H*, quartz, University of Illinois collections.

droxyls under ordinary firing conditions requires only the application of heat. Unlike the oxidation reaction, it is not dependent on the presence of oxygen and the escape of oxidation products. It is related to the ease of escape of the released water vapor, but under practical conditions, in the case of clay minerals like kaolinite, it is not possible to appreciably slow down the reaction by a reduced firing rate. In the case of clay minerals from which the hydroxyls are lost gradually, it is of course possible to slow down the reaction. In burning a clay composed of clay minerals whose dehydroxylation reaction cannot be slowed down it is obviously unnecessary, so far as the clay mineral is concerned, to try to fire slowly through the corresponding temperature interval. It is just as obvious that there might be other factors, for example, the presence of oxidizable components, which would require a reduction in heating rate. In the case of the three-layer clay minerals, when a dioctahedral component is present, it would also be impossible to reduce the rate of hydroxyl-water loss, and firing might as well, so far as this reaction is concerned, proceed through this temperature interval as rapidly as possible. The author is convinced that firing schedules have very frequently been prolonged by the erroneous idea that hydroxyl-loss reactions in every case could be and needed to be slowed down.

Accompanying the loss of hydroxyls, the structures of kaolinite and halloysite are changed but not completely destroyed. The hexagonal flake shape of kaolinite is retained (see pages 98–100). In the temperature interval following hydroxyl loss and below that of the crystallization of the first new high temperature phases (950 to 1000°C) the silica and alumina from the kaolinite are quite reactive. The alumina is readily soluble in acid and readily reacts with alkalies and alkaline earths.

In the case of the three-layer dioctahedral clay minerals, the structure is changed somewhat (Bradley and Grim, 1951) but is not lost when the hydroxyls are driven off. The structural order of these three-layer clay minerals is somewhat greater than that of the dehydrated kaolinite and halloysite with the result that the components are relatively not reactive between the temperatures of hydroxyl loss and the first new phase formation. For the trioctahedral three-layer minerals, the structure is largely lost accompanying the loss of hydroxyls so that reactive material would result. Theoretically, there should be large differences in the firing characteristics of dioctahedral and trioctahedral three-layer clay minerals, for example, in their vitrification temperature range, but so far there has been little specific investigation of this particular point. It should also be of great importance in the manufacture of portland cement and pozzolanas, where the reactivity of the dehydrated clay minerals is of major importance (see Chap. 8).

Carbonates lose carbon dioxide in the temperature interval from about

500 to 900°C with the exact temperature varying with the nature of the carbonate and its composition (Cuthbert and Rowland, 1947; Kerr and Kulp, 1948). An abundant literature portrays the reactions for the loss of carbon dioxide from carbonates. These reactions are abrupt and endothermic and would take place, therefore, when the material reaches the proper temperature. Slight increases in pressure because of the difficulty in the escape of the carbon dioxide would probably slightly increase the abruptness of the reaction.

The structure of the dehydrated form of the dioctahedral micas is lost by about 900°C, and all of the clay minerals are completely dehydrated by this temperature. In the presence of a large quantity (more than about 5 per cent) of iron, alkalies, and alkaline earths (fluxes) as components of the clay minerals, as adsorbed ions, or as nonclay mineral material, there may be little development of distinct high-temperature crystalline phases with the consequence that the clay material begins to fuse into a glassy mass at about this temperature.

Following the loss of hydroxyls from their structures, the clay minerals may, under some conditions, regain these hydroxyls and substantially develop their initial structures again. Grim (1953) has summarized data on such rehydration and indicated that, when there is little structural change accompanying the loss of hydroxyls, the rehydration and regain of structure is relatively easy and may take place under ordinary conditions of temperature and pressure. In cases where the loss of hydroxyls is accompanied by substantial structural changes, the rehydration and regain of structure is slow and may not take place to any substantial extent unless the dehydrated material is subjected to moderately elevated temperatures and pressures in the presence of water vapor.

In the absence of considerable quantities of fluxes, new crystalline phases develop from the clay minerals immediately, or after only a brief temperature interval, following the loss of the clay mineral structure and/or complete dehydration. New crystalline phases develop from all of the clay minerals except those containing large amounts of iron, alkalies, and/or alkaline earths in which case fusion may result after dehydration without any intervening crystalline phase. Frequently, there is a series of new high temperature phases developing in an overlapping sequence as the mineral is heated to successively higher temperatures. This is followed by eventual complete fusion of the mineral.

It has been shown that there may be a relationship between the structure of the original clay minerals and the initial high temperature phases; that is, there is a certain amount of structural inheritance (Bradley and Grim, 1951; Kulbicki and Grim, 1959; Brindley and Nakahira, 1959). However, such structural inheritance may be modified or nullified by the presence of very small quantities of extraneous compounds. Byrne (1954) has shown that some adsorbed organic molecules which are oxidized before the beginning of the crystallization of high temperature phases may have so influenced the clay mineral structure as to cause variations in high-temperature-phase development. Kulbicki (1958) has shown the very great variation in high temperature phases developed in montmorillonites with different exchangeable cations and following treatment with salts of varying concentrations. In general, it may be stated that data are available to predict the high temperature phases of most of the clay minerals with common exchangeable cations in the absence of impurities. Frequently, the data permit the prediction of only the initial high temperature phases and not the complete sequence up to fusion. In general, it may also be stated that the particular initial high temperature phases depend to a large extent on the structural character of the clay mineral, and the later high temperature phases depend more on the total composition. These two generalities apply, of course, to clay materials which do not contain considerable extraneous fluxes.

In the development of a high temperature phase, there first is frequently a nucleation of the new lattice configuration followed by a slow gradual growth of the new structure and an increase in its perfection when the temperature is raised slightly above that required for nucleation. This gradual change may be accompanied by a difference in form; thus, Lundin (1955) has shown that the mullite formed at low temperatures is in small, more or less equidimensional particles, and that the characteristic needlelike units do not develop until later. Brindley and Nakahira (1959) have shown that the parameters of mullite and its composition change as it develops with increasing temperatures. The nucleation is accompanied sometimes by a considerable release of energy and is shown on the differential thermal diagram by a sharp exothermic peak. At the temperature of the exothermic peak, X-ray analyses may not reveal the new phase causing the peak, because the new units may be too small or too imperfect to give appreciable diffraction intensity. Heating to a higher temperature and/or for considerable periods of time is necessary before the new phase is revealed by X-ray diffraction. Even more heating may be necessary before the new phase can be detected with a light microscope. Recent investigations with continuous X-ray diffraction at elevated temperatures using spectrometer techniques have provided very useful information on the temperature of formation and the rate of development of high temperature phases. Grim and Kulbicki (1957) have shown that a long heating period at the nucleation temperature is not always adequate to further develop the new phase; the temperature must be raised to increase atomic mobility so that the new structure can grow and develop. This is a matter of extreme importance in determining firing schedules, particularly if some definite high temperature phase is wanted, as for example, mullite in a refractory brick produced from a kaolinite clay. Thus, mullite begins to form from kaolinite at about 1000°C, but it generally does not develop rapidly until about 1250°C, and, so far as mullite development is concerned, firing should proceed to 1250°C as rapidly as possible.

It follows from the foregoing statements that differential thermal analyses frequently indicate the formation of a new high temperature phase before it is revealed by X-ray diffraction. The failure to appreciate this sequential development of new phases has been a major cause for the confusion and differences of opinion in the literature regarding high-temperature-phase development of the clay minerals.

As indicated previously, the presence of the fluxes in the clay material may cause vitrification and fusion at temperatures as low as 900°C. In the case of other clay materials, temperatures as high as 1900 to 2000°C are required to destroy the structures of the high temperature phases and cause complete fusion. Usually some of the high temperature phases will fuse before others and produce a glassy phase which knits together the still remaining structural units. There is, therefore, in most clay materials a gradual melting or a vitrification range during which liquid phases are produced from the crystalline components. In clay materials which are composed of mixtures of clay minerals such a vitrification range may be relatively long. A long vitrification range, of course, is desired in commercial firing operations so that the burning schedule need not be so precisely controlled.

Problems concerning the firing of ceramic products have their roots in high temperature phases developed from the clay minerals. Since any know-how that will reduce the time necessary to fire a ceramic product will effect large cost reductions, investigations of changes taking place during firing have tremendous economic impetus behind them. The literature is full of phase diagrams for mixtures of various oxides, and these data are extremely valuable for the consideration of firing problems. The writer would emphasize that the structure of the minerals in the starting clay and the presence of extremely small amounts of certain components are also important—in fact, they may determine a somewhat different sequence of events from that which would be predicted from an equilibrium system of pure oxides.

High-temperature-phase Development of the Clay Minerals

It is intended in this section to summarize pertinent available data on high-temperature-phase development for each of the clay minerals and to indicate variations that accrue because of variations in the adsorbed ions and the presence of small amounts of some extraneous materials. It must be emphasized that the data on the latter point are scant for many of the clay minerals, so that high-temperature-phase development cannot always be predicted for any given clay material solely on the basis of its clay mineral composition.

For some of the clay minerals the literature contains detailed analyses of the structural transition of one phase to another. This is considered to be out of the scope of this volume and will not be considered. For those interested, the work of Grim (1953), Bradley and Grim (1951), Brindley (1952), Brindley and Nakahira (1959), Kulbicki (1959), and others may be considered.

Another point requiring emphasis from a practical standpoint is the importance of the particle size of the component minerals of a clay. Thus, a clay composed of a mixture of quartz and kaolinite may have a composition of Al_2O_3 and SiO_2 indicating relatively low refractiveness on the basis of the phase diagram. Yet such clays find wide use as refractory materials because of the relatively long time required for elevated temperatures to cause reactions in the larger particles of these minerals.

KAOLINITE

There is no general agreement among investigators concerning the reactions taking place when kaolinite is heated to elevated temperatures even though this matter has been studied by many people. Grim (1953) and more recently Brindley and Nakahira (1959) have summarized the various conclusions that have been reached concerning these reactions. Since diffraction data obtained for kaolinites heated in the temperature interval from the loss of hydroxyl water ($\pm 500°C$) to about 1200°C are extremely poor, there can be many differences of opinion concerning their interpretation. At temperatures of the order of 1200°C, mullite and cristobalite are developed from kaolinite. The uncertainty concerns the character of the material resulting when kaolinite is heated in the temperature interval after dehydration to about 1200°C.

Many early investigators were of the opinion that following the loss of hydroxyls the material was an amorphous mixture of alumina and silica. In 1939 Tscheiswili et al. proved that this material had at least some residual structure related to that of kaolinite and from the available evidence suggested a structure in which the Si-O network of kaolinite remained largely intact after the dehydration and the Al-O network reorganized itself in the form of edge-shared Al-O octahedral chains. Electron microscope studies, particularly those by Comefero et al. (1948), showed that kaolinite particles retained their hexagonal outline far above the dehydration temperature. Comer et al. (1956) have presented excellent electron micrographs to illustrate this point. It is now generally agreed that this "metakaolin" has some structure related to that of kaolinite. Roy et al. (1955) have presented electron-diffraction data, and

Brindley and Hunter (1955), reasoning from studies of small flakes of nacrite, have shown that some degree of crystallinity persists after dehydration and that metakaolin has structural continuity with the parent material. Brindley and Nakahira (1959) have presented X-ray diffraction data for metakaolin derived from single crystals of kaolinite indicating that it has two-dimensional regularity in the *ab* plane and an absence of regularity in the third dimension. Thus, the layer structure of kaolinite persists in some modified form in metakaolin, but collapse of the layer destroys periodicity normal to the layers. These authors propose a structural model for metakaolin.

At a temperature of about 950°C, kaolinite experiences a sharp exothermic reaction and there has been much dispute concerning the explanation of this reaction. Insley and Ewell (1935) and many others have attributed it to the formation of gamma alumina. Other investigators have disagreed with this conclusion, for when pure amorphous alumina is heated, gamma alumina crystallizes over a long temperature interval and at a lower temperature. Furthermore, gamma alumina has a structure unlike one which would be anticipated from the sharpness and high intensity of this thermal reaction. Insley and Ewell (1935) attempted to explain these difficulties on the basis of some structural order in the dehydrated kaolinite which would delay the formation of gamma alumina until a relatively high temperature was reached with a sudden reaction releasing much energy. Comefero et al. (1948) have concluded that this exothermic reaction is to be explained by the formation of mullite. The difficulty with this explanation is that X-ray diffraction patterns obtained on material heated just above this thermal reaction reveal either no definite diffraction lines for mullite or only very faint ones. Johns (1953) has considered that the exothermic reaction is due to the nucleation of mullite and that further heating or a higher temperature is necessary for the development of the mineral to the extent required for good diffraction characteristics. Grim and Kulbicki (1957) have presented data supporting this conclusion. Roy et al. (1955) have also recently presented some electron-diffraction data supporting the same conclusion. Gerard-Hirne and Meneret (1956) have also arrived at the same conclusion. On the other hand, Richardson (1951) and Colegrave and Rigby (1952) have recently concluded that this exothermic reaction is to be explained by the formation of gamma alumina.

All investigators are agreed that at temperatures of the order of 1200°C any gamma alumina that might have been present has disappeared and mullite and cristobalite are the phases formed. The question essentially is whether gamma alumina is an intermediate phase forming from the metakaolin and from which mullite and cristobalite develop.

Brindley and Nakahira (1959) have recently investigated this matter in great detail using single crystals of kaolinite. They conclude that at about 950°C the metakaolin alters to gamma alumina, and the sharp exothermic reaction is a consequence of the formation of the gamma alumina. They further conclude that the gamma alumina has a spinel-type structure, and this phase carries some silicon. They point out a rather simple structural transformation from their proposed metakaolin structure to this cubic, silica-carrying, spinel-type structure. According to these authors, at about 1050°C the spinel-type structure transforms to a mullite phase. Silica is eliminated progressively as metakaolin transforms to the gamma alumina phase and thence to mullite. Above about 1100°C, the discarded silica appears on diffraction data as cristobalite. From 1200 to 1400°C there is continued development of cristobalite and mullite.

Vaughan (1955) has found that the evolution of heat at the abrupt exothermic reaction is from 8 to 40 cal per g for various kaolinites with usual values in the range of 16 to 25 cal per g.

The possible influence of the effect of variations in the crystallinity of the kaolinite on the high-temperature phases has been investigated by Glass (1954), Johns (1953), Wahl (1958), and by Roy et al. (1955). In general, these investigators all show that, at temperatures of the order of 1200°C, mullite and cristobalite are developed regardless of the degree of crystallinity of the kaolinite. They further show that X-ray diffraction data of well-crystallized kaolinite heated to just beyond the exothermic reaction are much more likely to show lines for mullite than data for poorly ordered kaolinite would. Johns (1953) has presented structural concepts showing that the transition from a probable structure for metakaolinite to mullite is much simpler for well-ordered kaolinite than for the poorly organized mineral. It seems quite certain that mullite and also cristobalite develop more easily from well-ordered than from poorly ordered kaolinite. Stubican (1959) has suggested that gamma alumina can form more readily from disordered kaolinite than from the well-ordered mineral.

Numerous investigators have studied the influence of traces of impurities on the high temperature reactions of kaolinite. Bertorelli and Williams (1949) have claimed that mullite formation is enhanced by heating in the presence of inert gases. Caillere et al. (1946) and Meneret (1957) have shown that very small amounts of various impurities may greatly affect the intensity of the 975°C exothermic reaction. Parmelee and Rodriguez (1942) showed that zinc, lithium, magnesium, iron, manganese, cerium, and molybdenum markedly enhanced the formation of mullite from kaolinite; boron and calcium enhanced it slightly; sodium, potassium, titanium, and tin retarded its formation; and the relative influence of these elements varied with temperature. Crookston (1949) found that the presence of potassium reduces markedly the formation of cristobalite from kaolinite; sodium reduces it slightly; and calcium, magnesium, and hydrogen have little effect.

Wahl (1958) has recently investigated this matter in some detail by the use of continuous X rays. He concluded that some mullite, which he calls primary mullite, is formed at the temperature of the 975°C exothermic reaction and that additional mullite, which he calls secondary mullite, is formed at a temperature of about 1200°C. He finds that considerable primary mullite is formed on the heating of well-organized kaolinite, whereas very little develops from poorly organized kaolinite or halloysite. He also finds that the secondary mullite develops abruptly from poorly organized minerals but more gradually and beginning at a lower temperature from well-organized kaolinite. Wahl's data show that magnesium, iron, lead, boron, and calcium, when present in trace amounts, enhance the formation of mullite and that its development is retarded by alkali ions. Of particular interest is his conclusion that these elements act particularly on the development of secondary mullite and have little influence on the material that is formed at the temperature of the exothermic reaction.

Wahl (1958) also recorded the formation of cristobalite at elevated temperatures. His data indicated that magnesium, fluorine, lead, calcium, and phosphorus in trace amounts enhance the development of cristobalite, whereas alkalies retard or prevent its development.

HALLOYSITE

In general the high temperature reactions of halloysite are like those of kaolinite, particularly the poorly ordered form. There is even less certainty concerning the precise nature of the high temperature reactions in halloysite than there is for kaolinite because the diffraction data obtained on heated samples are even poorer than those for kaolinite.

The hydroxyl water is lost on heating halloysite to temperatures above about 450°C, and an activation energy of 55 kcal is required for the dehydroxylization, according to Brindley and Nakahira (1937). Following the loss of hydroxyl water a poorly ordered phase develops which probably is similar in some ways to that of metakaolin. According to Roy et al. (1955), this metakaolin phase persists only to temperatures of the order of 675 to 700°C where it is lost and gamma alumina is simultaneously developed. According to these authors, the gamma-alumina phase persists until about 950°C where it is lost with the nucleation of mullite. Richardson (1951) and later Glass (1954) arrived at somewhat different conclusions. According to these authors, gamma alumina does not develop until about 950°C, and its development is responsible for the sharp exothermic reaction at this temperature. Visconte (1956) has pointed out that the tubular form of halloysite persists to 970°C, which is at least into the range of the high-temperature exothermic reaction. Stubican and Gunthard (1957) have indicated on the basis of infrared analyses that adsorbed water is present in halloysite following its heating to 850°C, whereas in well-ordered kaolinite no such water is present in material heated above 650°C. It can only be concluded that further research is necessary to elucidate the nature of halloysite after it is dehydrated and heated into the range of the intense exothermic reaction at about 950°C.

Richardson (1951) found that cristobalite develops at about 1100 to 1300°C and mullite at 1100 to 1350°C. Numerous other investigators have confirmed the presence of these minerals in this temperature range.

The presence of traces of elements appears to have about the same effect on high-temperature-phase development in halloysite as they do in kaolinite except that, as shown by Wahl (1958), the additives are relatively more effective in halloysite. Thus, in enhancing the development of cristobalite and mullite, those additives also develop these new phases at a somewhat lower temperature in halloysite than in kaolinite.

ILLITE

The loss of hydroxyls from illites begins at about 400°C and may continue to about 900°C. In the trioctahedral forms of the mineral, the dehydration appears to take place gradually; whereas in the dioctahedral forms DTA curves indicate an interval of relatively rapid dehydration between about 450 and 550°C. It has been shown that the dehydration of the micas is especially related to particle size (Grim and Bradley, 1951) and to the length of time they are heated (Roy, 1949). A decrease in particle size is accompanied by a reduction in the temperature at the beginning of the dehydration and by an increase in the interval during which it takes place. Dehydration is very slow at temperatures in the low end of the dehydration range (Fig. 3-17). As compared to kaolinite and halloysite, the dehydration of the illites is slow and gradual so that with moderate heating rates the mineral may not be completely dehy-

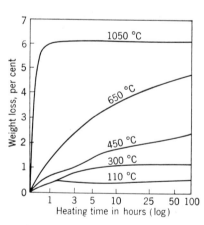

FIG. 3-17.   Dehydration curves for muscovite showing relation of water loss to time of heating, after Roy (1949).

drated until temperatures several hundred degrees higher than those adequate for the complete dehydration of kaolinite.

Grim and Bradley (1940) have shown that the loss of hydroxyl water in the dioctahedral illites studied by them is not accompanied by a loss of structure but only by a slight structural change of the kind described for montmorillonite (see page 107). According to these investigators, the structure of such illite is not destroyed until at least 850°C, and they correlate its destruction with the third endothermic reaction in the DTA curves. The illites studied by them had the muscovite type of crystallization. Maegdefrau and Hofmann (1937) have also reported the continuation of an illite-like structure beyond the loss of hydroxyl water, and in at least one of their samples it was retained to 1000°C.

According to Roy (1949), muscovite after dehydroxylation shows no further structural change until heated to about 940°C. The expulsion of at least most of the hydroxyl water is accompanied by a slight expansion of the lattice in the c dimension and not by complete destruction of the lattice. Phlogopite on heating exhibits the same characteristics as muscovite except that its structure is lost at a temperature of about 50°C lower. The biotite structure, according to Roy (1949), persists to about 1100°C and, therefore, also is not lost simultaneously with the expulsion of hydroxyl water. This is surprising in view of the reasoning of Bradley and Grim (1951) that anhydrite trioctahedral mica structures are not apt to occur. It would seem probable that the structure of trioctahedral illites would be lost gradually as they are dehydrated.

Roy (1949) reported that muscovite on firing to 1000°C develops gamma alumina and/or spinel (the X-ray data were too poor for a positive identification); at 1200°C the presence of gamma alumina was established definitely, and alpha alumina appears; and above 1400°C corundum (alpha alumina) and glass are the only phases present. Zwetsch (1934) has reported that muscovite changes at 1050°C to gamma alumina, alpha alumina, and leucite, and finally at 1300°C the crystalline phases are leucite and alpha alumina. On firing phlogopite, according to Roy (1949), spinel is formed at 1000°C and this persists as the only crystalline phase to 1550°C. On firing biotite to 1100°C the phases developed are high-iron magnetic spinel, leucite, and mullite; at about 1300°C the phases are the high-iron spinel and leucite; and at 1500°C only olivine and glass are to be found. In a biotite studied by Grim and Bradley (1940), leucite, gamma Fe_2O_3, and a spinel were identified after firing to 1200°C.

On heating several illites, Grim and Bradley (1940) found spinel appearing in all of them at about 850°C, and the spinel increased in amount and particle size up through about 1200°C. These investigators suggest that the octahedral sheet of the illite lattice carrying the alumina, magnesia, and iron goes into the formation of spinel and that the alkalies and the silica from the tetrahedral layers yield an amorphous glass.   They found that at 1300°C the spinel had been dissolved in the glass and that mullite became apparent at 1100°C and persisted to at least 1400°C.   The amounts of spinel and of mullite appeared to be complementary, and the specimens richer in spinel were subject to fusion at a somewhat lower temperature.   These investigators found no clear evidence of a quartz phase developing from their illites at elevated temperatures.

Grim and Kulbicki (1957) studied the high temperature reactions of illite by continuous X-ray diffraction.   In some samples which contained relatively large amounts of iron and alkalies, they were unable to detect the development of any crystalline phases following the complete loss of the dehydrated illite structure.   In all cases the diffraction characteristics of the high temperature phases were very poor, indicating only a small development of new crystalline phases, extremely small particle size, and/or a very low order of crystallinity.   In a sample from Fithian, Illinois, they found (Fig. 3-18) that the dehydrated illite structure persisted to about 1000°C and that this was followed immediately by the development of a spinel-type crystallization which persisted to about 1200°C, when mullite developed.

The effect of traces of additives on the high temperature reactions of illite is a subject for future researches.   In view of the presence of considerable fluxing material within the mineral, it would be expected that a major influence of such additives would be to decrease the formation of any high-temperature crystalline phases.   The foregoing data show that the various types of mica yield different high temperature phases.   This is to be expected because of the variations in composition within the micas.   Similarly, various illites would be expected to show different high temperature phases.

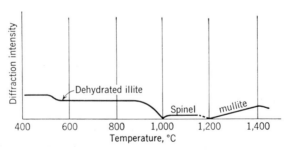

Fig. 3-18.   Phase changes on heating an illite (Fithian, Illinois) to elevated temperatures as shown by continuous X-ray diffraction, after Grim and Kulbicki (1947).

CHLORITE

The fact that clay mineral chlorite occurs mixed with other clay minerals in argillaceous materials has so far made it impossible to investigate the high temperature reactions of pure clay mineral chlorite. Based on investigations of well-crystallized chlorite which have been summarized by Grim (1953), it appears that the mineral dehydrates in two stages. The first stage, beginning about 400°C, corresponds to the loss of hydroxyls from the brucite part of the structure. In well-crystallized chlorites this reaction appears to be fairly abrupt; whereas in the clay mineral variety available data suggest that it is more gradual and begins at a somewhat lower temperature. The second stage, which corresponds to the loss of hydroxyls from the mica part of the structure, follows the dehydration of the brucite layer and may continue to temperatures of the order of 800 to 850°C. Again, the detailed characteristics of the second stage of dehydration would undoubtedly vary with particle size, degree of organization, and the dioctahedral or trioctahedral character of the mineral. Trioctahedral forms would be expected to show a more gradual dehydration, and poorly ordered extremely fine-grained material would be expected to show relatively more gradual dehydration beginning at a somewhat lower temperature.

Brindley and Ali (1955) have stated that the chlorite structure is modified but not destroyed as it dehydrates. They have discussed in some detail the nature of this modification for well-crystallized chlorites. At temperatures of the order of 800 to 900°C the modified chlorite structure disappears with the simultaneous appearance of olivine. Tooker (1952) has confirmed the presence of a modified chlorite structure between 700 and 850°C for dioctahedral forms. His data indicate that the trioctahedral form does not develop an anhydrite modification. Tooker also confirms the formation of olivine between 850 and 900°C.

Brindley and Ali (1950) have shown that the newly formed olivine phase has a high degree of preferential orientation relative to the structure of the original chlorite, and these authors have considered in detail the probable shifts in the lattice accompanying the formation of the olivine. They have shown that the temperature at which the lattice is destroyed and the temperature at which olivine forms vary for different chlorites. They have also indicated that other phases in addition to olivine form when various chlorites are heated and that the temperatures of formation of the additional phases are also variable. Thus, in some chlorites they record the formation of spinel and enstatite phases; in some instances these phases are not developed until temperatures of the order of 1100°C are reached. It is interesting that Brindley and Ali (1950) were unable to correlate in each case the thermal reactions shown by DTA curves and the phases developed as shown by X-ray diffraction. Grim (1953) has presented the following explanation for the lack of correlation.

> In some cases the new phase may develop slowly and/or involve only a slight structural shift so that it would not be accompanied by an intense or sudden energy change and, consequently, no thermal reaction would be expected on the differential thermal curve. In other cases the reaction might begin abruptly by a somewhat crude nucleation of the new phase which would involve a structural change of considerable magnitude and a definite thermal reaction, but would not yield discernible diffraction evidence of the new phase. Further heating or more time would be required to develop the new phase to the point where distinct diffraction effects become obvious. In the writer's experience the thermal reaction for a new phase frequently precedes its distinct appearance in X-ray reflections and the X-ray reflections further precede its appearance in optical measurements.

There appear to be no data available for the possible effect of traces of additives on the high temperature reactions of the chlorite minerals. On the basis of similar reasoning expressed for illites, it seems likely that such effect would be in the direction of decreasing the formation of high-temperature crystalline phases and the early development of fusion.

ALLOPHANE

No investigations appear to have been made on the high-temperature-phase reactions of allophane. Since the composition of this material can vary widely, great latitude in high-temperature-phase development of different samples would be expected. It appears that many allophanes have relatively high silica contents and rather small amounts of iron, alkalies, and alkaline earths. It would be expected that such materials would develop mullite and a silica phase, probably cristobalite, at temperatures in excess of about 1000°C. Other allophanes which contain fluxing components would be expected to develop either no high-temperature crystalline phases or perhaps those of the general character developed by the montmorillonites.

MONTMORILLONITES

The montmorillonite clay minerals lose their hydroxyl water in the range of 400 to 700°C. In general, specimens with substantial amounts of iron are in the low end of this range, and those with large amounts of magnesium are in the high end. Also, the dioctahedral forms tend to lose their hydroxyl water abruptly, whereas the loss is more gradual for the trioctahedral forms. Differential thermal curves for some montmorillonites show a dual endothermic reaction for the loss of hydroxyl water indicating a stepwise dehydration. The explanation for this characteristic is not always clear, but in some specimens, at least, it appears to be due definitely to a mixture of two forms of montmorillonite. Grim and Kulbicki (1959) have shown that many bentonites are composed of very intimate mixtures of two forms of montmorillonite, the forms varying in composition and perhaps also slightly in structural characteristics.

Thilo and Schunemann (1937) and Grim and Bradley (1940) have shown that the general layer type of structure of the dioctahedral montmorillonites and micas is able to survive the elimination of hydroxyl water with only moderate readjustments. According to Bradley and Grim (1951), removal of hydroxyl water is correlated with increases of 0.1 to 0.3 A in c axis periodicity and involves expulsion of about one-sixth of the oxygens of the octahedrally coordinated portion of the structure. An idealized rearrangement of the octahedral layers, which adequately accounts for the meager data observable is illustrated in Fig. 3-19. It represents merely the lifting of the adjacent oxygen layer out of the packed position with the immediate consequences that the vertical height is increased and the intensity of the 4.5 A diffraction line is augmented. The idealized scheme shown in Fig. 3-19 involves shared pairs of octahedral coordination faces for a dioctahedral form, and it is probably unstable. Applications of this same scheme to a trioctahedral type would demand sharing of three such pairs of the faces which is presumably impossible. No rearranged anhydrite was observed for hectorite and talc, which were the only two certain trioctahedral structures studied by Bradley and Grim (1951).

The anhydrite structure of many montmorillonites persists to temperatures of the order of 800 to 900°C. Differential thermal curves frequently show an endothermic reaction in this temperature interval, which is probably to be correlated with the loss of the anhydrite structure.

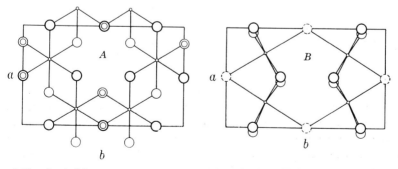

FIG. 3-19. Probable arrangement of dioctahedral montmorillonite before *A*, and following loss of hydroxyl water *B*, after Bradley and Grim (1951).

Bradley and Grim (1951) have shown that a considerable variety of high-temperature crystalline phases are formed when montmorillonites are heated above about 900°C and that they may persist to at least 1300°C. The high temperature phases developed are not the same for all montmorillonites, and this is to be expected because of the variations of chemical composition and possibly of structural variations within the group. The high temperature portion of thermal curves for montmorillonites is also quite variable, as would be expected. The high temperature phases formed include beta quartz, cristobalite, cordierite, mullite, enstatite, spinel, and anorthite.

On the basis of the study of a considerable number of samples, Bradley and Grim (1951) concluded that the high temperature portions of the DTA curves in montmorillonites tend to differentiate into two separate types: those which represent an S-shaped feature and those which exhibit a distinct shoulder directly above the third endothermic reaction. Clays yielding the S-shaped curves develop spinel following the first exothermic reaction, and the mineral is present in proportions equal in amount to the magnitude of the thermal effect. In the second group, the first prominent new phase appears to be quartz. The new phases thus seem to develop in the one case from the octahedral region in the mineral and in the other case from the tetrahedral region. From the point of view of the composition of the mineral, montmorillonites seemed to develop quartz if there was substantially no substitution in the tetrahedral layer and spinel if there was substantial substitution of aluminum in tetrahedral positions. The regularity in the composition of the tetrahedral scheme appears to endow it with ability to maintain its unity under conditions which disorganize substituted layers. Bradley and Grim (1951) discuss in some detail the structural changes involved in the development of high temperature phases when montmorillonites are heated.

Grim and Kulbicki (1957 and 1959) have studied the high-temperature-phase reactions of a large number of montmorillonites by continuous X rays. They confirmed the finding of Bradley and Grim (1951) that the high temperature reactions of various montmorillonites were somewhat different. According to them, iron-rich forms of the mineral and those carrying potassium as exchangeable cation showed very little, if any, development of new crystalline phases at elevated temperatures. These investigators reported the same high temperature phases identified by Bradley and Grim (1951) except that in many instances they did not record the initial development of spinel, perhaps because a longer time of firing at about 1000°C was required to develop this species than that used by Grim and Kulbicki in their continuous heating experiments. Grim and Kulbicki (1957) divided the aluminous montmorillonites into two types on the basis of their high temperature reactions (Fig. 3-20). One type, represented by a specimen of bentonite from Cheto, Arizona, loses all diffraction characteristics between about 800 and 850°C. At about 900°C, beta quartz appears which inverts to beta cristobalite beginning at about 1000°C. The cristobalite continues to develop until about 1200°C and then slowly disappears. A small amount of anorthite is present from about 1000° to 1150°C. Cordierite appears at about 1260°C. Both cordierite and cristobalite disappear at about 1450°C, above which temperature no crystalline phases are present.

The other type of montmorillonite, represented by samples of bentonite from Mendoza, Argentina, and from Wyoming, loses all diffraction characteristics at about 900°C. No diffraction effects are shown until about 1150°C, when mullite appears. Cristobalite develops above 1200°C, and the mullite and cristobalite persist to about 1500°C, above which temperature there are no crystalline phases.

Grim and Kulbicki (1959) show that the aluminous montmorillonites of many bentonites can be characterized as Wyoming type or Cheto type

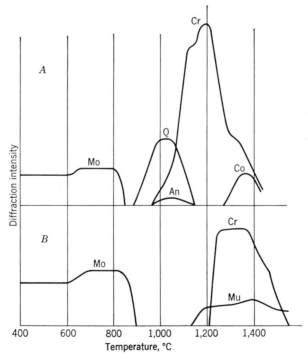

Fᴵɢ. 3-20. Phase changes on heating montmorillonite to elevated temperatures as shown by continuous X-ray diffraction, after Grim and Kulbicki (1957): *A,* Cheto type; *B,* Wyoming type; Mo, montmorillonite anhydrite; Q, beta quartz; Cr, beta cristobalite; An, anorthite; Co, cordierite; Mu, mullite.

or as a mixture of these types.   The differential thermal characteristics of these two types, in general, conform to the two groups distinguished by Bradley and Grim (1951).   However, detailed chemical analyses did not show any significant variation in the population of the tetrahedral layers of these two types and, hence, the suggestion that the amount of replacement of aluminum for silicon was a major distinction between the forms of aluminous montmorillonites could not be confirmed.   Grim and Kulbicki (1959) present data to indicate that a major difference resides in the population of the octahedral positions with the amount of

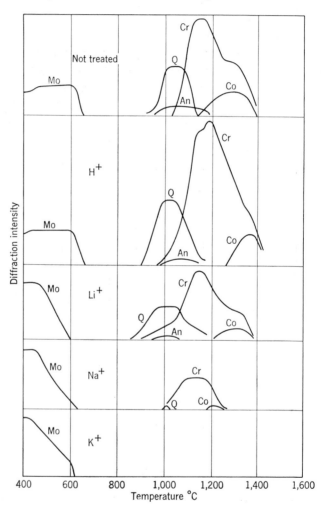

Fig. 3-21.   Phase changes on heating Cheto-type montmorillonite with various exchangeable cations to elevated temperatures as shown by continuous X-ray diffraction, after Grim and Kulbicki (1957).   See Fig. 3-20.

magnesium being larger in the Cheto than in the Wyoming type. These authors further suggest that the inversion of a small number of the silica tetrahedrons, as suggested by Edelman and Favejee (1940), might be a distinguishing characteristic of the two forms. They present evidence suggesting that there may be an appreciable amount of such inversion in the Cheto form and not in the Wyoming form.

Grim and Kulbicki (1957) showed the great influence of the exchangeable-cation composition of montmorillonite on the development of high temperature phases (Fig. 3-21). An investigation of a sample of Cheto-type montmorillonite showed an enhanced development of the high temperature phases when the exchangeable cations were replaced by hydrogen (and possibly also by some aluminum). The lithium form of the mineral showed a slight reduction in the intensity of the diffraction characteristics for the high-temperature phases. The sodium form showed a very great reduction in the development of high temperature phases and also reduced the maximum temperature to which they persisted from about 1400°C to slightly above 1250°C. In the potassium form of the mineral no high-temperature crystalline phases developed. These data show that additives or the presence of non-montmorillonite components in a natural montmorillonite clay would be likely to have a very great influence on the nature of the high temperature phases formed.

SEPIOLITE-ATTAPULGITE

The dehydration curve for sepiolite (Fig. 3-11) shows a large water loss below about 100°C and a gradual continuous loss above that temperature to complete dehydration at about 800°C. There is a relatively slight increase in water loss between 200 and 400°C and above 675°C. Migeon (1936) and Longchambon (1937) present similar dehydration data for sepiolite; according to them, there is no change in the structure of the mineral on heating to 350°C. Above this temperature, the loss of water is accompanied by a slight change in the dimensions of the structure. The modified form of sepiolite is said to persist to 700°C when it passes into a transient amorphous phase, according to Caillere (1936). Differential thermal curves of the mineral show an exothermic reaction at about 800°C, which is probably due to the development of a magnesium silicate phase. At 1000°C, Longchambon (1937) records the presence of enstatite and, at 1300°C, a mixture of enstatite and cristobalite.

Dehydration data for attapulgite show a sharp water loss below 100°C, abrupt water losses at 150 to 200°C and 375 to 425°C, and a gradual loss above 425°C, with complete dehydration at 700°C. Bradley (1940) stated that the water molecules in the channel-like interstices of the structure are lost below 100°C, and the water coordinated about the magnesium ions along the edges of the channel is lost at a slightly higher temperature,

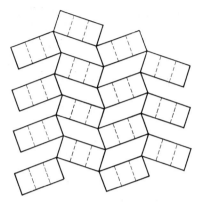

FIG. 3-22.   Dehydrated sepiolite projected on (001). The angle of tilting is arbitrary, after Preisinger (1957).

probably in the range 150 to 200°C. The loss of the hydroxyl water from the silicate unit probably begins at about the temperature of the third endothermic reaction (375°C). Apparently, some of this hydroxyl water is lost abruptly but most of it more slowly between 450 and about 700°C. According to Longchambon (1936 and 1938), the loss of water up to about 400°C is not accompanied by any structural changes, but at about 400°C there is a rapid contraction of the crystal lattice normal to the length of the fiber, and this modified structure persists to 775°C when the structure is destroyed and further shrinkage takes place.   Caillere and Henin (1951) state that the high temperature phases of some attapulgites are probably enstatite, sillimanite, and cristobalite.

Preisinger (1957) has shown that below 800°C the ribbons of sepiolite take a tilted position as indicated in Fig. 3-22.   Bradley and Kulbicki (1959) found that this tilting takes place in attapulgite at 300 to 350°C and in sepiolite at 350 to 450°C.   The original structure is readily regained by attapulgite unless heating is continued considerably above 350°C.   For sepiolite, the original structure is regained with difficulty when heated to 450°C.   According to Kulbicki (1959), the sepiolite structure is lost at about 800°C followed immediately by the nucleation of enstatite which develops slowly to a maximum at about 1350°C.   Beta cristobalite forms in some samples at 1075°C; in others only above 1350°C.   Both phases persist to above 1500°C, and the elongate units may persist to above 1400°C.

Kulbicki (1959) states that the attapulgite structure is lost at about 800°C followed immediately by the nucleation of mullite which develops slowly as the temperature is raised.   Beta quartz appears at about 1100°C, and both phases disappear at about 1200°C with the appearance of beta cristobalite, which persists above 1400°C.   The needlelike morphology begins to disappear at about 1200°C.   Exchangeable cations have about the same influence on the high temperature phases developed from attapulgite as from aluminous montmorillonites.

Dimensional Changes on Firing

Values for the linear firing shrinkage of the clay minerals are given in Table 3-11; the data for the last four minerals in this table are for single samples and should be considered only as indicating the order of magnitude of the shrinkage.

TABLE 3-11

LINEAR FIRING SHRINKAGE OF CLAY MINERALS
(in Per Cent)
(After White, 1945)

Kaolinite	2–17
Illite	9–15
Montmorillonite	20
Halloysite	11
Attapulgite	23
Allophane	50

The values indicate that the total shrinkages on firing of kaolinites and illites are small and substantially equal. The range in the per cent of shrinkage is due to variations in the size and shape of the clay mineral particles and in the case of the illites also to variations in composition. Koenig and Lyons (1955) have shown that for kaolinites the amount of shrinkage increases as the percentage of very small plate-shaped particles increases in relation to larger booklike masses of the mineral. Similar relations would be expected to apply to illites. In the case of illite increases in the amount of fluxing material would be expected to provide a relative increase in the amount of total firing shrinkage. Values for chlorites are probably similar to those for illites.

The value for halloysite given in Table 3-11 is relatively small. However, Hampel and Cutler (1953) have shown that halloysite may have relatively large shrinkage if the tubular particles have a relatively open packing arrangement and, further, that preferred orientation of the tubes may cause large differential firing shrinkage with a consequent cracking and breaking up of the fired piece. Firing shrinkage of montmorillonite would be expected to be variable depending on composition but in general rather large, perhaps about twice that of kaolinite, illite, or chlorite. The shrinkage of attapulgite appears to be about the same as that of montmorillonite. Data are not available to generalize on this property for allophanes, but the shrinkage would be expected to be quite high.

Firing shrinkage varies with the particle-size distribution tending to

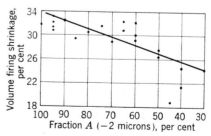

FIG. 3-23. Relation of volume firing shrinkage to the amount of minus 2 μ material in a series of illitic shales, after Grim (1941).

increase as the amount of small-particle-size material increases and as the sorting increases.   Figure 3-23 shows the general increase in the volume firing shrinkage of a series of illitic shales as the amount of fraction less than 2 μ (fraction *A*) tends to increase.   The firing shrinkage also varies with composition and tends to increase as the fluxing components increase with the production of relatively more glassy material and less high-temperature crystalline phases during the firing.   It is interesting that there is no correlation between the content of hydroxyls in the clay mineral structure and the firing shrinkage, indicating that this is not a significant factor in the amount of such shrinkage.

It must be remembered that constituents other than the clay minerals in a clay or shale may exert a controlling influence on firing shrinkage. Thus, the presence of a considerable amount of quartz may be important in reducing the shrinkage.   The clay minerals do, however, largely control the rate of shrinkage and the temperature intervals during which shrinkage takes place.

Hyslop and McMurdo (1938), Steger (1942), Norton (1952), and Kiefer (1952 and 1957) have presented data on the dimensional changes taking place in specific clay minerals as they are heated (Figs. 3-24 to 3-29).   They show that kaolinite and halloysite may exhibit an initial slight expansion up to about 500°C (Fig. 3-25).   This expansion is followed by modest shrinkage accompanying the loss of hydroxyl water, and beginning about 900°C it is followed by a more rapid and considerable shrinkage accompanying the formation of high-temperature crystalline phases. Kiefer (1957) has shown that above about 900°C there is a very rapid interval of shrinkage to about 1000°C followed by an interval of slight shrinkage to about 1200°C after which the shrinkage again becomes very

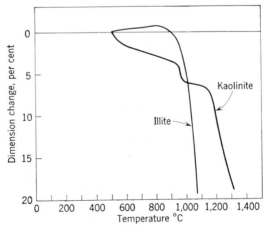

Fig. 3-24.   Dimensional changes on firing kaolinite and illite, after Kiefer (1952).

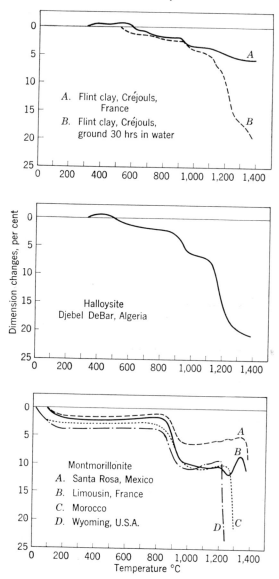

Fig. 3-25. Dimensional changes on firing kaolinite (flint clay), halloysite, and montmorillonite, after Kiefer (1957).

rapid (Fig. 3-25). He has correlated the first of these periods of rapid shrinkage with the formation of mullite and the second with the formation of cristobalite. Norton (1952) has presented data (Fig. 3-27) indicating the relatively more rapid rates of shrinkage for kaolinite in these same temperature intervals. Kiefer (1957) presents interesting data for

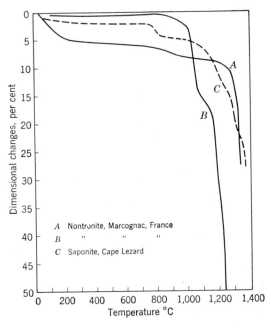

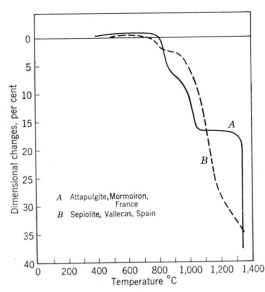

Fig. 3-26. Dimensional changes on firing nontronite, saponite, attapulgite, and sepiolite, after Kiefer (1957).

flint clay (Fig. 3-25) showing the increase in amount of shrinkage of this kaolinite clay as the particle size is reduced. The sample of halloysite investigated by Kiefer (1957) gave about the same results as those obtained for kaolinite (Fig. 3-25).

The data for illite (Fig. 3-24) show a slight expansion from about 450 to 800°C followed by a rapid continuous shrinkage. The expansion accompanied the development of the anhydrite structure and the shrinkage accompanied the loss of the structure. The relative rate of this high temperature shrinkage would be expected to be greater in samples of illite which showed the least development of high-temperature crystalline phases. Kiefer (1957) has presented data (Figs. 3-28 and 3-29) for muscovite and phlogopite showing the increase in shrinkage as the particle size is reduced by grinding. This author has also shown the much larger amount of expansion in the larger-sized particles of mica and the significant relation of the amount of expansion to preferred orientation in the samples of these minerals. The samples of illite investigated were dioctahedral forms, and probably no expansion would be expected for the trioctahedral forms since they do not develop an anhydrite structure. The trioctahedral forms would be expected to show gradual shrinkage developing as the clay mineral structure was lost.

No data are at hand for clay mineral chlorites, but they would probably show about the same characteristics as the illites.

The aluminous montmorillonites (Fig. 3-25) show no dimensional changes from about 200 to 800°C except for a slight expansion in some cases between about 600 and 800°C. Above about 800°C, there is a relatively rapid shrinkage to about 1000°C after which there is no change in dimension, except in some cases where there is a slight expansion, until fusion temperatures are reached, about 1200°C; at this temperature very

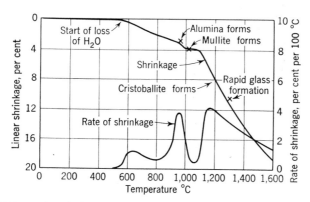

FIG. 3-27. Dimensional changes and rate of shrinkage on firing kaolinite, after Norton (1952).

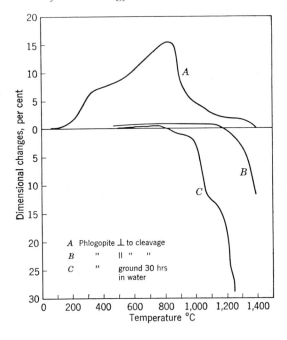

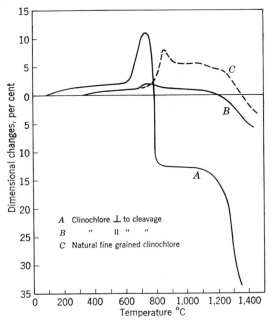

FIG. 3-28. Dimensional changes on firing phlogopite and chlorite, after Kiefer (1957).

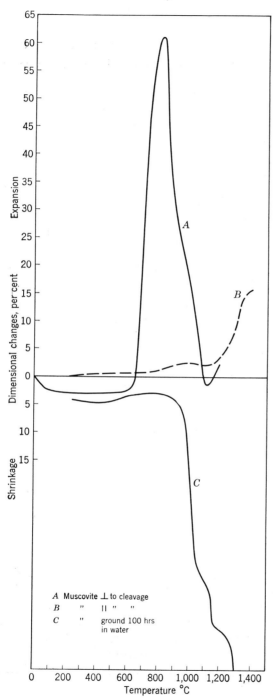

Fig. 3-29. Dimensional changes on firing muscovite, after Kiefer (1957).

rapid shrinkage again takes place. The dimensional changes above 1000°C vary greatly from one montmorillonite to another as would be expected by variations in composition with the consequent variations in the high temperature phases formed and the temperature of fusion.

Two samples of nontronite (Fig. 3-26) showed no interval of expansion on heating. In one example, there was little dimensional change from about 200 to 800°C. Following this there was rapid shrinkage from 800° to 1000°C and very rapid shrinkage above 1000°C. For the other sample of nontronite there was gradual shrinkage to about 1200°C, after which shrinkage became very rapid. A sample of saponite (Fig. 3-26) also showed no expansion but slight shrinkage to about 750°C followed by a brief interval (750 to 800°C) of more rapid shrinkage, then an interval of gradual shrinkage to 1100°C, after which the shrinkage again became very rapid.

Kiefer (1957) has shown (Fig. 3-26) that attapulgite expands slightly in the interval 400 to 800°C. This is followed by an interval of sharp shrinkage to about 1000°C. Above 1000°C there is little shrinkage until about 1300°C, after which very rapid shrinkage accompanies the fusion of the mineral. This same investigator found very little dimensional change for sepiolite (Fig. 3-26) until about 750°C. From 750 to about 800°C there was rapid shrinkage followed by an interval to 950°C of very slight shrinkage and then, above 950°C, continuous rapid shrinkage.

In general, it may be stated that the loss of hydroxyl water is accompanied by slight shrinkage if there is some loss of crystalline structure accompanying the loss of hydroxyls. If the structure is not substantially altered, as in the case of the dioctahedral micas and montmorillonites, the loss of hydroxyls may be accompanied by a slight expansion. This expansion accompanying the formation of an anhydride phase may not cause an over-all expansion in the fired piece as there may be adequate pore space to take care of the increase in dimension of the clay minerals. Also, it must be remembered that textural variations or the formation of gaseous material may cause expansion on heating which is not related to a volume change in the clay mineral structure. The major shrinkage begins at the temperatures corresponding to the formation of high-temperature crystalline phases and, in general, becomes most rapid as vitrification begins with the development of glassy material. Again, the development of glassy material during the vitrification interval may be accompanied by bloating, that is, an expansion of the dimensions of the test piece, if all gas-forming components have not been eliminated at lower temperatures.

Rieke and Mauve (1942) have presented some interesting data to show the changes in specific gravity of some of the clay minerals as they are heated to 1000°C. According to these authors and also Harmon and

Parmelee (1942), the specific gravity of kaolinite drops abruptly at about 450°C when the mineral is dehydrated and a poorly ordered structure develops. The specific gravity gradually increases as the kaolinite is heated to higher temperatures, probably indicating some development of order; at 950 to 1000°C there is an abrupt increase in specific gravity to a value higher than that of the original. This sudden increase in specific gravity can be correlated with the high-temperature crystalline phase developing at this temperature interval. Halloysite showed a similar series of changes except that there was an unexplained decrease in the specific gravity on heating from 950° to 1000°C. A sample of mica (an illite with some mixed-layer montmorillonite) from Sárospatak, Hungary, showed a decrease in specific gravity accompanying the loss of hydroxyl water above about 400°C. This decrease continued to 800°C after which there was no further change until about 1000°C when there was a slight increase in specific gravity accompanying the formation of a high-temperature crystalline phase. A sample of montmorillonite from Wyoming showed a decrease in specific gravity beginning about 700°C, which perhaps accompanied the formation of an anhydride phase. There was a slight increase in specific gravity at 950°C, which could be correlated with the development of a new high-temperature crystalline phase, with an unexplained decrease again at 1000°C.

Fusion Temperature

According to Norton (1949), kaolinite fuses at 1650 to 1775°C. The fusion point is preceded by a vitrification interval which may extend over several hundred degrees during which an amorphous component is an increasingly abundant phase. The fusion temperature of halloysite is about equal to that of the kaolinites. Halloysite, however, does not tend to gradually develop a glassy component prior to complete fusion; hence, the mineral is likely to crack into small pieces as the firing shrinkage develops. This makes halloysite difficult to use in ceramic ware. There are numerous instances in which a kaolin clay has caused very great difficulties in the firing of bodies because of the presence of a small amount of halloysite mixed with the kaolinite. The explanation for this firing characteristic of halloysite is not clear, but it probably is related to the tubular form of the mineral.

In general, all the other clay minerals, with the possible exception of some allophanes, which have the composition of halloysites, have a much lower fusion point than kaolinite or halloysite, because they contain iron, alkalies, and/or alkaline earths as essential constituents. Also, there is no definite fusion temperature for these clay minerals as the values vary within each clay mineral group with variations in the composition. In general, the fusion point ranges from about 1000 to 1500°C with the lower values being found in materials relatively rich in iron, alkalies, and the alkaline earths.

It must be emphasized again here that components other than the clay minerals may largely control the fusion temperature and, further, that the particle size of any nonclay minerals may exert a very significant influence.

Firing Color

The color developing when clays are heated to elevated temperatures usually depends much more on the nonclay minerals that are present and the conditions of firing than on the clay mineral composition. Thus, the presence of iron oxide, particularly in the free state, and the oxidizing-reducing conditions in the kiln are likely to be the determinative factors. The firing conditions may well determine whether the iron is present in a free state, locked up in a silicate structure, or in a glassy phase with a consequent great difference in color. Since kaolinite and halloysite contain no iron as essential constituents of their structure, the firing color of the pure mineral is white or a very light gray. The other clay minerals are likely to contain some iron, and there is no characteristic color that any of them develops.

Vitrification Range

By vitrification range is meant the temperature interval between the beginning of the development of a vitric bond in a ceramic body and the fusion of so much of the body that the shape of the ware is lost and the shrinkage is excessive. A long vitrification range is necessary practically so that the firing process can be safely controlled. In general, a mixture of mineral components in a clay will extend the vitrification range, since a likely consequence is an extended interval for the development of crystalline and glassy phases. The presence of some relatively large particles and a wide particle-size distribution will also tend to widen the vitrification range since the rate of fusion varies with particle size.

Vitrification can be expected to begin at temperatures somewhat above the formation of the initial high temperature phases. At the first high-temperature-phase development, a change in bonding and the nucleation of a new order takes place, probably without freeing much material that would be unorganized, i.e., glassy material that would act as a bond. Only at a higher temperature where there is substantial unorganized material left over from the high-temperature-phase requirements and when the high temperature phases have developed to a considerable extent and themselves caused bonding by the intergrowth of new crystalline forms would there be substantial development of hardness and strength in the clay body.

In Fig. 3-30, the shrinkage and adsorption characteristics of a kaolinite clay are shown in relation to firing temperature. It is seen that the shrinkage curve levels off at 2100°F and continues at a slower rate up to at least 2350°F. The adsorption curve also levels off. The contour of these curves suggests that at some temperature above 2350°F the shrinkage curve again rises sharply and the adsorption curve drops sharply. The interval from 2050 to 2350°F represents the shoulder commonly seen with kaolinitic clays, and it is the temperature interval in which the commercial product should be fired. Steel hardness is developed at 2200°F in this temperature range. The clay shows an interval of about 300°F following major shrinkage and the development of low adsorption before final rapid shrinkage accompanies complete fusion. There is, therefore, a long temperature interval for the satisfactory firing of this clay.

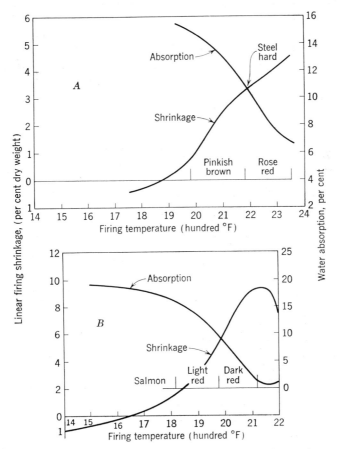

FIG. 3-30. Vitrification characteristics of *A*, a kaolinite clay and *B*, an illitic shale, after Stone (1957).

Also in Fig. 3-30 the firing characteristics of an illitic shale are shown. At 1800°F after the shrinkage begins to rise into a long sloping curve to a temperature of approximately 2050°F, there are no shoulders or breaks as are characteristic of the kaolinitic materials. The temperature of steel hardness, which corresponds very closely with that necessary to produce 10 per cent adsorption, is relatively low, in this case 1900°F. This particular shale has a very good firing range because of the relatively gentle slope of the shrinkage curve. The data indicate a firing range of about 200°F, between 1850 and 2000°F, which should make firing this material relatively easy.

Butterworth and Honeyborne (1952) have stated that kaolinite has a long vitrification range; whereas it is short for the illite and chlorite clay minerals. Stone's data are in accord with this conclusion but indicate that the range for illite may not be too short to cause difficult firing problems. In the case of the clay minerals other than kaolinite and halloysite, the vitrification range would be expected to decrease as the content of iron, alkalies, and alkaline earths increases. In other words, for these clay minerals no general correlation would be expected between vitrification range and the identity of the clay mineral, as the range would be expected to vary from relatively long to very short depending on the composition of the mineral including that of the adsorbed ions. Grimshaw (1957) has shown that fine-grained mica minerals give relatively more rapid and higher shrinkage at lower temperatures than coarser micas. However, the coarser micas may cause a large secondary contraction when the ware is heated again as in the case of refractory brick.

In refractory bodies of simple mineral composition, the presence of small amounts of fluxes may actually extend the vitrification range by causing some vitrification at lower temperatures and yet not significantly reducing the fusion point. The fluxes serve essentially to block the formation of high-temperature crystalline phases; that is, they cause the development of amorphous glassy material at relatively low temperatures. Meneret (1957) has shown that fluxes are much more effective when they are present as part of the clay mineral or as adsorbed ions than when they are present in other crystalline compounds. For example, potassium when present as a constituent of the clay minerals is a much more effective flux than when it is added to the body in a feldspar. Kiefer (1952) showed that muscovite lowered the vitrification temperature in a ceramic body more than feldspar for a given alkali content. These data emphasize the conclusion arrived at earlier that in considering the firing properties of a clay, particularly prior to complete fusion, the manner of the occurrence of the chemical components is likely to be extremely important, and phase-diagram data must be utilized with this in mind.

Calcium is well known by ceramists to have a potent tendency to reduce the vitrification range. It should be emphasized that the effect of fluxes depends somewhat on the particle size of the fluxing components. There are, for example, refractory clays of appreciable iron content in which the iron is present in sizable particles of pyrite, so that the effect of the iron is restricted to small areas, and the over-all refractoriness of a brick is not materially affected.

Rehydrated and Refired Kaolin

Hill (1953, 1956) has shown that when a test specimen of well-crystallized kaolinite is dehydrated at 600°C, rehydrated in saturated steam at 200°C, and then fired again at 600°C the compressive strength is increased manyfold from about 3,000 to 20,000 psi. This is explained by a breaking up of the kaolinite particles into smaller and more irregular units giving a greater bond between particles. The dehydration causing disorder and the subsequent rehydration must be continued long enough to regenerate the kaolinite; otherwise, the increase in strength is not developed. If the process is repeated through several cycles and/or the dehydration is continued for very long intervals, the gain in strength is much reduced, apparently because the dehydration causes so much disorder that rehydration develops little or no kaolinite. Hill (1956) found that the increase in strength also was not developed when he started with poorly ordered kaolinite.

Initial mullitization developed on firing to higher temperature was affected by the order of the kaolinites (Hill, 1956). Mullitization, for example, was considerably less at 1000°C in samples rehydrated slightly as compared to those subjected to intense rehydration with a consequent better regeneration of kaolinite. At higher temperatures where almost complete mullitization took place, the effect of rehydration and of kaolinite disorder tended to disappear. Hill's findings are in accord with those cited earlier from the work of Johns (1953) and Wahl (1959) that indicate a relationship between the order of the kaolinite crystallization and the development of mullite.

Data are not at hand to show the possible influence of dehydration and rehydration of the other clay minerals on their fired properties.

MISCELLANEOUS PROPERTIES

There are many additional properties of ceramic materials. Every type of product has specific properties and for some products, for example refractories, some of the desired ones vary depending on the particular use of the product. These properties may be dependent on the clay mineral composition or, to a large extent, on the other components in the body. They may also be dependent on the method of manufacturing, such as the forming procedure and intensity of firing. In many instances there are few or no data available on the fundamental factors controlling such properties. The following section, therefore, will be incomplete. Only those properties will be considered for which there are data indicating a significant influence of the clay mineral composition.

Scum and Efflorescence

Fired ceramic products may contain water-soluble components which will migrate to the surface when the ware dries. The precipitation of such salts on the surface of the ware causes the development of scum or efflorescent material. This condition may result if all potentially soluble ions are not locked up in glass or crystalline components in the ware. It may be a consequence of a relatively low firing temperature, a short time in the vitrification range, a large quantity of ions difficult to incorporate in crystalline phases or glass, and/or primary crystalline components which may resist breakdown during firing so that the potentially soluble ions are not released until too high a temperature is reached to fix them in an insoluble form.

Scum and efflorescence are more likely to be the result of nonclay mineral constituents than of the clay minerals. In the case of the clay minerals, those other than kaolinite or halloysite which have alkalies or alkaline earths in their structure or have high adsorptive capacity to carry such cations are most likely to cause this phenomenon. Considerable research has been devoted to finding the chemical additives which would aid in tying up potentially soluble constituents in the fired ware in an insoluble form. For example, Bauleke and Dodd (1957) showed that the addition of $\frac{1}{2}$ to 1 per cent of ammonium phosphate reduced or eliminated the development of scum in brick prepared from an illitic shale.

Permanent Moisture Expansion of Clay Products

Hosking and Hueber (1958) have found that substantially all clay products expand slightly once they leave the kiln and are exposed to the action of water vapor. These investigators and Demediuk and Cole (1958) have investigated this phenomenon in great detail, and the following statements are taken from their work. They have shown that reproducible maximum or total expansion usually many times greater than expansions so far reported under natural conditions are obtained by autoclaving the kiln-fresh samples in saturated steam at elevated temperatures until stable dimensions have been obtained. The investigation of a large variety of ceramic products showed that the relations between the expansion and firing temperature are most complex and cannot be expressed in general terms. The relationships vary according to the composition and structure of the different bodies, and for any particular body they depend on the stage and the progress of the expansion. For some bodies the total expansion increases as the temperature increases up to the maximum of practical firing, in which case well-vitrified and bloated samples expand most of all. In some cases, the relationships are reversed; in others, the maximum expansion occurs at an intermediate temperature; and for some bodies, there is little difference in the amount of expansion throughout the whole firing range. In general, the rate of expansion of lightly burned products is much faster in the early stages of reaction than the rate of expansion of harder-burned products, and the lighter-burned products reach their total expansion in a shorter time.

The expansion is due to the hydration and possibly recrystallization of the components of the fired bodies. In the case of ware fired to relatively low temperatures, the hydration may be of the clay minerals or of modified clay mineral structures. In such instances the clay minerals which preserve their structural characteristics to relatively high temperatures would probably be the most susceptive. In the case of ware fired to relatively high temperatures, expansion may be due to the hydration and crystallization of glassy materials. In such cases, glassy material containing appreciable quantities of alkalies and alkaline earths would probably be most susceptible. Natural volcanic glasses of certain compositions readily hydrate and devitrify as is illustrated in the formation of bentonite clays.

Clay minerals, such as kaolinite and halloysite, which on vitrification produce crystalline high-temperature phases of considerable stability, such as mullite and cristobalite, and amorphous material without alkalies or alkaline earths, would be expected to be most resistant to hydration under ordinary conditions.

Translucency

In the production of white ware a high degree of translucency is frequently desired in the finished product. This is attained by firing the ware as close to the fusion point as possible without losing shape, that is, with the development of the maximum amount of glassy material. It is enhanced in some ware by the addition of phosphates, as for example, in the production of bone china. From the clay mineral standpoint, it is interesting that the presence of small amounts of halloysite replacing kaolinite in the body is claimed to increase the translucency. No satisfactory explanation of this phenomenon has been offered.

Glaze Properties

In manufacture of many ceramic products a veneer of glass known as a *glaze* is put on the surface. Glazes are frequently classified into three main groups: salt glazes, slip glazes, and compounded glazes.

Salt glazes are developed by adding a salt to the kiln when it has attained about its maximum temperature. The salt is volatilized by the intense heat, and the salt vapor circulates and deposits itself on the surface of the ware where it undergoes a chemical reaction leading to the formation of a glaze.

Slip glazes are produced from natural clays deposited on the ware from a suspension; they have a melting point so low as to form a glassy coating within the firing range of the body. Extremely fine-grained clays composed of the nonrefractory clay minerals are used frequently. The fine-grained character is necessary to provide good dispersion characteristics. Frequently calcareous clays are used as the presence of calcium tends to enhance the development of the glassy phase.

Compounded glazes are sometimes known as synthetic or fritted, and they comprise by far the largest portion of glazes used today. This type of glaze is composed of many finely ground ingredients, among which are oxides for coloring agents, whiting, feldspar, china clay, flint, borax, frit (finely ground synthetic glass with a low melting temperature), and auxiliary plastics. Clays are used in such glazes for their ability to carry the other materials in a water suspension and for their chemical composition, and those composed of montmorillonite and possibly attapulgite are used because of their very high suspending properties which permit them to be used in very small quantities. The thixotropic character and high shrinkage properties of montmorillonites are generally not serious deterrents to their use in glazes because only very small quantities of the minerals are required. Koppen and Oberlies (1954) have stated that in some compositions the presence of montmorillonite tends to produce a less glossy surface than that developed when illite and kaolinites are used as components of glazes. Depending on the desired properties, this attribute may influence the selection of the type of clay mineral for the glaze.

Some kaolinite and illite clays possess the required suspending power for use in glazes. Such clays would be those composed of relatively fine-particle-sized material with relatively poorly ordered clay minerals. They would be expected to have less shrinkage and less thixotropic character than the montmorillonite, which would be factors in their favor; however, a larger quantity would probably be required to obtain the desired properties. Some such clays, for example some Ball clays, contain small amounts of montmorillonite which may enhance their value for this purpose.

Porcelain-enamel Properties

Porcelain-enamel ware is prepared by spraying a metal surface with a slip or slurry of somewhat the same composition as that used in the compounded or fritted glazes noted above.

Montmorillonite clays and very fine-grained kaolinite and illite clays, frequently in combination, are commonly used as the clay components of porcelain-enamel bodies. Since color is extremely important in porcelain enamels, clays which have a white or very light firing color are desired; consequently, montmorillonites and illites very low in iron are desired. A further property desired is opacity, which is frequently attained by the addition of titanium oxide to the formula; however, it can also be attained to some extent by the development of extremely small air bubbles in the glaze, and this seems to be favored by the presence of some organic material in the formula. Ball clays frequently carry such organic material, which may favor their use.

Reheat Volume Changes

Volume changes in refractory brick at the service temperatures are sometimes extremely important factors determining the use of such brick. Norton (1949) has summarized the available data, and, in general, factors other than clay mineral composition exert a controlling influence.

Frequently an expansion of the brick takes place on reheating (secondary expansion), which may be desirable as it tends to seal the joints between the brick. Some fireclay brick made from clays composed of kaolinite and illite exhibit an appreciable secondary expansion and this characteristic seems to be enhanced by the presence of illite. This is not to say that secondary expansion cannot be developed by other means in fireclays which contain little or no illite.

CLAY MATERIALS USED FOR VARIOUS CERAMIC PRODUCTS

It is desired to briefly summarize here the clay mineral composition of the clays that have been found most satisfactory for the manufacture of various types of ceramic products.

Brick

Almost any composition is satisfactory for the manufacture of *common brick* unless it contains a large percentage of coarse stony material which cannot be eliminated in the preparation process or ground to adequate fineness. Further, a high concentration of nonclay material in a silt-size range may cause difficulties by reducing the green and fired strength of the ware. Montmorillonite should be absent or present only in very small amounts as otherwise the shrinkage may be excessive. Clays composed of mixtures of clay minerals with appreciable amounts (25 to 50 per cent) of unsorted fine-grained nonclay minerals are most satisfactory. An abundance of kaolinite is not to be preferred as it would tend to increase the temperature required for firing. Large amounts of iron, alkalies, and alkaline earths, either in the clay minerals or as other constituents, are detrimental because they cause too much shrinkage and reduce the vitrification range. Thus, a clay with a substantial amount of calcareous material is not desirable.

Shales and sedimentary clays with a wide range of ages are used in the manufacture of brick. Surficial soil material is also widely used, although the presence of appreciable organic material may make firing somewhat difficult.

Face brick which are generally considered to be somewhat higher in quality than common brick can be made from about the same types of material found satisfactory for the manufacture of common brick except that it is even more desirable to avoid the detrimental components mentioned above, and the presence of kaolinite may be desirable. In cases where a light buff or gray face brick are desired, the presence of considerable amounts of kaolinite in the clay is essential.

Shales composed of illite and quartz frequently with some chlorite and kaolinite are widely used in the manufacture of face brick. Also, in many parts of the world the "underclays" which occur beneath beds of Carboniferous coal are widely used. These underclays are mixtures of kaolinite, illite, and quartz and frequently have excellent ceramic properties.

Adobe brick, which develop adequate strength for use without firing, are widely used in regions of very low rainfall. Such brick are frequently made from surface clays which contain relatively large amounts of fine-grained nonclay mineral material, considerable organic material, and carbonates. It is not known whether any particular clay mineral composition would be beneficial.

Tile

Roofing and *structural tile* are commonly made from material with about the same clay mineral composition as that preferred for face brick. The presence of kaolinite would not be desirable because a light burning color is not required and the increased firing temperature would be undesirable. Such units are rather large so that a relatively large amount of nonclay mineral material would be helpful to reduce shrinkage. Also, a mixture of clay minerals would be preferred to provide a long vitrification range.

Drain tile have a high porosity which is frequently attained by firing at relatively low temperatures. Frequently, drain tile are made from clays with a very large amount of fine-grained nonclay mineral material (75 per cent ±) and clay mineral components which provide high green and dry strength and a low fusion point. In the United States such tile are frequently made from surficial loessal materials which are essentially silts in which the clay mineral component is montmorillonite providing the strength and the low fusion point.

Terra Cotta, Stoneware, Sewer Pipe, Paving Brick

Clay materials of about the same composition are preferred for all of these products. They are composed of a mixture of clay minerals with relatively fine-grained unsorted quartz present in amounts ranging from 25 to 50 per cent. Clay mineral components are illite and kaolinite, frequently present in about equal amounts; a small amount of chlorite may also be present. In general, such clays have relatively low shrinkage, good plastic properties, and a long vitrification range. A small amount of montmorillonite can be tolerated, but a large amount would give undesirable shrinkage and drying properties.

In many parts of the world, Carboniferous underclays with about the above composition are found in many areas, and they are widely used for the production of these products (Grim and Allen, 1938).

White Ware

Porcelain and dinnerware bodies are made up of about equal amounts of kaolin, Ball clay, flint (ground quartz), and feldspar or some other white-burning fluxing material, e.g., talc and nepheline.

The kaolin used is composed of well-ordered particles of kaolinite which may be sedimentary or residual in origin. In the United States, sedimentary kaolins are widely used, whereas in Great Britain the kaolins are mostly residual ones from the Cornwall district. Elsewhere both types of kaolins find use. Some kaolins, particularly those of the residual type, occasionally contain halloysite in addition to the kaolinite. This constituent may be desirable in enhancing the translucency of the ware, but, in appreciable quantities, it is likely to cause difficulty in firing because of the development of cracks and broken pieces.

In their natural state some residual kaolins produced by the alteration of granitic rocks contain considerable quantities of quartz and feldspar; that is, they may be made up of three of the essential constituents for a white-ware body. Such material, called *china stone,* has been used in the manufacture of this ware. However, because of the variability of the composition of the natural product, the use of china stone is generally not feasible for the production of the highest-quality ware. It is necessary to separate the kaolinite from the parent material by a washing process and then blend together the other constituents in order to obtain a uniform body with controllable properties.

The use of the term "residual" to characterize many of these kaolins is misleading because they have been produced by hydrothermal alteration and are not residual in the sense that they are a residue from a surficial weathering process. Thus, the kaolins in the Cornwall area in Great Britain have had a hydrothermal origin (Davison, 1930). In other instances, as for example in the residual kaolins in the Appalachian area of the United States, it is difficult to establish whether they are the result of hydrothermal or weathering processes or a combination of both of them.

Ball clays are white burning, highly plastic, and easily dispersible. They largely provide the plasticity necessary in the forming of the ware and an adequate green and dry strength for handling. Such clays are composed mostly of extremely fine-grained and relatively poorly organized kaolinite. Some Ball clays also contain small amounts of illite and/or small amounts of montmorillonite, which may add to their desired properties. Also, many Ball clays contain a small but appreciable amount of organic material, which appears also to enhance their desired properties.

Clays with properties required of Ball clays are not very widely distributed throughout the world. They are extensively produced in western Kentucky and Tennessee, and Mississippi in the United States from sedimentary deposits of the Upper Cretaceous and Lower Tertiary ages. In England they are extensively produced from Tertiary beds in North Devon, South Devon, and Dorset (Holderidge, 1956). So far as the writer is aware, there are no residual kaolins with the plastic and shrinkage properties required in Ball clays.

Material classed as pottery may be made from a body with the same composition as just described for porcelain and dinnerware. Much pottery is made from a body composed of a single clay such as that used in the manufacture of terra cotta and stoneware. Generally, in such ware the surface is coated with a glaze so that the fired color of the underlying body is not very important.

Cheaper dinnerware, which may be heavily glazed, also may be prepared from a body composed of a single clay with about the same composition as that indicated for stoneware and terra cotta.

Sanitary ware is frequently manufactured from a body which is a mixture of kaolin, Ball clay, flint, and a fluxing component similar to that used for porcelain. Even though sanitary ware is generally coated with a glaze, the underlying body is generally a prepared mixture rather than a single clay so that the desired properties may be attained and controlled.

Refractories

Refractory brick are produced from clays and a wide variety of other natural materials, e.g., chromite and magnesite. Only clay refractories will be considered herein.

Clays satisfactory for the manufacture of refractories are dominantly composed of kaolinite. The absence of iron, alkalies, and alkaline earths in kaolinite provides the necessary high fusion point. Both sedimentary and residual kaolins are widely used in the manufacture of refractory brick.

For many refractory uses a somewhat lower fusion point than that provided by pure kaolinite may be adequate, so that clay materials with a moderate amount of other components in addition to kaolinite are satisfactory. In some cases such other components, as for example illite in moderate amounts, may actually be desirable by providing the necessary reheat expansion. Thus, brick used in lining steel ladles in many instances are made from clays composed of illite, kaolinite, and quartz, because they possess desirable properties even though their refractoriness is not very high. The underclays of Carboniferous age which are essentially kaolinitic but contain illite and quartz in addition to the kaolinite are widely used in the manufacture of refractory brick.

High-alumina clays are also extensively used for the manufacture of special types of refractories. Such clays may be bauxites composed essentially of an aluminum hydrate mineral (gibbsite, boehmite) and kaolinite, or they may be diaspore clays which are composed of the aluminum monohydrate, diaspore, with varying small amounts of kaolinite. These latter clays are produced in Missouri and also in France (Halm, 1951). Their origin has been the subject of much discussion and is still not settled. According to Keller (1952), those found in Missouri have had a sedimentary origin and are of Carboniferous age.

An interesting type of clay widely used in the manufacture of refractories is so-called flint clay. As its name would suggest, this clay is very hard and has very slight plasticity even when finely ground. Flint clays are essentially pure, extremely fine-grained kaolinite clays. In some cases the hardness appears to be due to the presence of a small amount of free silica which acts as a cement to bind together the kaolinite particles. In other instances, there seems to be no excess silica, and the hardness has been explained (John, 1953) on the basis of an intergrowth of the extremely small kaolinite particles. A further interesting fact is that the kaolinite units are extremely well organized. The origin of flint clays has also been the subject of much discussion and is by no means settled. It often occurs as irregular and lenticular masses associated with plastic kaolinite clays in a manner that seems to have no definite pattern or regularity. It has been suggested that flint clays may be essentially chemical precipitates or the result of the crystallization of colloidal amorphous material (Keller, 1954). Flint clays in the United States are mined in Missouri and the Appalachian area where they occur in Carboniferous beds; such clays appear to be absent or at least uncommon in other than Carboniferous beds.

In recent years there has been much development of plastic refractories.

Such material is applied in the plastic state where it is to be used and then burned into place to provide a monolithic unit. Materials of a wide variety of compositions are used for this purpose, but, in general, clays similar to those used in producing fired units are used. Sometimes highly plastic materials of low refractoriness, such as bentonite, are added in amounts which are small enough not to reduce the fusion point seriously but large enough to enhance somewhat the plasticity. Frequently, some of the clay is calcined so that the plastic refractory is a mixture of grog (calcined clay) and unburned clay. Also the composition often contains relatively large particles of chert, which, along with the grog, serve to reduce shrinkage.

Porcelain Enamels and Glazes

The compositions preferred in clays used for these products have been stated under Miscellaneous Properties.

Ball clays similar to those used in white-ware bodies are commonly used in porcelain enamels. Sedimentary kaolins composed mostly of poorly ordered kaolinite of Tertiary age are mined in Florida, Germany, and elsewhere in the world for this purpose. Vallander clay produced in Germany is an example of such a clay. Sometimes these clays contain small amounts of illite or montmorillonite and/or a small amount of a bentonite, preferably composed of a low-iron montmorillonite, may be added to supplement the suspending power of the clay. Such clays could in many instances be classed as Ball clays—they need not, however, necessarily have the low shrinkage preferred in Ball clays.

REFERENCES

Anonymous, "Kaolin Clays and Their Industrial Uses," Huber Corporation, New York (1955).
Atterberg, A., Die Plastizität der Tone, *Intern. Mitt. Bodenk.*, **I**, 4–37 (1911).
———, Die Konsistenz und Bindigkeit der Boden, *Intern. Mitt. Bodenk.*, **II**, (1912).
Barshad, I., Vermiculite and Its Relation to Biotite as Revealed by Base Exchange Reactions, X-ray Analyses, Differential Thermal Curves, and Water Content, *Am. Mineralogist* **33**, 655–678 (1948).
Bauleke, M. P., and C. M. Dodd, Effect of Ammonium Salts on an Illitic Shale, *J. Am. Ceram. Soc.*, **40**, 325–334 (1957).
Bertorelli, O. L., and I. Williams, Preparation of Mullite, U.S. Patent 2,536,122 (1949).
Bloor, E. C., Plasticity: A Critical Survey, *Trans. Brit. Ceram. Soc.*, **56**, 423–481 (1957).
Bradley, W. F., The Structural Scheme of Attapulgite, *Am. Mineralogist*, **25**, 405–413 (1940).
——— and R. E. Grim, High Temperature Thermal Effects of Clay and Related Materials, *Am. Mineralogist*, **36**, 182–201 (1951).

—— and G. Kulbicki, "Structural Changes on Dehydration of Sepiolite and Attapulgite," manuscript (1959).

Brindley, G. W., Structural Aspects of Some Thermal and Chemical Transformations of Layer Silicate Minerals, *Proc. Intern. Symposium on Reactivity of Solids*, pp. 349–369, Gotheburg, Sweden (1952).

—— and S. Z. Ali, Thermal Transformations in Magnesian Chlorites, *Acta Cryst.*, **3**, 25–30 (1950).

—— and K. Hunter, Thermal Reactions of Nacrite and the Formation of Metakaolin, Gamma-Alumina, and Mullite, *Mineral. Mag.*, **30**, 575–584 (1955).

—— and M. Nakahira, Kinetics of Dehydroxylation of Kaolinite and Halloysite, *J. Am. Ceram. Soc.*, **40**, 346–350 (1957).

—— and ——, The Kaolinite-Mullite Reactions Series: Parts I, II, III, *J. Am. Ceram. Soc.*, **42**, 311–314, 314–318, 319–324 (1959).

Butterworth, B., and D. B. Honeyborne, Bricks and Clays of the Hastings Beds, *Trans. Brit. Ceram. Soc.*, **51**, 211–259 (1952).

Byrne, P. J. S., Some Observations on Montmorillonite-Organic Complexes, *Natl. Acad. Sci. Publ.* 327, pp. 241–253 (1954).

Caillere, S., Étude de quelques silicates magnésiens a facies asbestiforme ou papyrace n'appartenant pas du groupe de l'antigorite, *Bull. soc. franç. minéral.*, **59**, 353–386 (1936).

—— and S. Henin, Palygorskite-Attapulgite, "X-ray Identification and Crystal Structures of the Clay Minerals," chap. IX, pp. 239–243, Mineralogical Society of Great Britain Monograph (1957).

——, ——, and S. Ture, Étude de analyse thermique differentielle des argiles, *Compt. rend.*, **223**, 383–384 (1946).

Colegrave, E. B., and G. R. Rigby, The Decomposition of Kaolinite by Heat, *Trans. Brit. Ceram. Soc.*, **57**, 355–367 (1952).

Comefero, J. E., R. B. Fischer, and W. F. Bradley, Mullitization of Kaolinite, *J. Am. Ceram. Soc.*, **31**, 254–259 (1948).

Comer, J. J., J. H. Koenig, and S. C. Lyons, What Are Ceramic Bodies Really Like?, *Ceram. Ind.*, **67**, 96–105 (1956).

Crookston, J. A., "The Effect of Exchangeable Bases on the Fired Properties of Fireclays," Ph.D. thesis, University of Illinois (1949).

Cuthbert, F. L., and R. A. Rowland, Differential Thermal Analyses of Some Carbonate Minerals, *Am. Mineralogist*, **32**, 111–116 (1947).

Davison, E. H., The Geology and Economics of the West of England China-clay Deposits, *Trans. Roy. Geol. Soc. (Cornwall)*, **16**, 113–116 (1930).

Demediuk, T., and W. F. Cole, A New Approach to the Investigation of the Cause of Moisture Expansion of Ceramic Bodies, *Nature,* **182**, 1223–1224 (1958).

Edelman, C. H., and J. C. L. Favejee, On the Crystal Structure of Montmorillonite and Halloysite, *Z. Krist.*, **102**, 417–431 (1940).

Eitel, W., "The Physical Chemistry of the Silicates," University of Chicago Press, Chicago (1954).

Endell, K., H. Fendius, and U. Hofmann, Basenaustauschfähigkeit von Tonen und Formsgebungsprobleme in der Keramik, *Ber. deut. keram. Ges.*, **15**, 595–625 (1934).

—— and C. Wens, Über die Steigerung der Plastizität durch Bentonitzusatz, *Ber. deut. keram. Ges.*, **15**, 271–281 (1934).

Fendius, H., and K. Endell, Über die Bestimmung der Verformbarkeit und Plastizität verschiedener Tone und Massen, *Sprechsaal*, 14 (1935).

Gerard-Hirne, J., and J. Meneret, Les réactions thermique à haute temperature des kaolins et argiles, *Bull. soc. franç. céram.*, 30, 25–33 (1956).

Glass, H. D., High Temperature Phases from Kaolinite and Halloysite, *Am. Mineralogist*, 39, 193–207 (1954).

Goldschmidt, V. M., Undersokelser over lepsedimenter, *Nord. Jordbrugs-forskn.*, nos. 4–7, pp. 434–441 (1926).

Graham, R. P., and J. D. Sullivan, Workability of Clays, *J. Am. Ceram. Soc.*, 22, 152–157 (1939).

———, Effect of Exchangeable Bases on Adsorption and Transverse Strength of Clay Bodies, *J. Am. Ceram. Soc.*, 23, 52–56 (1940).

Greene-Kelley, R., Irreversible Dehydration in Montmorillonite, *Clay Minerals Bull.* 2, pp. 52–56 (1953).

Grim, R. E., Petrographic and Ceramic Properties of Pennsylvania Shales of Illinois, *J. Am. Ceram. Soc.*, 24, 23–28 (1941).

———, Some Fundamental Properties Influencing the Properties of Soil Materials, *Proc. Intern. Conf. Soil Mech., 2nd Conf.*, III, 8–12 (1948).

———, Method and Application of Differential Thermal Analysis, *Ann. N.Y. Acad. Sci.*, 53, 1031–1053 (1951).

———, "Clay Mineralogy," McGraw-Hill Book Company, Inc., New York (1953).

——— and V. T. Allen, Petrology of the Pennsylvanian Underclays of Illinois, *Bull. Geol. Soc. Am.*, 49, 1485–1513 (1938).

——— and W. F. Bradley, Investigation of the Effect of Heat on the Clay Minerals Illite and Montmorillonite, *J. Am. Ceram. Soc.*, 23, 242–248 (1940).

——— and ———, The Mica Clay Minerals, "X-ray Identification and Crystal Structures of Clay Minerals," chap. V, pp. 138–172, Mineralogical Society of Great Britain Monograph (1951).

——— and F. L. Cuthbert, Some Clay-Water Properties of Certain Clay Minerals, *J. Am. Ceram. Soc.*, 28, 90–95 (1945).

——— and ———, The Bonding Action of Clays: Pt. 2, Clays in Dry Molding Sands, *Illinois State Geol. Survey Rept. Invest.* 110 (1946).

——— and G. Kulbicki, Études des réactions de hautes temperatures dans les minéraux argileux au moyen des rayons-X, *Bull. soc. franç. céram.*, 36, 21–28 (1957).

———, "Montmorillonite: High Temperature Reactions and Classification," manuscript, *Am. Mineralogist*, In Press.

Grimshaw, R. W., Fundamental Aspects of Fireclay Research and Technology: Importance of Particle Size Distribution, *Refractories J.*, 33, 528–535 (1957).

Hampel, B. F., and T. B. Cutler, Some Ceramic Properties of Halloysite, *J. Am. Ceram. Soc.*, 36, 30–34 (1953).

Harman, C. G., and F. Fraulini, Properties of Kaolinite as a Function of Its Particle Size, *J. Am. Ceram. Soc.*, 23, 252–258 (1940).

——— and C. W. Parmelee, Testing and Classification of Ball Clays—Thermal History, *Bull. Am. Ceram. Soc.*, 21, 280–286 (1942).

Hauser, E., "Colloidal Phenomena," McGraw-Hill Book Company, Inc., New York (1939).

Hendricks, S. B., and M. E. Jefferson, Structure of Kaolin and Talc-Pynophyllite Hydrates and Their Bearing on Water Sorption of Clays, *Am. Mineralogist*, 23, 863–875 (1938).

———, R. A. Nelson, and L. T. Alexander, Hydration Mechanism of Clay

Mineral Montmorillonite Saturated with Various Ions, *J. Am. Chem. Soc.,* **62,** 1457–1464 (1940).

Henry, E. C., Measurement of Workability of Ceramic Bodies for Plastic Molding Processes, *J. Am. Ceram. Soc.,* **26,** 37–39 (1943).

——— and A. C. Siefert, Plastic and Drying Properties of Certain Clays as Influenced by Electrolytic Content, *J. Am. Ceram. Soc.,* **24,** 281–285 (1941).

Hill, R. D., The Rehydration of Fired Clay and Associated Minerals, *Trans. Brit. Ceram. Soc.,* **52,** 589–613 (1953).

———, Studies on Rehydrated and Refired Kaolinite Minerals, *Trans. Brit. Ceram. Soc.,* **55,** 441–456 (1956).

Hind, S. R., The Plasticity of Clays: Pt. I, The Mechanical Methods of Measurement, *Trans. Brit. Ceram. Soc.,* **29,** 177–207 (1930).

Hofmann, U., "Fullstoffe und keramische Rohmaterialien, "Rapport Europees Congres Electronenmicroscopie," pp. 161–172, Gent (1954).

———, W. Czerch, and E. Scharrer, Über die Ursachen der trockenbiegefestigkeit der Tone, *Ber. deut. keram. Ges.,* **35,** 219–225 (1958).

——— and J. Endell, Die Abhangigkeit des Kationaustausches und der Quellung bei Montmorillonit von der Voresitzung, *Z. Ver. deut. Chemiker,* **10,** 35 (1939).

Holderidge, D. A., Ball Clays and Their Properties, *Trans. Brit. Ceram. Soc.,* **55,** 369–440 (1956).

——— and F. Moore, Clay-Water Relationships in Ceramics, *Clay Minerals Bull.* **2,** pp. 26–33 (1953).

Holm, L., Contribution à l'étude des argiles françaises-alumineuses, *Bull. soc. franç. céram.,* **12,** 31–39 (1951).

Hosking, J. S., and H. V. Hueber, Permanent Moisture Expansion of Clay Products on Autoclaving, *Nature,* **182,** 1142–1144 (1958).

Hoyos, A., and J. Rodriguez, Alteraciones de la superficie de bentonitas homoionicas por tratamiento thermico, *Anales edafol. y fisiol. vegetal (Madrid),* **13,** 225–266 (1954).

Hyslop, J. F., and A. McMurdo, The Thermal Expansion of Some Clay Minerals, *Trans. Brit. Ceram. Soc.,* **37,** 180–186 (1938).

Insley, H., and R. H. Ewell, Thermal Behavior of Kaolin Minerals, *J. Research Natl. Bur. Standards,* **14,** 615–627 (1935).

Johns, W. D., High Temperature Phase Changes in Kaolinite, *Mineral. Mag.,* **30,** 186–198 (1953).

Keller, W. D., Observations on the Origin of Missouri High Alumina Clays, "Problems of Clay and Laterite Genesis," American Institute of Mining and Metallurgical Engineers, pp. 115–134 (1952).

———, The Origin of Missouri Fireclay, *Natl. Acad. Sci. Publ.* 325, pp. 7–46 (1954).

Keppeler, G., and H. Gotthardt, Untersuchungen der Kaoline und Tone, *Sprechsaal,* **64,** 883–887 (1931).

Kerr, P. F., and J. L. Kulp, Multiple Differential Thermal Analysis, *Am. Mineralogist,* **33,** 387–419 (1948).

Kiefer, C., Importance et influence de la nature minéralogique des constituants sur le comportement des masses céramique, *Bull. soc. franç. céram.,* **17,** 14–33 (1952).

———, Propriétés dilatométriques des minéraux phylliteux entre 0 et 1,400°, *Bull. soc. franç. céram.,* **35,** 95–114 (1957).

Koenig, J. H., and S. C. Lyons, Some Ceramic Mechanisms and New Methods, *Ceram. Age,* **65,** 26–36 (1955).

Koppen, N., and F. Oberlies, Clay Coating, a Decorative Coating for Ceramics, *Ber. deut. keram. Ges.,* **31,** 287–301 (1954).

Kruyt, H. R., "Colloid Science," Elsevier Press, Inc., New York (1952). Trans. by L. C. Jackson.

Kulbicki, G., High Temperature Phases in Montmorillonites, *Natl. Acad. Sci. Publ.* 566, pp. 144–158 (1958).

——, High Temperature Phases in Sepiolite, Attapulgite and Saponite, *Am. Mineralogist,* **44,** 752–764 (1959).

Longchambon, H., Sur certaines caractéristiques des palygorskites, *Compt. rend.,* **203,** 672–674 (1936).

——, Sur certaines caractéristiques de la sepiolite d'Ampandandrava et la formule des sepiolites, *Bull. soc. franç. minéral,* pp. 232–276 (1937).

——, Plasticité des matériaux argileux, *Compt. rend. 18e intern. congr. chim. ind.,* pp. 784–787 (1938).

——, Recueil des communicationes du congrès technique de l'Industrie de Céramique, pp. 75–141 (1938).

Low, P. F., and C. W. Lovell, Jr., The Factor of Moisture in Frost Action, presented at U.S. Highway Research Board Symposium, "Highway Pavement Design in Frost Areas" (1958).

Lundin, S. T., Electron Optical and X-ray Studies on the Formation of Porcelain: Mullite and Microstructure of the Mullite Phase, *Geol. Fören. i Stockholm Förh.,* **77,** 404–421 (1955).

Maegdefrau, E., and U. Hofmann, Glimmerartige Mineralien als Tonsubstanzen, *Z. Krist.,* **98,** 31–39 (1937).

Migeon, G., Contribution à l'étude de la définition des sepiolites, *Bull. soc. franç. minéral.,* **59,** 6–133 (1936).

Meneret, J., Influence des alcalins et des alcalins-terreux sur les propriétés physicochimiques des kaolins, *Bull. soc. franç. céram.,* **35,** 35–41 (1957).

Mering, J., The Hydration of Montmorillonite, *Trans. Faraday Soc.,* **42B,** 205–219 (1946).

—— and R. Glaesser, Sur le rôle de la valence des cations exchangeables dans le montmorillonite, *Bull. soc. franç. minéral.,* **77,** 519–530 (1954).

Norton, F. H., "Refractories," 3d ed., McGraw-Hill Book Company, Inc., New York (1949).

——, "Elements of Ceramics," Addison-Wesley Publishing Company, Reading, Mass. (1952).

Nutting, P. C., Some Standard Thermal Dehydration Curves, *U.S. Geol. Survey Profess. Paper* 197-E, pp. 197–216 (1943).

Parmelee, C. W., and A. R. Rodriguez, Catalytic Mullitization of Kaolinite by Metallic Oxides, *J. Am. Ceram. Soc.,* **25,** 1–10 (1942).

Pfefferkorn, F., Untersuchungen über die Plastizität von Tonen, *Sprechsaal,* **57,** 297–299 (1924).

Platen, H., and H. G. F. Winkler, Plastizität und Thixotropic von fraktionierter Tonmineralen, *Kolloid-Z.,* **158,** 3–22 (1958).

Preisinger, A., An X-ray Study of the Structure of Sepiolite, *Proc. Natl. Clay Conf., 6th Conf.,* pp. 61–67, Pergamon Press, New York (1959).

Richardson, H. M., Phase Changes Which Occur on Heating Kaolin Clays, "X-ray Identification and Crystal Structures of the Clay Minerals," chap. III, pp. 76–85, Mineralogical Society of Great Britain Monograph (1951).

Rieke, R., Untersuchungen an deutschen Kaolinen, *Ber. deut. keram. Ges.,* 4, 176–187 (1923).

———— and L. Mauve, Zur Frage des Nachweises des mineralischen Bestandteile der Kaoline, *Ber. deut. keram. Ges.,* 23, 119–150 (1942).

Ries, H., "Clays, Occurrence, Properties, and Uses," 3d ed., John Wiley & Sons, Inc., New York (1927).

Ross, C. S., and P. F. Kerr, The Kaolin Minerals, *U.S. Geol. Survey Profess. Paper* 165-E, pp. 151–175 (1931).

————, Halloysite and Allophane, *U.S. Geol. Survey Profess. Paper* 185-G, pp. 135–148 (1934).

———— and S. B. Hendricks, Minerals of the Montmorillonite Group, *U.S. Geol. Survey Profess. Paper* 205-B, pp. 23–80 (1945).

Roy, R., Decomposition and Resynthesis of the Micas, *J. Am. Ceram. Soc.,* 32, 202–210 (1949).

————, D. M. Roy, and E. E. Francis, New Data on Thermal Decomposition of Kaolinite and Halloysite, *J. Am. Ceram. Soc.,* 38, 198–205 (1955).

Searle, A. B., and R. W. Grimshaw, "The Chemistry and Physics of Clays," 3d ed., Interscience Publishers, Inc., New York (1959).

Speil, S., Effect of Adsorbed Electrolytes on Properties of Monodispersed Clay-Water Systems, *J. Am. Ceram. Soc.,* 23, 33–38 (1940).

Steger, W., Die Langenanderunger von Kaolinen und einigen anderen Ton-mineralien beim Brennen bis 1100°C., *Ber. deut. keram. Ges.,* 23, 46–92; 157–174 (1942).

Stone, R. L., Determinative Tests of Aid in the Design of Driers and Kilns, *Bull. Am. Ceram. Soc.,* 36, 1–5 (1957).

Stubican, V., Residual Hydroxyls Groups in the Metakaolin Range, *Mineral. Mag.,* 32, 38–52 (1959).

———— and H. H. Gunthard, Infra-red Spectra of High Temperature Phases of Kaolinite and Halloysite, *Nature,* 179, 542 (1957).

Sullivan, J. D., Physico-Chemical Control of Properties of Clay, *Trans. Electrochem. Soc.,* 75, 71–97 (1939).

———— and R. P. Graham, Effect of Exchangeable Bases on Torsion Properties of Clays, *J. Am. Ceram. Soc.,* 23, 39–51 (1940).

———— and ————, Effect of Exchangeable Bases on Drying Clay Bodies, *J. Am. Ceram. Soc.,* 23, 57–60 (1940).

Thilo, E., and H. Schunemann, Chemical Studies of Silicates: IV, Behavior of Pyrophyllite on Heating and the Existence of a "Water-free" Pyrophyllite, *Z. anorg. u. allgem. Chem.,* 230, 321–325 (1937).

Tooker, E. W., "Thermal Transformations of Some Layer Silicates," Ph.D. thesis, University of Illinois (1952).

Tscheiswili, L., W. Bussem, and W. Weyl, Metakaolin, *Ber. deut. keram. Ges.,* 20, 249–276 (1939).

Vaughan, F., Energy Changes When Kaolin Minerals Are Heated, *Clay Minerals Bull.* 2, pp. 265–274 (1955).

Visconti, Y. S., "New Observations Relative to Tubular Kaolins by Means of Chemical Dispersion and Electron Microscopy," Second Conference on Ceramics, Brazil (1956).

Wahl, F. M., "Reactions in Kaolin-type Minerals at Elevated Temperatures as Investigated by Continuous X-ray Diffraction," Ph.D. thesis, University of Illinois (1958).

West, H. F., and J. H. Veale, Blast-furnace Operation, U.S. Patent 2,660,534 (1953).

White, W. A., The Properties of Clays, M.S. thesis, University of Illinois (1947).

———, Allophanes from Lawrence County, Indiana, *Am. Mineralogist*, **38**, 634–652 (1953).

——— and E. Pichler, Water Sorption Characteristics of Clay Minerals, *Illinois State Geol. Survey Circ.* 266 (1959).

Whittemore, J. W., Mechanical Method for Measurement of Plasticity of Clay, *J. Am. Ceram. Soc.,* **18**, 352–360 (1935).

Williamson, W. O., Some Structures of Unfired Pottery Bodies Revealed by a New Technique, *Trans. Brit. Ceram. Soc.,* **40**, 225–241 (1941).

———, Oriented Aggregation, Differential Drying Shrinkage and Recovery from Deformation of a Kaolinite-Illite Clay, *Trans. Brit. Ceram. Soc.,* **54**, 413–442 (1955).

Zschokke, K., *Bull. soc. encour.* (1902). See reference in Endell, Fendius, and Hofmann (1934).

Zwetsch, A., Röntgenuntersuchungen in der Keramik, *Ber. deut. keram. Ges.,* **14**, 2–4 (1934).

CHAPTER 4

Clays in Foundry Molding Sands

INTRODUCTION

Molding sands, which are composed essentially of sand and clay, are used extensively in the metallurgical industry in the shaping of metal by the casting process. By the use of a pattern, a cavity of the desired shape is formed in the sand, and into this, molten metal is poured and then allowed to cool.

The molding sand may be a natural sand containing clay or a synthetically prepared mixture of a clean quartz sand and clay. Synthetic sands are widely used because they can be prepared to meet property specifications, and their properties are more easily controlled as they are used. Granular particles other than quartz sand, e.g., calcined clay, olivine, zircon, may be used in rare special instances. Natural sands frequently contain other components, such as limonite, in addition to the sand and clay. Ground bituminous coal (Sea Coal) and cereal binders may be added to the sand-clay mixture to develop certain properties.

A small amount of water, called *tempering water,* must be added to the molding sand to make it somewhat plastic, to develop cohesive strength so that the sand can be molded around the pattern, and to give it sufficient strength to maintain the cavity after the pattern is removed and while the metal is poured into it. These properties vary greatly with the amount of tempering water. A sand with the amount of water necessary to give the optimum molding properties is said to be at the temper point.

In foundry practice the prepared mold may be used while the tempering water is retained (green state), or the mold may be dried (dry state) before the metal is poured. The drying may be at an ordinary or at an elevated temperature.

The same molding sand is used over and over again—in a mechanized foundry with an efficient sand-handling system, the reuse period may be an hour or less. The high temperature of the metal dehydrates and vitrifies some of the clay, thereby partially destroying the desirable properties of the mixture; as a consequence, fresh clay must be added con-

141

tinuously as the sand is used.   In modern sand practice the properties are tested continuously, and sufficient clay is added to maintain the properties at the desired level.   The burned clay must occasionally be removed from the sand in order that this component does not exceed a given percentage and thereby cause detrimental properties.

Frequently one sand is used for the bulk of the mold (heap sand) and another sand for the surface against the casting (facing sand).   The facing sand is often a new sand-clay mixture, which after the first use goes into the heap sand.   The addition of clay to the heap sand may be by way of the facing sand, or it may also be added directly to the heap sand.

In addition to sands tempered with water, clay-bonded sands tempered with an oil are used occasionally.   The clay in such sands is previously treated with an organic compound so that the clay mineral particles become hydrophobic and oleophilic.

MOLDING-SAND PROPERTIES

The properties of molding sands that determine their utility are dependent on a variety of factors of which the following are the most important:

1. Kind (clay mineral composition) and amount of clay
2. Kind of granular particles, i.e., quartz, calcined clay, etc.
3. Amount, particle-size distribution, and shape of the granular grains
4. Amount of tempering water
5. Nature and abundance of exchangeable ions and soluble salts
6. Miscellaneous components, such as limonite and Sea Coal

The present discussion will consider the influence of the clay mineral composition and exchangeable ions on the properties of molding sands, and the manner in which this influence varies with the amount of tempering water.   Also a concept of the bonding action of clays in molding sands will be presented.   An abundant literature, especially in the *Transactions of the American Foundrymen's Society* (A.F.S.) and the *Journal of the Iron and Steel Institute* (*Great Britain*), considers the influence of other factors of composition on molding-sand properties.

The properties listed below are usually found adequate to characterize and evaluate molding sands.   No property is adequate in itself, and indeed the final test of evaluation is that the sand produce satisfactory castings in actual use.   Also the desired properties vary with the metal being cast, the size of the castings, and in general with the actual practice in each individual foundry.

In the publication "Testing and Grading Foundry Sands and Clays," sixth edition, published by the A.F.S. in 1952, standard procedures for the testing of molding sands are given. The reader is referred to this publication for information on test procedures. Except where indicated, the A.F.S. procedures were used to obtain the test data reported herein.

Green Compression Strength is the compressive force necessary to cause failure in a test specimen of a definite size containing tempering water and compacted by ramming. The test is made on a series of preparations for which the only variable is the amount of tempering water. The tempering water is determined on the basis of the weight of the tempered sand. The test results are plotted on a curve of green compression strength versus tempering water (Figs. 4-2 to 4-7). As the amount of tempering water added to a dry mixture is increased, the compression strength increases to a maximum and then decreases. The temper point at which a sand has optimum molding properties is on the wet side of the maximum green strength. At maximum green strength the sand is in general too brittle and insufficiently plastic for use. A green-compression-strength curve that does not show a sharp maximum is desirable because then the moisture content is less critical and more of the potential strength can be used.

Some idea of the desired green compression strength can be gained from the fact that the sands used in steel foundries vary in strength from about 2.5 to 11.5 psi depending on the type of mold desired. Strengths in the range from 5 to 7.5 psi are common.

Bulk Density is the weight per unit volume of green sand compacted by ramming. It varies with the amount of tempering water, and the test results are usually presented in the form of a curve of weight per unit volume versus tempering water. As moisture is added to a dry sand, the bulk density increases slightly then decreases to a minimum after which it rises again (Fig. 4-1). Minimum bulk density is reached with a larger amount of tempering water than that required from maximum green strength. However, as will be shown presently, the difference is small for some types of clay minerals and large for other types.

Dietert and Valtier (1931) described temper point as developing at a moisture content providing the minimum weight per unit volume, and Hofmann (1958) points out that it corresponds closely to minimum bulk density. This correla-

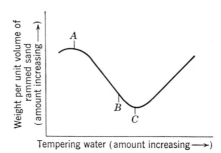

Fig. 4-1. Curve showing the typical relation of bulk density to tempering water in molding sands, after Grim and Cuthbert (1945): *A,* minimum bulk density; *B,* maximum green strength; *C,* minimum bulk density.

tion is more likely to be true for some types of clay minerals than for others (see page 156). In actual practice the tendency is to use sands slightly on the wet side of minimum bulk density.

Dry Compression Strength is the compressive force necessary to cause failure in a rammed test specimen that has been dried in an oven to remove all tempering water and then allowed to cool in a desiccator. Again the strength varies with the amount of tempering water, and the results are presented in curves of dry strength versus tempering water (Figs. 4-15 to 4-19). In general the strength increases with an increasing amount of water up to a maximum value which is maintained over a considerable moisture range and beyond which the strength decreases. Maximum dry compression strength is attained at a higher moisture content than maximum green strength. Maximum dry strength can frequently be obtained at about minimum bulk density and at temper point, although slightly more water may sometimes be required.

In steel foundries the usual range of required dry strength is from 75 to 100 psi. For other types of metal, lower strength may be adequate.

Dry strength is greater than green strength. If the tempering water is removed quickly by drying in an oven, the strength is relatively greater than that developed by slow drying in air (Grim and Cuthbert, 1946). For montmorillonite and illite clay-bonded sands there is a gradual increase in strength as the tempering water is lost. For kaolinite and halloysite clay-bonded sands a greatly increased strength develops with slight loss of tempering water, i.e., air-set strength (see page 169). With further loss of water the strength tends to decrease slightly, and with still further loss of water there may be an increase in strength again. In some cases there is no further gain in strength, and the air-set strength is higher than the standard dry strength.

Since the manner and rate of drying a molding sand are critical in the strength developed, empirical test data are not likely to parallel plant practice. The drying of large masses of sand in a mold is not likely to be comparable to laboratory procedures. Test data for dry strength do show differences between types of clay, but their correlation in detail with plant practice demands caution.

Hot Strength is the compressive force necessary to cause failure of a rammed test specimen heated to an elevated temperature; it is determined while the sample is in the furnace at a given temperature (Figs. 4-26 and 4-27). The hot strength varies with the amount of tempering water used to prepare the specimen, but details of this variation are not known for the different types of clay minerals. Davies and Rees (1946) have shown that frequently the hot strength is higher for specimens prepared at the temper point than for those with lower moisture contents. It is customary to present hot-strength data for specimens prepared at about the temper point.

In general the compressive strengths of specimens allowed to cool after heating are much lower than the strengths of the specimens while at the elevated temperature (see page 175).

Flowability is the property of a molding sand which enables it to flow or conform to the shape of the pattern with a minimum of ramming or squeezing. It is measured on the A.F.S. sand rammer by an Ames dial attached so that changes in the length of the sand specimen may be read for any blow of the rammer. It is believed that a sand of good flowability will take the form of the standard sand specimen with the first few blows and that additional blows will cause very little change in the length. A sand of poor flowability, however, will not compress as much the first two or three blows but will continue to decrease gradually in volume with several additional blows. Flowability is measured by the change in length caused by the fifth blow of the rammer. Zero change in length equals 100 per cent flowability, and a change in length of 0.1 in. equals zero flowability. Usual values desired in practice are between 65 and 90.

In general with an increasing amount of tempering water added to the dry sand-clay mixture, flowability decreases to a minimum value slightly on the wet side of maximum green strength at about maximum dry strength and minimum bulk density. With larger amounts of moisture, flowability tends to remain about the same or increase slightly. This increase is particularly noticed in sands with high clay contents (10+).

Permeability may be determined on the green or dried specimen. The particle-size distribution of the quartz grains exerts a major influence on permeability. The kind and amount of clay is relatively unimportant in determining this property, and hence it will not be considered in detail. Further, molding sands of such relatively low permeability have been found useful in foundries that this property is often not determined in evaluating molding sands.

Briggs and Morey (1939) have shown that permeability tends to increase with increasing amounts of tempering water to a maximum at about the point of minimum bulk density. With further increases of moisture, it decreases. As the amount of clay increases up to about 6 per cent, the permeability decreases. With larger amounts of clay, up to about 10 per cent, the permeability remains approximately the same. Green and dry permeability show about the same relation to tempering water, except that slightly more water is required to produce maximum dry permeability than maximum green permeability.

Durability is related to the strength of the sand that is retained after use. It may be measured by the strength of the sand after repeated use without clay additions (Casberg and Schubert, 1936). Recently Hofmann (1958) has suggested a method whereby the sand is heated to successively higher temperatures, and the compression strength is determined at the temper point after each heating—the heating is carried finally to a temperature causing the complete loss of strength.

Durability is difficult to evaluate in the laboratory. When metal is poured into molds, very large temperature gradients are set up so that the clay bond is subjected to a wide range of temperatures which vary with the size of the casting, pouring temperature, etc. Such conditions are difficult to duplicate in the laboratory. Fundamentally the durability of a molding is determined by the effect of elevated temperatures on the structural changes in its clay bond, and this will be considered later.

Surface refers to the character of the surface of the metal casting. The smoother the surface is and the lower the amount of "burning on" of the sand, the lower the cost of cleaning and milling the casting will be and, therefore, the more satisfactory the sand. The character of the surface is related, in part, to the character of the clay bond. Another factor, however, such as the presence of Sea Coal or the use of special highly refractory facing materials, may be the controlling one.

Other tests have been used to evaluate the properties of clays in molding sands, but the ones discussed here are adequate for a consideration of the differences in properties of the important types of clay minerals and for the development of a concept of the bonding action of clays in molding sands.

It must be emphasized continuously that property determinations only serve to compare clays and to show that a given clay is *likely* to be satisfactory for use in molding sands. It is necessary to try the clay in actual use to be certain that castings free from defects can be produced on a continuing basis. Many casting defects are due primarily to factors other than the kind of clay: for example, too much tempering water and improper ramming; however, the type of clay may make the sand susceptible to such difficulties. Thus, if the strength varies sharply with moisture content, it may be difficult to control the moisture in the essential narrow range. Sometimes sands bonded with certain types of clay are relatively less prone to defects. Thus, illite clay-bonded sands seem to be remarkably free from any tendency to develop "pin holes" in malleable iron castings (Jones and Grim, 1959).

TYPES OF CLAY USED IN MOLDING SANDS

Bentonites, composed essentially of montmorillonite, are used very extensively in bonding molding sands—in fact, this is the largest single commercial use of bentonites. In the United States, bentonite for foundry use is mined principally in the Wyoming area and in Mississippi. Bentonites are also mined for this purpose in England, Germany, Switzerland, Italy, Yugoslavia, Greece, U.S.S.R., Algeria, Morocco, South Africa, India, Japan, Australia, and Argentina. Much of the montmorillonite in the bentonite produced in the Wyoming area carries sodium as the principal exchangeable cation, whereas the montmorillonite in all the other bentonites with some few possible exceptions, for example, some of the Algerian bentonites, carries calcium, magnesium, and/or hydrogen as the major exchangeable cations. To a considerable extent, but not solely because of this difference in adsorbed-cation composition, much of the Wyoming bentonite has different properties from most other bentonites. It is common practice to treat the other bentonites chemically, often with soda ash, to change their properties in the direction of those possessed by the Wyoming clay. Such treatment frequently accomplishes a significant change in properties, but usually the properties of the Wyoming clay are not attained completely (Hofmann, 1959). This author has recently proposed a classification of bentonites for foundry use based on their cation-exchange properties and chemical composition. For many types of molding-sand use, the properties of the nonsodium montmorillonite clays are equal to, or even more desirable than, those composed of sodium montmorillonite. As a consequence large tonnages of the former are mined and used without any chemical treatment.

Plastic clays composed largely of kaolinite, but with small amounts of illite and at times montmorillonite, are widely used in bonding molding sands. These clays are frequently called *fireclays* because of their relatively high refractoriness. In the United States such clays are mined extensively in Illinois and Ohio from beds of Carboniferous age where they occur directly beneath beds of coal (underclays). Similar clays of similar geological occurrence are mined elsewhere, notably in England, Germany, and France. Other sedimentary, plastic, kaolinite-type clays, such as the ceramic Ball clays, may have similar bonding properties. The kaolinite-type clays have lower bonding strength than the montmorillonite clays, but their other properties and their accessibility frequently make their use desirable, either alone or mixed with bentonite. The plastic kaolins are composed of extremely small particles of relatively poorly crystallized kaolinite. The coarser kaolin clays composed of large well-crystallized particles of kaolinite have bonding strengths too low to permit their commercial use as components of molding sands.

The third type of clay used in foundries is composed essentially of illite. Most illite clays have a bonding strength (Hofmann, 1959) and plasticity too low for bonding use, but there are some varieties that have a bonding strength approaching that of montmorillonite and have other properties which make them highly desirable. Illite bonding clays are produced extensively in Illinois. The illite in these clays is finer-grained and more easily dispersible in water than the relatively less plastic illite in many clays and shales. This is probably because some weathering has partially removed the potassium from between the unit layers. It is interesting that the bonding component of many natural sands is illite (Grim and Schubert, 1940).

Clays composed of halloysite in an intermediate state of hydration have considerable bonding strength, whereas halloysite in either the $2H_2O$ or $4H_2O$ form is relatively nonplastic and without bonding strength. Halloysite clays of intermediate hydration have other excellent properties; for example, they yield excellent casting surfaces. However, the difficulty of maintaining such clays in the proper state of hydration prior to use has precluded, so far as the author knows, any commercial use of halloysite clays in foundries.

Attapulgite-sepiolite clays appear not to be used in molding sands tempered with water, although it seems likely that they would have satisfactory bonding strength and other desirable properties. Hofmann (1959) has recently tested an attapulgite sample which had green strengths about equal to kaolinite clays. It has been claimed (Anon., 1959) that attapulgite gives desirable properties in oil-bound sand systems (see page 202).

The author knows of no foundry use of clays composed largely of chlorite. It would be expected that some weathered chlorites might have similar properties to the illite and kaolinite clays.

White (1953) has shown that some allophane possesses little or no bonding strength. It is conceivable that some allophane clays might have high bonding strength, but such clays apparently have not yet been reported.

PROPERTIES OF VARIOUS TYPES OF CLAYS

Green Compression Strength

A series of curves showing the considerable variation in green compression strength within a group of montmorillonite clays is given in Fig. 4-2. Curves presenting the relation between green compression strength and the amount of tempering water for varying amounts of a commonly used sodium montmorillonite clay and a calcium montmorillonite clay are given in Figs. 4-3 and 4-4. Similar curves for halloysite clay, illite clay, and kaolinite clay are given in Figs. 4-5 to 4-7. In the crude state the kaolinite clay contained a small amount of quartz which was removed by wet sedimentation before the determinations were

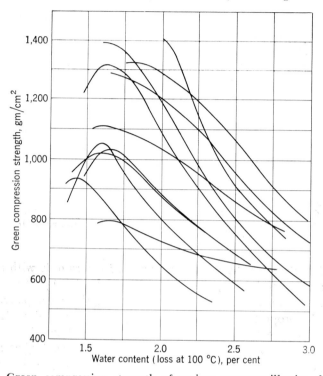

FIG. 4-2. Green compression strength of various montmorillonite clays, after Hofmann (1956).

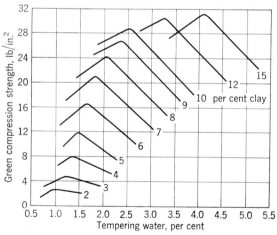

FIG. 4-3. Green compression strength versus amount of tempering water in sands bonded with varying amounts of sodium montmorillonite clay, after Grim and Cuthbert (1945).

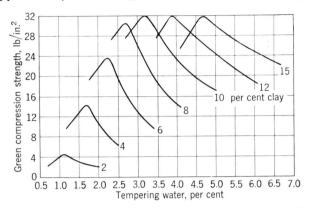

Fig. 4-4. Green compression strength versus amounts of tempering water in sands bonded with varying amounts of calcium montmorillonite clay, after Grim and Cuthbert (1945).

made. The data for the halloysite clay are for a sample with an intermediate state of hydration, which provides relatively high strength.

It must not be assumed that all clays with these components have precisely the properties reported for these particular samples. Thus, for kaolinite and illite, better-crystallized examples would have lower strength and poorer-crystallized examples would perhaps have higher strength. The data do, however, illustrate the general green-strength characteristics of the clay minerals.

For sand-clay mixtures with 4 per cent or less of any of the clays, the curves showing the relation of tempering water to green compression strength are relatively flat. In the range from 4 to 15 per cent clay, the

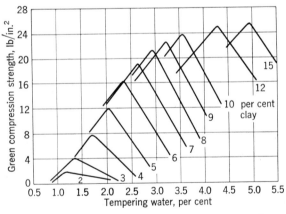

Fig. 4-5. Green compression strength versus amount of tempering water in sands bonded with varying amounts of halloysite clay, after Grim and Cuthbert (1945).

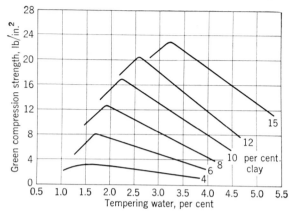

Green compression strength versus amount of tempering water in sands bonded with varying amounts of illite clay, after Grim and Cuthbert (1945).

maximum green strength is attained within narrow moisture limits. The narrowness of the limit is not the same for all types of clay. Thus the highest strength is reached in a relatively wide moisture range for kaolinite and illite clays, in a narrow range for the calcium montmorillonite and halloysite clays, and in an intermediate range for the sodium montmorillonite clays.

Figure 4-8 shows the maximum green compression strength for varying amounts of each type of clay up to 15 per cent. The calcium montmorillonite gives the highest strength at all clay contents. The sodium montmorillonite and halloysite have about the same strength in mixtures up to about 6 per cent clay; with larger amounts of clay, the montmorillonite is the stronger. The kaolinite and illite have about the same strength; the kaolinite is slightly higher in mixtures up to about 12 per

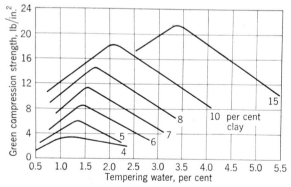

Fɪɢ. 4-7. Green compression strength versus amount of tempering water in sands bonded with varying amounts of kaolinite clay, after Grim and Cuthbert (1945).

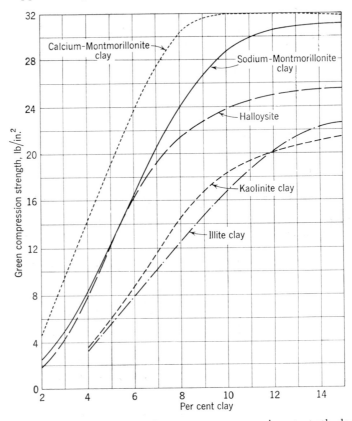

Fig. 4-8. Curves showing the maximum green compression strength developed by each type of clay in relation to the amount of clay in the sand-clay mixture, after Grim and Cuthbert (1945).

cent clay, and the illite is slightly higher when the clay content is larger.

In sands bonded with the calcium montmorillonite clay, the strength increases approximately in proportion to the amount of clay up to about 8 per cent clay. Additional clay up to 10 per cent causes only a very slight increase in strength, and the addition of clay in excess of 10 per cent causes no increase in strength. Sands bonded with the sodium montmorillonite and halloysite clays show a similar relation between maximum green compression strength and the amount of clay, except that the reduction in strength per unit of added clay above about 8 per cent is less than for the calcium montmorillonite. The kaolinite and illite clay-bonded sands show a continuing increase in maximum green compression strength as up to 15 per cent clay is added, but the rate of increase is somewhat reduced above about 10 per cent for kaolinite and 12 per cent for illite.

Table 4-1 shows clearly that the maximum strength for all the clays is developed in sands when they contain rather narrowly limited amounts of bond. With lesser or greater amounts of bond, the strength developed per unit of clay remains about the same or decreases. The optimum clay content for the development of maximum green strength is 7 to 9 per cent with sodium montmorillonite, 6 to 8 per cent with calcium montmorillonite and halloysite, and 9 to 12 per cent with kaolinite and illite clay-bonded sands. This means that the relative difference in maximum green compression strength developed by the different types of clay is greatest in sands of low clay content. In sands with a high clay content, the difference in bonding power of the various types of clay decreases considerably.

Figure 4-9 presents curves showing the green compression strength at minimum bulk density in mixtures with clay contents up to 15 per cent. In mixtures with less than about 6.5 per cent clay, the calcium montmorillonite clay-bonded sands are the strongest; in sands with from 6.5 to about 12 per cent clay, the halloysite clay-bonded sands are strongest,

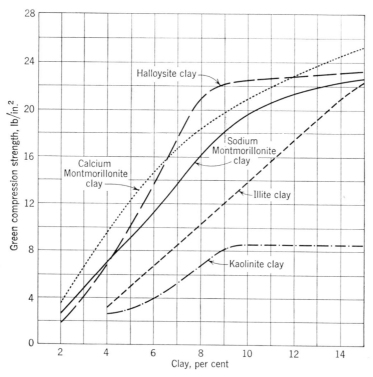

FIG. 4-9. Curves showing the green compression strength at the minimum bulk-density point developed by each type of clay in relation to the amount of clay in the sand-clay mixture, after Grim and Cuthbert (1945).

and with from 12 to 15 per cent, the calcium montmorillonite clay-bonded sands are strongest.   Sands bonded with sodium montmorillonite have less strength than those bonded with calcium montmorillonite at all clay contents up to at least 15 per cent.

Sands bonded with illite clay are weaker than those bonded with either montmorillonite or halloysite clays in all mixtures except those with high clay contents in which the strengths are about equal.

The sands bonded with kaolinite clay are lower in strength than those bonded with the other clays.   A reason for this characteristic is that minimum bulk density is developed at very high moisture contents in sands bonded with large amounts of this clay, and consequently the strength is low.   The kaolinite-clay curve flattens above 10 per cent indicating that there is no increase in strength at minimum bulk density as clay in excess of 10 per cent is added to mixtures.

Unlike kaolinite clay, illite clay-bonded sands with high clay content develop minimum bulk density at relatively low moisture contents.   Consequently the illite clay-bonded sands with a high clay content are strong at this point—as strong, in fact, as those bonded with either montmorillonite or halloysite clays.

In the halloysite clay-bonded sands, the increase in strength at minimum bulk density is proportionate to the amount of clay up to about 8 per cent clay.   With more than 8 per cent clay, the strength increases only slightly as the clay content increases.

With the calcium and sodium montmorillonite clays, the strength increases in proportion to the amount of clay up to about 9 per cent.   In mixtures with more than this amount, the relative increase in strength is slightly reduced for the calcium montmorillonite and considerably reduced for the sodium montmorillonite clay.

The relative bonding strength of the various types of clay is shown also in Table 4-1, which gives the bonding strength per unit of clay at minimum bulk density for each clay in mixtures up to 15 per cent clay.   The data in the table indicate the same conclusions as those derived from a consideration of the curves in Fig. 4-9.

A comparison of the maximum green compression strength and the strength at minimum bulk density brings out the following conclusions. The strength of the halloysite clay-bonded sands at minimum bulk density is only slightly less than the maximum strength, whereas the strength of sands bonded with both montmorillonite clays is considerably less.   The explanation is that minimum bulk density is developed with the halloysite with only slightly more water than that required for maximum green strength, whereas in sands bonded with either type of montmorillonite clay considerably more water is required for the minimum bulk density than for maximum green strength.   Because of this fact,

TABLE 4-1

GREEN COMPRESSION STRENGTH PER UNIT OF CLAY
(in Pounds per Square Inch)
(After Grim and Cuthbert, 1945)

Per cent clay	Sodium mont-morillonite clay	Calcium mont-morillonite clay	Halloysite clay	Illite clay	Kaolinite clay
At maximum green compression strength
2	0.060	0.117	0.047		
3	0.079	0.156	0.070		
4	0.101	0.178	0.098	0.041	0.044
5	0.114	0.191	0.121	0.058	0.060
6	0.137	0.197	0.137	0.067	0.072
7	0.148	0.196	0.132	0.071	0.082
8	0.150	0.191	0.133	0.079	0.092
9	0.150	0.176	0.126	0.082	0.094
10	0.146	0.160	0.119	0.084	0.092
12	0.127	0.132	0.104	0.084	0.084
15	0.103	0.106	0.085	0.076	0.072
At minimum bulk density
2	0.070	0.082	0.050		
3	0.080	0.108	0.069		
4	0.087	0.118	0.087	0.040	0.034
5	0.091	0.119	0.124	0.061	0.037
6	0.090	0.120	0.114	0.057	0.033
7	0.091	0.119	0.124	0.061	0.037
8	0.101	0.114	0.130	0.064	0.042
9	0.101	0.109	0.122	0.068	0.045
10	0.098	0.104	0.112	0.069	0.043
12	0.089	0.095	0.095	0.073	0.036
15	0.075	0.084	0.078	0.075	0.029

the halloysite clay-bonded sands are stronger at minimum bulk density for some clay contents than are sands bonded with the montmorillonite clays.

Similarly the illite clay-bonded sands develop minimum bulk density at moisture contents only slightly above that required for maximum green strength, hence the strength at minimum bulk density is only slightly less than the maximum. This is particularly true for high-clay-content sands and explains why the illite clay-bonded sands have about the same strength at minimum bulk density as high-clay-content sands bonded with either montmorillonite or the halloysite clays.

Hofmann (1956 and 1958) has shown that treatment of calcium montmorillonite clays with sodium has only a slight effect on green strength. The change may be a slight increase or decrease. Natural calcium montmorillonites have higher green strength than sodium montmorillonites so that any increase would not be expected—the occasional increase can, however, be explained by a dispersing effect of the sodium, which would tend to break up the montmorillonite particles into smaller and thinner units so that a larger amount of bonding surface per unit of clay would be released. In some instances this might outweigh the effect of the sodium on the tempering water, which tends to reduce green strength (see pages 152–155). The same author has shown that potassium treatment reduces green strength. This is expected since the effect of potassium would be to reduce the amount of dispersion. Data are not available on the effect of other cations on the green strength of montmorillonite clays or of various cations on the bonding strength of other clays. One would expect that treatment with sodium and lithium would have a dispersing effect and tend to increase the green compression

TABLE 4-2

RELATION OF PLASTIC LIMIT TO MOISTURE CONTENT
AT MAXIMUM GREEN COMPRESSION STRENGTH

Clay	Plastic limit	Moisture content at maximum green compression strength		
		Clay, %		
		4	8	15
Sodium montmorillonite.....	97	54	44	42
Calcium montmorillonite.....	82	63	51	46
Illite....................	42	54	33	28
Kaolinite	37	48	46	35
Halloysite	58	64	57	50

strength of illite and kaolinite clays. The effect of alkaline-earth cations and potassium would probably be to reduce green strength.

A comparison of moisture values at which maximum green strength is developed with the plastic-limit values (page 207) computed on a comparable basis (Table 4-2) shows that for the montmorillonite clays, maximum green strength develops with considerably less water than the plastic-limit value, especially in high-clay-content sands. For illite, halloysite, and kaolinite clay-bonded sands, the moisture content for maximum green strength is slightly larger than the plastic limit in low-clay-content sands (4 per cent) and about equal or slightly less in the high-clay-content sands (15 per cent plus).

Bulk Density

In Figs. 4-10 to 4-14 curves are presented showing the weight per unit volume of mixtures containing different amounts of clay with varying amounts of tempering water. For each mixture the curve passes through a minimum point which is often taken as the temper point. However, the best working conditions frequently prevail when the sands are slightly on the wet side of the minimum weight.

The curves for the sodium montmorillonite clay-bonded sands are steep on the dry side and moderately steep on the wet side, indicating that the bulk density changes rapidly with moisture content below minimum bulk density and gradually with moisture content above it. The slope of the curves on the dry side becomes more gentle as the amount of clay increases, and consequently the minimum–bulk-density point is less sharp in higher clay content mixtures.

The upward shift of successive curves for the sodium montmorillonite

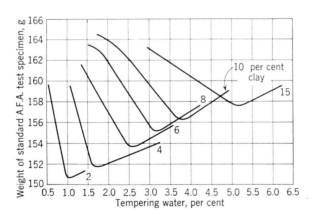

FIG. 4-10. Bulk density versus amount of tempering water in sands bonded with varying amounts of sodium montmorillonite clay, after Grim and Cuthbert (1945).

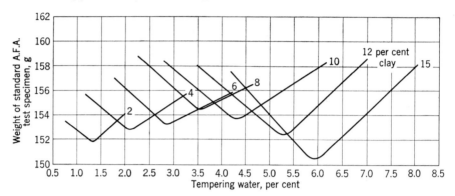

Fɪɢ. 4-11. Bulk density versus amount of tempering water in sands bonded with varying amounts of calcium montmorillonite clay, after Grim and Cuthbert (1945).

clay indicates an increase in weight per unit volume at the minimum point as the amount of clay increases in the mixtures. The amount of increase in weight becomes relatively less as the clay content increases; thus a mixture with 15 per cent clay is only slightly heavier than one with 10 per cent clay at the minimum point, and the mixture with 10 per cent clay is considerably heavier than the one with 5 per cent clay.

The character of the curves for the calcium montmorillonite clay is about the same regardless of the clay content. They have relatively gentle slopes on both dry and wet sides of the minimum. Unlike the sodium montmorillonite, in mixtures with up to 8 per cent clay, there is only a very slight upward shift of successive curves, indicating a very small increase in weight per unit volume at the minimum point as the clay increases. In mixtures with more than 8 per cent clay there is a decrease in weight at the minimum point as the amount of clay increases.

The curves for the halloysite clay-bonded sands are U-shaped, indicating very great changes in bulk density with slight variations in the amount

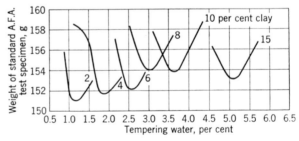

Fɪɢ. 4-12. Bulk density versus amount of tempering water in sands bonded with varying amounts of halloysite clay, after Grim and Cuthbert (1945).

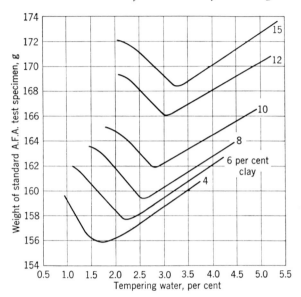

Fɪɢ. 4-13.   Bulk density versus amount of tempering water in sands bonded with varying amounts of illite clay, after Grim and Cuthbert (1945).

of tempering water on both sides of the minimum point.   The variation of bulk density with amount of tempering water is greater for sands bonded with the halloysite clay than with any other type of clay.   The weight per unit volume at minimum bulk density increases with increasing amounts of halloysite in mixtures with up to 8 per cent clay.

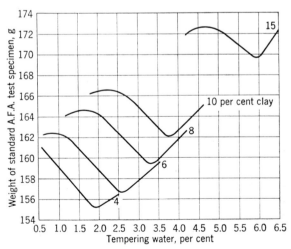

Fɪɢ. 4-14.   Bulk density versus amount of tempering water in sands bonded with varying amounts of kaolinite clay, after Grim and Cuthbert (1945).

The character of the curves for sands bonded with the illite and kaolinite clays is the same within the limits of experimental error. The curves have gentle slopes on both the dry and wet side of the minimum point. The weight per unit volume at minimum bulk density for a given amount of clay is about the same in sands bonded with either the kaolinite clay or illite clay. In both cases the weight per unit volume is greater than that of the montmorillonite or the halloysite clay-bonded sands containing equal amounts of tempering water. In sands bonded with either the illite or kaolinite clay, the weight per unit volume at the minimum point increases sharply as the amount of clay increases.

The curves for the illite clay-bonded sands are distinctive in that increasing amounts of clay cause only very slight shifts to the right. This results from the fact that sands bonded with large amounts of the illite develop minimum bulk density with smaller amounts of tempering water per unit of clay than do sands bonded with the same amount of the other types of clay.

The dry side of the curves for the kaolinite-clay mixtures with more than 4 per cent clay shows a reversal at the dry end. Curves for some of the sands bonded with other types of clay also suggest that the gradual increase in weight on the dry side of the minimum point is reversed at very low moisture contents.

For the sodium montmorillonite clay, minimum bulk density is developed at moisture contents lower than the plastic limit in all the sands of various clay content. For the calcium montmorillonite clay, minimum bulk density is developed below the plastic limit in low-clay-content sands and at about the plastic limit in high-clay-content sands. Minimum bulk density develops at higher moisture contents than the plastic limit for the illite clay-bonded sands with low clay content and at lower moisture contents when the clay content is high. For the halloysite clay-bonded sands, minimum bulk density develops above the plastic limit for low-clay-content sands and about at the plastic limit when the clay content is high. For the kaolinite clay-bonded sands, minimum bulk density develops above the plastic limit for all clay contents.

Dry Compression Strength

The relation between dry compression strength and amount of tempering water for mixtures with various quantities of the clays is shown in Figs. 4-15 to 4-19.

The curves for the sodium montmorillonite clay-bonded sands show the very high dry strength developed in sands bonded with this type of clay and the very great variation in dry strength with extremely small variations in amount of tempering water. Thus, a variation of less than 0.1 per cent water may cause a change in strength of more than 10 psi.

The curves indicate that strengths in excess of 100 psi are developed in any mixture with as much as 4 per cent of this clay by adjusting the amount of tempering water. On the basis of data from other types of clay, it is probable that the maximum dry strength would increase with the amount of clay.

It is clear from the curves in Fig. 4-15 that a certain amount of tempering water is required for the development of any dry strength, and that this initial water increases in amount as the amount of clay increases. Computation (Grim and Cuthbert, 1946) indicates that the required water is equal to an amount slightly in excess of that necessary to develop a sheet of water 2 molecular layers thick on each unit of the

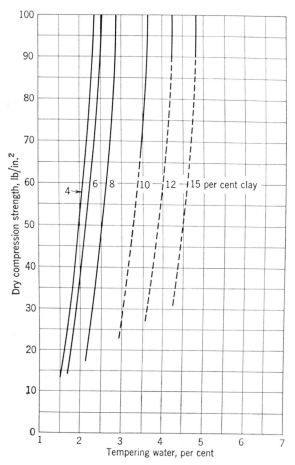

Fig. 4-15. Dry compression strength versus amount of tempering water in sands bonded with varying amounts of sodium montmorillonite clay, after Grim and Cuthbert (1946).

montmorillonite. Actual dry strengths below about 10 psi cannot be measured, so that somewhat more tempering water than this value is required for appreciable dry strength. Since a water layer 3 molecules thick is probably rigid (Grim and Cuthbert, 1945) and a thicker one loses some rigidity (see pages 180–186), it can be concluded that a water content about equal to that which can be held rigidly is necessary for any dry strength, and that water slightly in excess of this amount causes a very rapid increase in dry strength.

As shown in Fig. 4-16, sands bonded with the calcium montmorillonite clay require a certain minimum amount of tempering water to develop any dry strength, and above this minimum, the dry strength increases with amount of tempering water up to a maximum value which is reached abruptly. A striking feature of this clay is that maximum dry compression strength is about the same for mixtures containing 6, 10, 12, and 15 per cent clay. The maximum values for 8 per cent mixtures are slightly higher, but the difference is probably within experimental error. This means that it is impossible to get more than a certain dry strength regardless of the amount of this clay used. The use of more clay merely makes it necessary to use more tempering water to develop the same maximum strength.

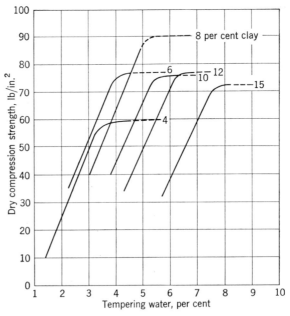

Fig. 4-16. Dry compression strength versus amount of tempering water in sands bonded with varying amounts of calcium montmorillonite clay, after Grim and Cuthbert (1946).

For the initiation of dry strength, the calcium montmorillonite clay requires water slightly in excess of that necessary to develop 3 molecular layers of water per unit cell of montmorillonite. It has been suggested (Grim and Cuthbert, 1945) that this type of montmorillonite holds water layers 4 molecules thick with complete rigidity, and it seems, therefore, that some dry strength develops before there is enough water to provide incompletely rigid water. This is not a certain conclusion for this type of clay, however, because not all the unit-cell surfaces may be available to water, so that the amount present on available surfaces may be greater than the computed values. Maximum dry compression strength is developed when there is water equivalent to more than 5 molecular layers per unit cell. This is probably more water than can be held in a completely rigid condition. In general it would seem that the development of relatively high dry strength of any class of clay requires some incompletely rigid water between the clay units so that adjustment of clay units can take place easily (see pages 197–199). It would seem further that only a certain amount of water would provide all possible adjustment of flakes, so that water in excess of the given amount would not necessarily cause greater strength.

Hofmann (1956) has shown that treating some calcium montmorillonite clays with sodium salts increases dry strength, whereas for others there is no change. Treatment with an acid or a potassium salt reduces dry strength.

The curves in Fig. 4-17, showing the relation of dry compression strength to tempering water for various amounts of halloysite clay, indicate that this type of clay develops low dry strength. However, as will be shown presently, the halloysite clay has high air-set properties, so that strengths greater than dry strengths are developed without much loss of tempering water when a rammed specimen stands for some minutes in the air. Also this clay is unique in that complete removal of water on drying does not increase strength above that which will develop with considerable retained water (see page 171). The maximum strength increases as the amount of clay increases and is about directly proportional to the amount of clay. Unlike other types of clay the maximum strength is attained gradually rather than abruptly.

A striking feature of halloysite clay-bonded sands is the small amount of tempering water necessary to start dry strength. Water does not readily penetrate to all of the halloysite particle surfaces as it does in the case of montmorillonite, so that less water would be required to permit adjustment between particles.

As shown in Fig. 4-18, illite clay develops high dry compression strength. The maximum dry strength increases with the amount of clay and develops abruptly. A distinctive character of this clay is that

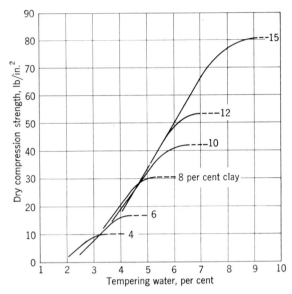

Fig. 4-17. Dry compression strength versus amount of tempering water in sands bonded with varying amounts of halloysite clay, after Grim and Cuthbert (1946).

maximum strength is developed with relatively small amounts of tempering water. The amount of water necessary to begin the formation of dry strength does not increase very much as the amount of clay increases, and the rate of increase of strength with increasing tempering water is the same for all amounts of clay, provided it is in excess of a minimum value. For example, at 3.5 per cent tempering water, sands with 6, 8, 10, 12, and 15 per cent clay all develop the same dry strength, 56 to 62 psi.

Figure 4-19 shows that the maximum dry compression strength obtainable with kaolinite clay is reached abruptly and increases with the amount of clay in the mixture. In general this clay yields less dry strength than the illite clay, and slightly more water is required to develop equivalent strength in a given mixture. As in the case of the illite clay, the amount of water necessary to start the formation of dry strength is about the same for all amounts of clay, and the rate of increase of strength with increasing tempering water is the same for all amounts of clay up to 15 per cent. This means that the dry compression strength for practical purposes will be the same in all mixtures tempered with equal amounts of water regardless of the amount of clay, provided the clay and water are more abundant than a certain minimum amount.

Dry compression strength for any given amount of tempering water in a workable range can be represented by the formula $DC = (T - M)K$

when T is the amount of tempering water, M is the tempering water in per cent required before any dry compression strength is developed, and K is an empirical coefficient. The M value is indicated by the intersection of the curves with the base line, and K is essentially the dry compression strength per unit of tempering water in excess of that required for the initial development of dry strength. These values, given in Table 4-3, permit a comparison of the bonding strength of the various types of clay. The maximum possible dry strength for mixtures with a given clay content decreases with the type of bond as follows: sodium montmorillonite, illite, kaolinite, and halloysite. The calcium montmorillonite is unique in that maximum attainable dry strength increases as the amount of clay increases up to about 8 per cent, but with larger

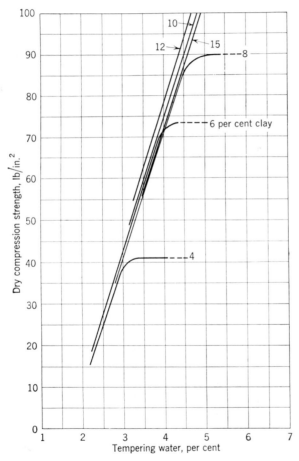

Fig. 4-18.   Dry compression strength versus amount of tempering water in sands bonded with varying amounts of illite clay, after Grim and Cuthbert (1946).

amounts of clay there is no further improvement in strength. The maximum dry strength of sands bonded with up to 8 per cent calcium montmorillonite is about equal to that of sands bonded with equal amounts of illite. With more than 8 per cent clay, illite clay-bonded sands have a higher maximum strength.

The K value is much higher for the sodium montmorillonite than for any other type of clay—the dry compression strength shows the largest change with variation in the amount of tempering water. In this clay, variations of 0.1 per cent water cause changes of 5 to 20 psi in dry strength. Halloysite has the lowest K value. Values for calcium montmorillonite, illite, and kaolinite are intermediate but are much closer to halloysite than to the sodium montmorillonite clay.

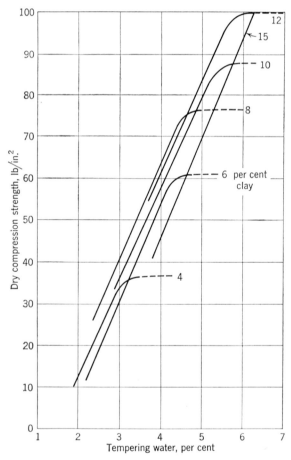

Fig. 4-19. Dry compression strength versus amount of tempering water in sands bonded with varying amounts of kaolinite clay, after Grim and Cuthbert (1946).

The M value increases with increasing amounts of clay in the montmorillonite and halloysite clays. Since the calcium montmorillonite and halloysite clays also have low K values, rather large amounts of water are required to develop much dry strength in mixtures bonded with these

TABLE 4-3

MAXIMUM DRY STRENGTH, K AND M VALUES FOR MIXTURES WITH
DIFFERENT AMOUNTS OF BONDING CLAY OF EACH CLASS
(After Grim and Cuthbert, 1946)

Per cent clay	Sodium montmorillonite clay			Calcium montmorillonite clay		
	Max. DC	M	K	Max. DC	M	K
4	100+	1.25	50–200	60	1	22
6	100+	1.4	50–200	77	1	22
8	100+	1.8	50–200	90	1.5	22
10	100+	2.5	50–200	76	2	22
12	100+	3.1	50–200	77	2.7	22
15	100+	3.75	50–200	73	4.2	22

Per cent clay	Halloysite clay			Illite clay			Kaolinite clay		
	Max. DC	M	K	Max. DC	M	K	Max. DC	M	K
4	10	1.8	8.0	41	1.6	30	37	1.6	23
6	17	2.2	9.5	73	1.6	30	61	1.6	23
8	30	2.4	13.5	90	1.6	30	77	1.6	23
10	42	2.6	13.5	100+	1.6	30	88	1.6	23
12	53	2.9	16.5	100+	1.6	30	100	1.6	23
15	80	2.9	16.5	100+	1.6	30	100+	1.6	23

clays. A condition is rapidly approached wherein the sands are so wet that no more adjustment of clay mineral particles is possible with additional water, and, as a consequence, the maximum dry strength is relatively low. In the case of sands bonded with the sodium montmorillonite, the K value is so high that extremely high strength is developed in sands with relatively low moisture contents.

In sands bonded with illite and kaolinite clay, the M value is low and constant so that, even though the K value is moderate, high maximum strength is attained in mixtures with relatively large clay contents containing moderate amounts of tempering water. Illite and kaolinite clays are unique in that both the M and K values are constant for all amounts of clay up to at least 15 per cent. This means that a certain dry strength develops at a given moisture content regardless of the

TABLE 4-4

TEMPERING WATER VALUES FOR MIXTURES WITH VARYING AMOUNTS OF TYPE CLAYS
(After Grim and Cuthbert, 1946)

Type and amount of clay in mixture, %	M	Per cent tempering water at—		
		Maximum green compression strength	Minimum bulk density	Maximum dry compression strength
Sodium montmorillonite:				
4...................	1.25	1.35	1.7	2.3+
6...................	1.4	1.7	2.6	2.5+
8...................	1.8	2.1	3.2	2.9+
10..................	2.5	2.6	3.6	3.6+
12..................	3.1	3.3	3.6	4.2+
15..................	3.75	4.1	5.2	4.9+
Calcium montmorillonite:				
4...................	1	1.7	2.1	3.5
6...................	1	2.2	2.6	4
8...................	1.5	2.7	3.5	5
10..................	2	3.2	4.3	5.5
12..................	2.7	3.9	5.3	6.5
15..................	4.2	4.7	5.9	7.5
Halloysite:				
4...................	1.8	1.7	1.85	3
6...................	2.2	2.35	2.6	4
8...................	2.4	2.9	3.0	5
10..................	2.6	3.6	3.7	6
12..................	2.9	4.3	...	7
15..................	2.9	4.9	5.1	8.5
Illite:				
4...................	1.6	1.6	1.75	3.3
6...................	1.6	1.7	2.2	4
8...................	1.6	1.9	2.6	5
10..................	1.6	2.2	2.8	5+
12..................	1.6	2.6	3.1	5+
15..................	1.6	3.2	3.3	5+
Kaolinite:				
4...................	1.6	1.1	1.9	3.5
6...................	1.6	1.4	2.5	4.5
8...................	1.6	1.7	3.3	5
10..................	1.6	2.1	3.8	5.5
12..................	1.6	...	...	6
15..................	1.6	3.4	5.9	6+

amount of clay provided it is in excess of the amount that develops a maximum strength at the moisture content used.

Table 4-4 shows the moisture content at which maximum green strength, minimum bulk density, and maximum dry strength are developed; it also shows the amount of water necessary for any dry strength (M value). For the montmorillonite clays maximum green strength develops just slightly in excess of the M value. This is true also for halloysite and illite clays when the mixtures contain small amounts of clay. With more than about 6 to 8 per cent halloysite or illite clay in the sand, maximum green strength requires increasingly more water than the M value. Kaolinite is unique in that with less than 6 per cent clay in the sand maximum green strength develops with less water than the M value. Minimum bulk density requires a larger amount of water than the M value, and the amount becomes greater as the clay content increases. Maximum dry compression strength requires a higher moisture content than either maximum green compression strength or minimum bulk density.

Comparison of the moisture content for maximum dry compression strength and limit values computed on a comparable basis show that maximum dry strength develops on the wet side of the plastic limit for all the types of clay (with the possible exception of sodium montmorillonite clay for which water values at maximum dry strength are not available).

Air-set Strength

Grim and Cuthbert (1945) discovered that sands bonded with halloysite and kaolinite clays developed greatly increased strength when rammed specimens were allowed to stand in the air for short periods of time. This increased strength is developed without much loss of moisture; this condition was not found in sands bonded with the other types of clay. Halloysite and kaolinite clays have, therefore, another type of strength in addition to green and dry strengths called *air-set strength*.

Figures 4-20 to 4-24 show the results of tests in which moldable mixtures of each type of clay were prepared at two moisture contents, one at about temper and one on the wet side of temper. Compression strength and moisture were determined on rammed specimens after they were allowed to stand in the air or in a 100°F oven for varying periods of time up to 10 hr. By the use of air drying and oven drying at 100°F, loss of moisture at two different rates was attained, and 10 hr proved adequate for the removal of essentially all of the tempering water.

With sodium montmorillonite clay bond there is only a slight increase in strength accompanying the first loss of water, but following this the

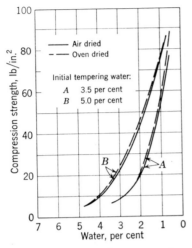

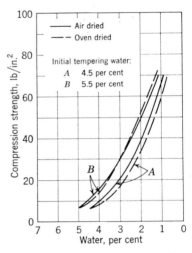

Fig. 4-20.   Compression strength of sands bonded with 6 per cent sodium montmorillonite clay developed on drying in air and in a 100°F oven to various moisture contents, after Grim and Cuthbert (1946).

Fig. 4-21.   Compression strength of sands bonded with 6 per cent calcium montmorillonite clay developed on drying in air and in a 100°F oven to various moisture contents, after Grim and Cuthbert (1946).

strength increases in direct relation to the loss of water (Fig. 4-20).   There is no suggestion of air-set strength.   The strength developed during gradual drying is dependent on the initial moisture content as well as on the moisture remaining at any given time—the strength is higher for the higher initial moisture content.   An increased rate of drying causes a more rapid loss of water and a more rapid increase in strength, so that after any intermediate time the samples dried at 100°F are stronger than those dried in air.

Dry compression tests of the sodium montmorillonite clay in mixtures with 6 per cent clay tempered with either 5.0 or 3.5 per cent water made according to standard A.F.S. procedure, which involves very rapid drying at 220°F and yielded values in excess of 270 psi, whereas similar batches with the same initial moisture content dried slowly in air or at 100°F to a very low moisture content (0.5 per cent) developed only about 90 psi compression strength.   This indicates that the very high A.F.S. dry strength of this clay is due either to an effect of the 220°F temperature or to the fact that the rate of drying influences the strength developed. It is clear that a regular A.F.S. dry-compression-strength test for this clay gives no indication of the strength in a dry sand mold unless the mold has been dried very rapidly and completely.

The curves in Fig. 4-21 indicate that sands bonded with calcium montmorillonite clay also show a direct gain in strength with loss of water on gradual drying. There is no air-set strength. The maximum attainable dry strength for a sand bonded with 6 per cent of calcium montmorillonite clay is about 77 psi (Fig. 4-16). This value is closely approached by gradual drying. Unlike the sodium montmorillonite, the calcium montmorillonite clay develops a strength on slow drying about equal to that developed on rapid drying if there is enough time for almost complete loss of moisture.

The strength of sands bonded with illite clay (Fig. 4-22) gradually increases as the tempering water is lost during slow drying without any suggestion of air-set strength. The increase in strength begins immediately with the loss of the first water. Samples with the same initial moisture content dried at 100°F develop slightly greater strength than those dried in the air to the same moisture content. After substantially complete drying in either the air or a 100°F oven, the strength increases to about 80 psi which is, however, still considerably less than the A.F.S. dry strength (270 psi) developed on rapid drying of similar sands at 220°F. In sands bonded with illite clay, therefore, molds dried at a relatively slow rate do not develop the strength that would be anticipated on the basis of the standard A.F.S. dry-compression tests.

The curves in Fig. 4-23 show that drying of halloysite clay-bonded sands

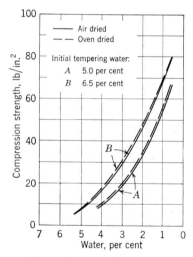

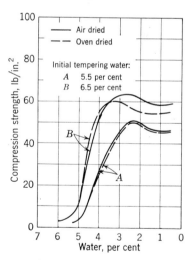

Fig. 4-22. Compression strength of sands bonded with 12 per cent illite clay developed on drying in air and in a 100°F oven to various moisture contents, after Grim and Cuthbert (1946).

Fig. 4-23. Compression strength of sands bonded with 12 per cent halloysite clay developed on drying in air and in a 100°F oven to various moisture contents, after Grim and Cuthbert (1946).

causes little increase in strength until a certain definite moisture content is reached (about 5 per cent for 12 per cent clay mixtures) and that with further loss of water there is an abrupt increase in strength until, with about 2.4 to 3.5 per cent retained water, a strength about 25 times greater than green strength is developed. There is a slight decrease in strength on drying to less than 2.5 per cent water. The striking feature of sands bonded with halloysite clay is that they develop a higher strength when they still retain a considerable amount of tempering water than they do when essentially all the water is removed. This is air-set strength, and for halloysite clay-bonded sands it is higher than dry strength. Also air-set strength is much greater than the maximum green strength.

The curves in Fig. 4-23 indicate that slightly higher air-set strength develops as the rate of drying is decreased. The effect of the rate of drying seems to be more pronounced in sands with higher initial water contents. The sands with higher initial amounts of tempering water develop higher air-set strength just as they develop higher dry strength. However, the moisture content at which maximum air-set strength develops varies only slightly with the amount of initial tempering water.

Computations (Grim and Cuthbert, 1946) show that maximum air-set strength is reached when there is enough water to coat the basal surface of each unit cell of halloysite with a film of water about 4 to 5 A thick. Since not all the basal surfaces of the halloysite units are available to water, the actual thickness of water on the available surface is in excess of this value, perhaps about 6 A or the thickness of a water layer 2 molecules thick. It is interesting that the maximum green strength is attained when the computed water per unit basal surface is 7 A thick as compared to 4 to 5 A for air-set strength. The difference is about 3 A or the thickness of a single molecular water layer. This may be a fortuitous situation because the most probable theory of air-set strength (see page 196) suggests that many more basal surfaces are coated with water at air-set strength than at green strength.

It is well known that increased ramming tends to increase the strength characteristics of sand molds. Figure 4-24 presents the results of compression tests made on two batches of halloysite clay-bonded sands from which test specimens were prepared with ramming both three and six times. Increased ramming increases the air-set strength as well as the green and dry strengths. From the similarity of the curves for both amounts of ramming, it would seem that increased ramming has no unusual effect on air-set strength. It does not decrease the tendency for air-set strength to develop nor change the moisture content at which the maximum strength develops.

The curves in Fig. 4-25 show that sands bonded with kaolinite clay, like those bonded with halloysite clay, develop air-set strength. When sands bonded with 10 per cent kaolinite clay are dried, the strength increases sharply until a maximum is reached when the moisture content is reduced to 1.5 to 3 per cent. With further decrease in moisture content there is a slight decrease in strength, followed again by an increase in strength at very low moisture contents when true A.F.S. dry strength is attained. The air-set strength developed with 1.5 to 3 per cent moisture is 5 to 10 times that of green strength and one-third to one-half that of A.F.S. dry strength. The air-set strength characteristics of halloysite and kaolinite clays are somewhat different in that A.F.S. dry strength is slightly less than air-set strength in halloysite clay-bonded sands and considerably higher for kaolinite clay-bonded sands.

For kaolinite clays, an increase in the amount of tempering water increases somewhat the amount of air-set strength. Variations in rate of drying seem to have no effect on the air-set strength in sands with relatively small amounts of tempering water. In wet sands the amount of air-set strength is also about the same, regardless of the rate of drying, but it develops at a slightly higher moisture content when the rate of drying is rapid.

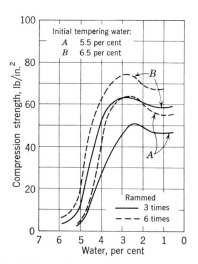

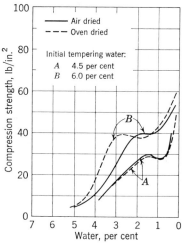

Fig. 4-24. Compression strength of sands bonded with 12 per cent halloysite clay, rammed three and six times, after drying in air to various moisture contents, after Grim and Cuthbert (1946).

Fig. 4-25. Compression strength of sands bonded with 10 per cent kaolinite clay developed on drying in air and in a 100°F oven to various moisture contents, after Grim and Cuthbert (1946).

Hot Strength

Figure 4-26 shows that the compression strength of sodium montmorillonite clay-bonded sands increases slowly up to about 1000°F, then rapidly increases to 1800°F, after which it declines abruptly. In Fig. 4-27 contours show the effect of soaking time and initial tempering water on hot strength. The data show that rapid heating causes the development of higher maximum hot strength and that increased tempering water also favors higher hot strength for the sodium montmorillonite clay-bonded sands. Figure 4-28 shows that the strength of a specimen which is allowed to cool after heating is much less than its hot strength and that maximum strength develops at a much lower temperature. In fact, specimens cooled from the temperature of maximum hot strength lose strength completely.

Calcium montmorillonite clay-bonded sands develop maximum hot strength at about the same temperature as the sodium montmorillonite clay-bonded sands, but the maximum hot strength is much less (Fig. 4-26). Also, on cooling, the sands show the same loss of strength as do the sodium montmorillonite clay-bonded sands (Fig. 4-28).

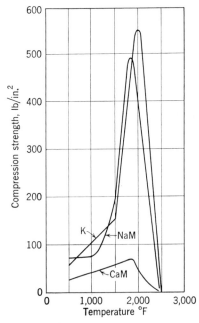

Kaolinite clay-bonded sands (Fig. 4-26) develop strengths about equal to, or slightly greater than, dry strength on heating up to about 1500°F after which the strength increases rapidly up to 2000°F. At higher temperatures the strength decreases rapidly. The maximum strength for kaolinite clay-bonded sands is developed at about 200°C higher than for montmorillonite clay-bonded sands. Figure 4-28 shows that for kaolinite as for montmorillonite clay-bonded sands the hot strength is not retained after the specimens are allowed to cool.

Fig. 4-26. Hot compression strength of sands bonded with sodium montmorillonite (NaM), calcium montmorillonite (CaM), kaolinite (K) clays: with 12 per cent K, 5 per cent NaM, 4 per cent CaM, at about temper point, modified after Dunbeck (1942).

The high strength shown by the montmorillonite clay-bonded sands on cooling following heating to about 2200°F is due to the fusion of

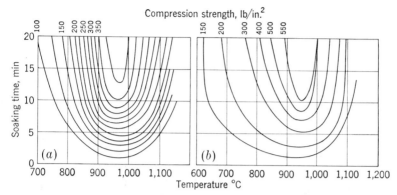

Fig. 4-27.   Hot compression strength of sands bonded with 5 per cent sodium montmorillonite clay with (*a*) 2.5 per cent and (*b*) 5 per cent tempering water, after Davies and Rees (1946).

the clay mineral, which at the high temperature provides a liquid phase (and low strength) and, on cooling, a glassy phase which binds the sand grains together.

   Data are not available for the hot strength of halloysite and illite clay-bonded sands.   However, based on general considerations of the structure, composition, and high temperature reactions of the clay minerals, one might predict that halloysite clays would produce results similar to kaolinite clays and that illite clays would produce results similar to montmorillonite clays, probably intermediate between the sodium and calcium varieties.

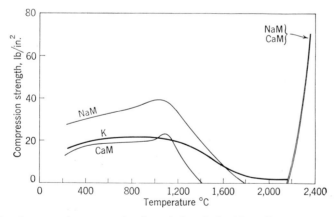

Fig. 4-28.   Compression strength of sands bonded with sodium montmorillonite (NaM), calcium montmorillonite (CaM), and kaolinite (K) clays: with 3.5 per cent NaM, 3.25 per cent CaM, and 8.8 per cent K, at about temper point after heating to temperature indicated and then cooled, after Hofmann (1958).

Flowability

Briggs and Morey (1939) have presented data (Fig. 4-29) showing the relation of flowability to tempering water in sands bonded with varying amounts of sodium montmorillonite clay. The flowability decreases slightly as the amount of clay increases up to 8 per cent. A sudden drop is recorded above 8 per cent. As the amount of tempering water increases, the flowability decreases to a minimum which is reached at about the minimum-bulk density point. With further increase of moisture the flowability gradually increases. The abruptness of the decrease on the dry side is greater as the amount of clay becomes larger.

It would seem that for all types of clay, the flowability would decrease as the amount of clay in the sand increased and that, as tempering water was added, flowability would decrease to a minimum at minimum bulk density and then increase. The increase on the wet side of the minimum density point would probably be abrupt and rapid so that a little additional water would increase flowability substantially.

Dunbeck (1942) has listed flowability in relation to clay mineral composition as follows, in decreasing order: calcium montmorillonite, illite, kaolinite, and sodium montmorillonite. The flowability of the first three clay minerals would probably be about the same and considerably different from that of the sodium montmorillonite. Data are not available for the effect of chemical treatment on the flowability of illite and kaolinite, but treatment with sodium would be expected to increase it, i.e., the relative effect of sodium and calcium would be the opposite of that for montmorillonite clays.

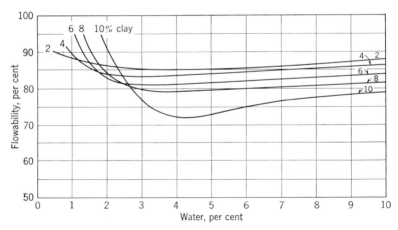

Fig. 4-29. Relation of flowability to amount of tempering water for sands bonded with a sodium montmorillonite clay, after Briggs and Morey (1939).

Grim and Johns (1957) have presented data on the composition properties of clay-bonded sands showing that flowability for montmorillonite clays is very sensitive to moisture change and that good flowability may require tempering water considerably in excess of that necessary for maximum green strength. For kaolinite and illite clay-bonded sand the amount of tempering water is much less critical in determining flowability, and a large amount beyond that yielding maximum green strength is not required for adequate flowability.

Durability

Casberg and Schubert (1936) investigated the durability of sands bonded with fireclay (kaolinite) and with bentonite (montmorillonite) by repeatedly pouring cast iron into molds made with the sands and measuring the strengths after each casting. They found that the bentonite molding sand gradually decreased in both green and dry strengths during the tests. The green strength of the fireclay-bonded sand first increased and then decreased, and there was a gradual decrease in dry strength while the green strength increased. The increase in green strength was attributed primarily to the breaking down of larger clay particles into smaller ones as the sand was used. The breaking down of the larger particles probably took place during the mulling operation of repeated tests.

Hofmann (1958), determining the decrease in strength as sands are heated to successively higher temperatures, has shown (Fig. 4-30) that sodium montmorillonite clay-bonded sands retain their green strength after moderate heating so that it decreases only after heating above 600°C. The green bonding capacity of calcium montmorillonite clay, however, starts to decrease gradually after heating to temperatures of a little over 100°C. The values for dry strength have much the same trend as the green-strength values. This difference of thermal resistance, according to Hofmann (1958), is a characteristic distinction between sodium and calcium montmorillonite clays. As a consequence, the calcium bentonite has better shake-out properties, not because of lower dry strength as is generally assumed, but because of a much faster decrease of bonding capacity. Sands bonded with calcium montmorillonite clay burn out to a much higher degree during the casting operation. Conversely the durability of sands with sodium montmorillonite clay is higher; less clay is required to recondition such sands.

Hofmann (1958) also determined the effect of treatment with sodium and potassium salts on the thermal resistance of calcium montmorillonite clays from Italy and Switzerland. He found that sodium treatment does not cause a decisive increase in the temperature at which the final loss of bonding capacity occurs; however, the rate of loss of the bonding capacity of the clay is improved by sodium carbonate treatment, and in some cases it becomes equal to that of the natural sodium montmorillonite clays. Dry strength is not essentially altered by sodium treatment. In contrast, potassium carbonate treatment causes green strength and dry strength to drop drastically, but the residual bonding capacity is maintained over a large range with increasing temperature.

The illite sample studied by Hofmann showed an abrupt loss of strength on heating to 400°C, but this might well not be characteristic of all illites. Kaolinite showed a gradual loss of strength on heating, but again this might well not be characteristic of all kaolinites or their strength development in actual use.

Dunbeck (1942) has listed durability, in decreasing order, in relation to clay mineral composition as follows: kaolinite, sodium montmoril-

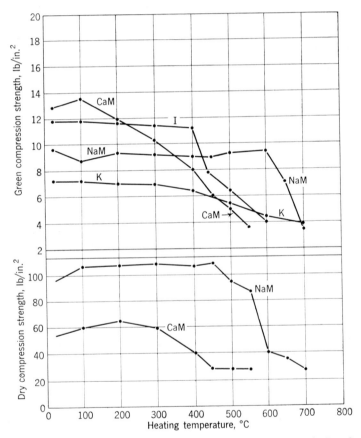

Fig. 4-30. Relation of heating temperature to strength of sands bonded with sodium montmorillonite (NaM), calcium montmorillonite (CaM), illite (I), and kaolinite (K) clays, after Hofmann (1958 and 1959).

lonite, illite, calcium montmorillonite. Grim and Cuthbert (1945) have arrived at somewhat different conclusions. They agree that kaolinite clay has the greatest durability but state that illite and calcium montmorillonite would be more durable than sodium montmorillonite because of their lesser dispersibility which causes them to occur in sands in larger particles (see pages 180–189).

Davidson and White (1953) investigated the reduction of strength following the heating of montmorillonite clay-bonded sands to elevated temperatures. They found that all the montmorillonite clays studied lost most of their bonding properties after heating to temperatures over 600°C but that considerable differences exist for such clays regarding their deterioration in the range 200 to 600°C. These authors obtained data suggesting that the sodium montmorillonite clays were most heat resistant in this temperature interval and also that these montmorillonites with low Si:Al ratios and fairly high iron contents were relatively less heat resistant. These authors also found that three of the bentonites which had the least resistance to heat, as assessed by green strength, were the most resistant on the basis of dry strength. No explanation is offered for this apparent anomaly.

SANDS BONDED WITH MIXTURES OF CLAY TYPES

Dunbeck pointed out (1942) that often in foundry practice there were advantages to using more than one type of clay in preparing a synthetic molding sand. In general this permits greater flexibility in obtaining precisely the properties desired in the sand. Middleton and White (1955) have emphasized the value of blending bonding clays. They have indicated that, in addition to a better control of properties, there may be increased durability. Thus, they found that mixtures of a kaolinite clay and bentonite retain their green strength after heating better than do bentonites alone.

CHARACTER OF THE CLAY COATING OF SAND GRAINS AND DISTRIBUTION OF TEMPERING WATER IN GREEN SANDS

The discussion of this subject is taken from the work of Grim and Cuthbert (1945).

Sodium Montmorillonite Clay

As illustrated in Fig. 4-31, the quartz grains in sands bonded with this clay have a smooth regular coating. The clay is made up of flake-shaped units, and when mulled with sand and water it is broken down to extremely small flakes which are plastered regularly on top of each

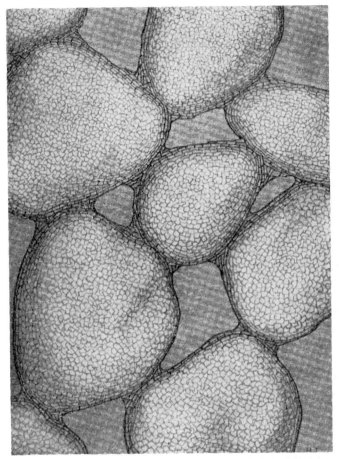

Fɪɢ. 4-31.   Sketch of sodium montmorillonite clay-bonded sand, based on micro-scopic examination, to illustrate the smooth even coating of the quartz grains with flakes of montmorillonite, and the wedge-shaped blocks at the junction of the clay-coated quartz grains holding the grains in place, after Grim and Cuthbert (1945).

other to make up the coating of the quartz grains.   A distinctive feature of the coating is the absence of aggregates or larger particles which have not been broken down.

When water is added to the sand-clay mixture, it penetrates into the montmorillonite and forms a film that coats the surfaces of each indi-vidual flake.   When the film is thin, the water molecules composing the film occupy definite fixed positions with respect to the surface of the montmorillonite-flake units.   Such water in which the molecules are oriented and fixed in position is not fluid, but solid and rigid.   It follows that the first tempering water added to a sand-clay mixture assumes a rigid condition on the surface of the montmorillonite flakes. As additional water is added the film becomes thicker in stepwise fashion, that is, the first water forms a layer 1 molecule thick, additional water forms a second layer another molecule thick, and so on. The orientation of the water molecules and the consequent rigidity is caused by the arrangement of the atoms that make up the montmorillonite itself. The effect of the atomic arrangement in the montmorillonite extends to a limited distance from the surface of the flakes; hence, the rigid character of the water also extends to a limited distance from the surface.

The thicknesses of the water and montmorillonite films surrounding the quartz grains given in Table 4-5 are based on the assumption, which is probably valid for this montmorillonite, that water penetrates between each unit flake. The data indicate that, in all mixtures containing more than enough clay to have pronounced bonding value (5 per cent), the thickness of the water film at maximum green compression strength is approximately 8 A which is equal to about the thickness of 3 water molecules. This computation further assumes that the water molecules are loosely packed and have the structure suggested by Hendricks and Jefferson (1938).

It seems certain that the effect of montmorillonite in causing water to become rigid would extend at least through three water molecules and, therefore, that the water coating the montmorillonite flakes is in a rigid condition when maximum green compression strength is developed. Since the bonding agents, clay and water, are both in a rigid condition when maximum green strength is developed, it follows that a concept

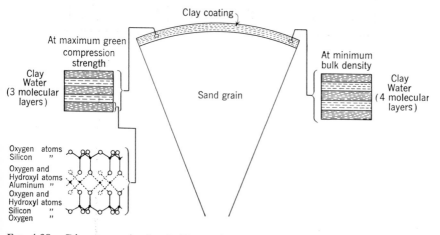

FIG. 4-32. Diagrammatic sketch illustrating the character of the coating of the quartz grains in sands bonded with sodium montmorillonite clay, after Grim and Cuthbert (1945).

of green bonding in molding sands must be based on a rigid condition of the material causing bonding. The thickness of the water film (8 A) is slightly less than the thickness of the individual units of montmorillonite (9.5 A). The coating of each quartz grain may, therefore, be

TABLE 4-5

COMPUTATIONS OF CLAY AND WATER FILM THICKNESS FOR
SANDS BONDED WITH SODIUM MONTMORILLONITE CLAY

Per cent clay	Per cent water	Water lost at 110°C, cc[a]	Thickness of clay film, unit cells of mont-morillonite	Total thickness of water film, μ	Thickness of water film per unit cell of mont-morillonite, angstroms	Ratio of water film to clay film thickness
			Values at maximum green compression strength			
2	1.0	20.0	631	0.946	15.0	1.63
3	1.25	25.0	955	1.19	12.5	1.36
4	1.35	27.0	1,288	1.30	10.1	1.10
5	1.45	29.0	1,626	1.41	8.6	0.93
6	1.65	33.0	1,973	1.63	8.3	0.90
7	1.85	37.0	2,326	1.84	7.9	0.86
8	2.10	42.0	2,681	2.12	7.9	0.86
9	2.40	48.0	3,057	2.45	8.0	0.87
10	2.60	52.0	3,426	2.68	7.8	0.85
12	3.30	66.0	4,214	3.47	8.1	0.88
15	4.15	83.0	5,454	4.52	8.3	0.90
			Values at minimum bulk density			
2	1.1	22.0	631	1.041	16.5	1.8
4	1.7	34.0	1,288	1.642	12.8	1.4
6	2.6	52.0	1,973	2.564	12.9	1.4
8	3.15	63.0	2,681	3.174	11.8	1.28
10	3.8	76.0	3,426	3.915	11.4	1.24
15	5.15	103.0	5,454	5.617	10.3	1.12

[a] Values based on 2,000-g mixtures.

visualized (Fig. 4-32) as an alternation of layers of montmorillonite and rigid solid water with the water layers slightly thinner than the clay layers.

The thickness of the water and montmorillonite films surrounding the quartz grains when there is just enough water to develop minimum bulk density is given also in Table 4-5. The data show that mixtures with enough clay to have pronounced bonding value develop minimum density when there is enough water to coat each flake surface with a film of water about 12 A thick, which is equal to a layer slightly thicker than 4 water molecules. It is significant that minimum bulk density is developed when the water per sheet of montmorillonite is about 1 molecule thicker than that required for maximum green compression strength.

It will be indicated later that the minimum density for sands bonded with this type of clay is developed when the water film is thick enough to begin to lose its rigidity. The coating of the quartz grains at minimum bulk density can be visualized as an alternation of layers of montmorillonite and water with the water layer somewhat thicker than the montmorillonite layers. The individual water layers are not uniformly rigid, the central portion of each layer being less rigid than that part directly in contact with the montmorillonite.

Calcium Montmorillonite Clay

Microscopic study of sands bonded with this clay shows that the quartz grains have a smooth even coating and that there are no large aggregates or particles present in the coating. The value for the water film thickness per flake of montmorillonite is 12.7 A in 4 per cent clay mixtures and 9.4 A in 15 per cent clay mixtures (Table 4-6). This decrease in thickness of water film per unit of montmorillonite is probably more apparent than real because it is likely that water does not penetrate all of the unit surfaces of this type of montmorillonite and because relatively more such surfaces would be unavailable to water in the mixtures with higher contents of clay.

The computed thickness of the water film in mixtures with more than 6 per cent clay is greater than a sheet of water 3 molecules thick and less than a sheet 4 molecules thick. Since, as noted above, there are probably some surfaces unavailable to water, a logical conclusion seems to be that the available surfaces of the units of montmorillonite are coated by a film of water 4 molecules thick at maximum green compression strength. The calcium montmorillonite differs, therefore, from the sodium montmorillonite in holding four instead of three molecules of water per unit of montmorillonite at maximum green compression strength. It appears therefore that the calcium montmorillonite can retain four molecules of water in a rigid condition whereas the sodium montmorillonite can retain only three molecules in a rigid condition—the fourth molecular layer showing a distinct reduction of rigidity. Later it will be shown that this extra water-retaining power provides an explanation for the higher green strength of the calcium montmorillonite clay. The cause of the difference in water-retaining power of the two montmorillonite clays probably resides largely in the exchangeable cations which they carry.

The data given in Table 4-6 indicate that the computed thickness of the water film per unit of montmorillonite at minimum bulk density is about 13 A in mixtures with more than 6 per cent clay. This thickness is slightly less than that of a sheet of water 5 molecules thick. It seems likely that the actual water-film thickness on available units of montmorillonite at minimum bulk density would be 5 molecules, or 1 molecule thicker than that required for maximum green compression strength.

Halloysite Clay

The quartz grains of sands bonded with this clay have a fairly smooth regular coating. Halloysite is made up of thin elongate lath-shaped or

TABLE 4-6

COMPUTATIONS OF CLAY AND WATER FILM THICKNESS FOR SANDS BONDED WITH CALCIUM MONTMORILLONITE CLAY

Per cent clay	Per cent water	Water lost at 110°C, cc[a]	Thickness of clay film, unit cells of montmorillonite	Total thickness of water film, μ	Thickness of water film per unit cell of montmorillonite, angstroms	Ratio of water film to clay film thickness
\multicolumn{7}{c}{Values at maximum green compression strength}
2	1.15	23.0	631	1.09	17.3	1.88
4	1.7	34.0	1,288	1.64	12.7	1.39
6	2.25	45.0	1,973	2.22	11.2	1.22
8	2.7	54.0	2,681	2.72	10.1	1.10
10	3.2	64.0	3,426	3.29	9.6	1.04
12	3.85	77.0	4,212	4.06	9.6	1.04
15	4.7	94.0	5,454	5.13	9.4	1.02
\multicolumn{7}{c}{Values at minimum bulk density}
2	1.35	27.0	631	1.27	20.1	2.18
4	2.1	42.0	1,288	2.03	15.8	1.72
6	2.85	57.0	1,973	2.81	14.2	1.54
8	3.55	71.0	2,681	3.58	13.4	1.46
10	4.3	86.0	3,426	4.43	12.9	1.40
12	5.3	106.0	4,212	5.58	13.2	1.44
15	5.95	119.0	5,454	6.55	12.0	1.30

[a] Values based on 2,000-g mixtures.

tubular units, and the coating appears to be composed of such units plastered regularly on top of each other.

Computations of the thickness of the water film reveal that maximum green compression strength is developed in sands with more than 6 per

TABLE 4-7

COMPUTATIONS OF CLAY AND WATER FILM THICKNESS FOR
SANDS BONDED WITH HALLOYSITE CLAY

Per cent clay	Per cent water	Water lost at 110°C, cc[a]	Thickness of clay film, unit cells of halloysite	Total thickness of water film, μ	Thickness of water film per unit cell of halloysite, angstroms	Ratio of water film to clay film thickness
Values at maximum green compression strength						
2	1.15	23.0	1,009	1.088	10.8	1.54
3	1.35	27.0	1,531	1.291	8.4	1.20
4	1.70	34.0	2,055	1.642	8.0	1.14
5	2.05	41.0	2,606	2.000	7.7	1.10
6	2.35	47.0	3,161	2.318	7.3	1.04
7	2.60	52.0	3,727	2.590	6.9	0.97
8	2.95	59.0	4,306	2.973	6.9	0.96
9	3.25	65.0	4,898	3.312	6.8	0.94
10	3.60	72.0	5,503	3.709	6.7	0.94
12	4.30	86.0	6,754	4.480	6.6	0.92
15	4.95	99.0	8,740	5.400	6.2	0.86
Values at minimum bulk density						
2	1.2	24.0	1,009	1.131	11.2	1.60
4	1.9	38.0	2,055	1.835	8.9	1.27
6	2.55	51.0	3,161	2.515	7.9	1.13
8	3.05	61.0	4,306	3.074	7.0	0.99
10	3.65	73.0	5,503	3.760	6.8	0.95
15	5.15	103.0	8,740	5.617	6.4	0.89

[a] Values based on 2,000-g mixtures.

cent clay when the tempering water is equal to a film of water 6 to 7 A thick for the basal surface of each unit of halloysite (Table 4-7). This value is intermediate between the thickness of 2 and 3 water layers. Because of the structural characteristics of halloysite, it is likely that not all of the individual unit surfaces are available to water and that the actual thickness of the water sheets on available surfaces is greater than the computed values—probably at least 3 molecular layers.

Halloysite clay-bonded sands possess air-set strength which suggests that such sands immediately after ramming are composed of quartz grains with alternate layers of clay and rigid water plus some liquid water. As air-set strength develops, the liquid-water molecules further penetrate between the silicate units, assume a fixed position, and become completely rigid.

The amounts of water required to develop minimum bulk density (Table 4-7) suggest that the thickness of the water film per unit of clay decreases as the content of clay in the sand increases. In mixtures with more than 8 per cent clay, the decrease is very small and is not greater than the experimental error in determining the values. The amount of water required for minimum density is only slightly greater than that for maximum green compression strength. Minimum bulk density and maximum green compression strength both appear to be developed when the amount of water present is equal to a film of water at least 3 molecules thick on the available surfaces of the individual laths of halloysite.

Illite Clay

A microscopic examination of sands bonded with illite clay shows that the coating is composed of minute flake-shaped units that are regularly plastered around the quartz grains plus larger particles that are stuck irregularly in the fine particles to give the coating an irregular appearance. Unlike montmorillonite, which breaks down readily on mulling, illite is broken down only in part to very small flake-shaped particles. The remainder is in the form of larger particles and aggregates. Computations of the thickness of the water per unit surface of illite given in Table 4-8 are based on the assumption that all the illite unit surfaces are available; this assumption cannot be correct for sands bonded with illite clay, as is indicated by the presence of larger particles in the coating of the quartz grains. Thus, the thickness on the available surfaces is probably at least 3 molecules of water, whereas the computed thickness is equal to only 2 water layers.

The values for the water required to develop minimum bulk density (Table 4-8) indicate that the amount of water per unit of clay decreases as the clay content increases. At least in part this decrease can be explained by relatively more of the illite being unavailable to penetration by water in the high-clay-content sands. These values also indicate that minimum bulk density is attained with very little more water than that required for maximum green compression strength. The difference between the two requirements is largest at intermediate clay contents and smaller at high or low clay contents.

TABLE 4-8

COMPUTATIONS OF CLAY AND WATER FILM THICKNESS FOR
SANDS BONDED WITH ILLITE CLAY

Per cent clay	Per cent water	Water lost at 110°C, cc[a]	Thickness of clay film, unit cells of illite	Total thickness of water film, μ	Thickness of water film per unit cell of illite, angstroms	Ratio of water film to clay film thickness
Values at maximum green compression strength						
4	1.65	33.0	1,486	1.593	10.7	1.07
6	1.70	34.0	2,276	1.677	7.37	6.74
8	1.93	38.6	3,101	1.945	6.27	0.63
10	2.22	44.0	3,962	2.287	5.77	0.58
12	2.57	51.4	4,863	2.709	5.57	0.65
15	3.22	64.4	6,293	3.513	5.58	0.56
Values at minimum bulk density						
4	1.77	35.4	1,486	1.710	11.5	1.15
6	2.2	44.0	2,276	2.170	9.53	0.95
8	2.55	51.0	3,101	2.570	8.29	0.83
10	2.8	56.0	3,962	2.885	7.28	0.73
12	3.06	60.12	4,863	3.167	6.51	0.65
15	3.30	66.0	6,293	3.60	5.72	0.57

[a] Values based on 2,000-g mixtures.

Kaolinite Clay

A microscopic examination of the coating of quartz grains with kaolinite clay (Fig. 4-33) shows it to be composed of large particles and aggregates disseminated through a matrix of small clay mineral flakes. The coating differs from that in sands bonded with illite clay by being more irregular and having a greater proportion of large particles. Kaolinite, like illite and unlike montmorillonite, is not readily reduced to extremely small units when it is mulled with sand and water. In kaolinite, water does not penetrate between the individual units, and it is, therefore, not possible to make significant computations of water-film thicknesses.

The values in Table 4-9 indicate that the amount of water per unit of clay necessary for maximum green strength is about constant regardless of the amount of clay in excess of that required (6 per cent) to develop appreciable bonding action. In mixtures with more than 6 per cent clay, water makes up about 60 per cent of the volume of the coating. Kaolinite clay-bonded sands develop air-set strength so that immediately after ramming some of the water is not completely rigid. This water probably becomes more rigid, or at least some of it becomes more rigid, when air-set strength develops. The relatively smaller proportion of water to clay required to develop maximum green strength in kaolinite clay-bonded sands than in those bonded with montmorillonite clays is explained by the smaller amount of clay mineral surface available in coatings made up of kaolinite clay.

The data in Table 4-9 show that sands bonded with all amounts of

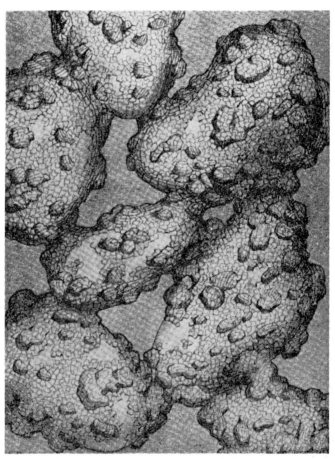

FIG. 4-33. Sketch of kaolinite clay-bonded sand, based on microscopic examination, to illustrate the irregular coating of the quartz grains with small flakes and large lumps of flakes, and the wedge-shaped blocks at the junction of the clay-coated quartz grains holding the grains in place, after Grim and Cuthbert (1945).

TABLE 4-9

COMPUTATIONS OF CLAY AND WATER FILM THICKNESS FOR
SANDS BONDED WITH KAOLINITE CLAY

Per cent clay	Per cent water	Water lost at 110°C, cc[a]	Thickness of clay film, μ	Total thickness of water film, μ	Ratio of water film to clay film thickness
Values at maximum green compression strength					
4	1.15	23.0	1.486	1.11	0.75
5	1.35	27.0	1.877	1.32	0.70
6	1.40	28.0	2.276	1.40	0.62
7	1.55	31.0	2.684	1.54	0.57
8	1.70	34.0	3.101	1.73	0.56
10	2.10	42.0	3.962	2.16	0.55
15	3.40	68.0	6.293	3.71	0.59
Values at minimum bulk density					
4	1.9	38.0	1.486	1.835	1.2
6	2.55	51.0	2.276	2.515	1.1
8	3.3	66.0	3.101	3.326	1.1
10	3.8	76.0	3.962	3.915	1.0
15	6.05	121.0	6.293	6.60	1.0

[a] Values based on 2,000-g mixtures.

kaolinite clay require considerably more tempering water to develop minimum bulk density than maximum green strength and that the amount of water per unit of clay at minimum density decreases very slightly with increasing amounts of clay in the mixture. The coating of the quartz grains at minimum bulk density has the same characteristics as at maximum green strength except that the proportion of water to clay is greater and there is more incompletely rigid water immediately after ramming. At minimum bulk density the volume of water and clay is about equal in sands with more than about 6 per cent clay.

CONCEPT OF THE BONDING ACTION OF CLAY IN MOLDING SANDS

Green Strength

Grim and Cuthbert (1945) suggested that the concept which best agrees with experimental data is that of a wedge and block at the contact of the sand grains holding them in place. Davies (1947) quite independently suggested about the same concept. As illustrated in Figs. 4-31 and 4-33, the clay-water coating forms a wedge-shaped mass where the quartz grains are in contact with each other. It is this wedge-shaped block, which has maximum solidity and rigidity at maximum green compression strength, that locks the sand grains in position and gives the mixture its strength. Each grain is, of course, fixed in place by a number of clay wedges.

The bonding action of clay and water in molding sands is not that of glue or adhesive causing the grains to stick together. The evidence suggesting the wedge-block concept and at the same time opposing any theory of gluing action is summarized and discussed below.

1. Green sands have very low tensile strength.

2. The maximum green compression strength is developed when all the water molecules are in a solid, rigid condition. The strength is reduced greatly by the presence of very small amounts of water above that required for maximum strength which is considered not to be in a highly rigid state. It is unlikely that very slight changes in the character and amount of water would cause such great changes in strength if bonding action were a gluing phenomenon.

3. The concept satisfactorily takes into account the green-strength properties that are distinctive for the various types of bonding clays.

4. The wedge-block concept provides a satisfactory basis for an understanding of how variations in the intensity of mulling produce different effects on the green strength of the various types of clays.

5. The variation in the durability of the different types of bonding clay can be explained satisfactorily on the basis of the wedge-block concept.

6. Air-set strength can be accounted for satisfactorily by this concept.

7. The wedge-block is entirely consistent with dry-strength properties.

The strongest block of a given size offering the greatest resistance to the movement of the sand grains would be homogeneous, completely rigid, and free from planes of weakness. The clay coating of the sands of the montmorillonite clay-bonded sands is essentially homogeneous (Fig. 4-31), and at maximum green strength all the tempering water is probably rigid. It follows that the blocks holding the grains in place are strong and the sand has high strength. On the other hand the sand grains in the kaolinite clay-bonded sands have an irregular coating containing large particles which provide planes of weakness (Fig. 4-33). It follows, therefore, that the wedge-blocks are weaker for kaolinite than for montmorillonite clay-bonded sands.

It has been shown that sands bonded with sodium montmorillonite clay have coatings containing sheets of water 3 water molecules thick per unit of montmorillonite and that in the case of the calcium montmorillonite clay the coating is 4 water molecules thick at maximum green compression strength. Therefore in sands of the same clay content, the coating would be thicker when the latter clay is used. The wedge-block between the grains therefore would be larger, and since the water is rigid and the coating is homogeneous in both cases, the larger block would be expected to be the stronger. Thus an explanation is provided for the higher green strength of the calcium montmorillonite clay.

It is characteristic of sands bonded with all types of clay when there is more than 4 to 6 per cent clay in the mixture that the maximum green strength is developed in a very narrow moisture range. This also follows from the wedge-block concept if it is assumed that there is a definite maximum thickness of water that is fixed rigidly on each clay mineral basal surface, because a slight amount of incompletely rigid water would greatly weaken the wedge or block. This assumption seems valid because it agrees with structural data regarding clay and water (Hendricks and Jefferson, 1938) and because it permits an understanding of bulk-density variations in rammed sand-clay mixtures. The great variation in strength with slight variations in the amount of tempering water cannot be explained by any "gluing" concept of bonding action, since a slight change in amount of water should only slightly change the bonding power of a glue.

The curves showing tempering water in relation to green compression strength are relatively flat for mixtures with less than 4 to 6 per cent clay regardless of the type of clay. A probable explanation is that the amount of clay is so small that other factors, such as adhesion of quartz and water, also play a part in the bonding action. When there is enough clay to exert appreciable bonding strength, the curves develop a characteristic shape.

A comparison of the tempering water versus green-strength curves for the various types of clay shows that the curves for halloysite clay-bonded sands are the steepest. The explanation is probably somehow related to the property of halloysite (see discussion of minimum bulk density) to hold adsorbed water to a given amount in a rigid condition with any additional water being completely nonrigid. It will be indicated later that this additional water is held with gradually reduced rigidity in the other clay minerals, with the possible exception of the illites.

Hofmann (1959) has shown that treating a calcium montmorillonite clay-bonded sand with Na_2CO_3 reduces the sharpness of the peak of the green compression–tempering-water curve. Since sodium tends to reduce the abruptness of the transition of rigid to liquid water, this change would be expected.

It is a well-known fact that the mixing of a small amount of montmorillonite clay with a clay belonging to one of the other types causes an increase in bonding strength out of proportion to the amount of montmorillonite clay added.   The explanation based on the suggested concept is that the montmorillonite breaks down into extremely small particles which occupy the open spaces in the coating developed by the larger particles of the other clay minerals.   The montmorillonite acts to fill and seal the spaces, thereby eliminating planes of weakness and increasing strength.   It should be emphasized that there must be comparatively few planes of weakness in a coating of kaolinite or illite clay or there will be no bonding strength.   By the same token only a very little montmorillonite clay is required to heal the few planes of weakness, and the resulting effect is large.

In mixtures with more than about 10 per cent clay, the maximum bonding strength per unit of clay increases more for the illite and kaolinite clays than for the montmorillonite and halloysite clays.   That is, for the types of clay that provide homogeneous coatings and wedges, once a wedge-block of a certain size is attained, a larger wedge-block gives little more strength.   On the other hand, for the types of clay providing nonhomogeneous wedge-blocks, the larger the wedge-block, the greater the strength provided.   This seems logical, because the larger a nonhomogeneous block is, the less likelihood there would be for a plane of weakness to penetrate completely through it.

The initial strength of a clay depends largely on the degree to which it is broken down in the mulling operation, because this determines the uniformity of the coating of the quartz grains and, therefore, the strength of the wedge-blocks.

In the case of montmorillonite clay-bonded sands, maximum green compression strength is developed at moisture contents much below the plastic limit.   The plastic-limit moisture content includes pore water, rigidly fixed adsorbed water, and some water less rigid and easily disrupted by pressure.   The adsorptive power of the surfaces of montmorillonites is such that it would be expected that all water added up to a certain point would be rigid and that no pore water would develop until all demands of the surface were satisfied.   Maximum green strength develops with the water at maximum rigidity; therefore it would be expected to develop at a lower moisture content than the plastic limit by a difference equal to the less rigid water and the pore water.   The expected difference would be largest in sodium montmorillonites because they have relatively more adsorbed water in a moderate degree of rigidity.

In the case of the other clay minerals, maximum green compression strength is developed at higher moisture contents than the plastic limit in low-clay-content sands and at equal or lower moisture contents in high-clay-content sands.   A probable explanation for the difference between these and the montmorillonite clay-bonded sands is the relatively lower adsorbing power of these clay minerals so that in no case would there be an absence of pore water. A relatively larger amount of such pore water would be expected in low-clay-content sands.

Intensity of Mulling

It is a well-known fact and follows from the foregoing discussion of the bonding action of clays that, as the mulling action applied to a sand with an illite or kaolinite clay is intensified or lengthened, the number of larger particles in the coating of the quartz grains will be reduced, thereby increasing the uniformity of the coating and accordingly increasing the strength. As shown in Table 4-10, the same thing does not

TABLE 4-10

EFFECT OF TIME OF MULLING[a] ON GREEN COMPRESSION STRENGTH

Mulling time, min	Green compression strength, psi	
	Mixture with 12% kaolinite clay at 2.8% tempering water	Mixture with 4% sodium montmorillonite clay at 2.2% tempering water
1	6.6	4.0
2	7.6	4.4
3	8.4	4.6
5	9.6	4.9
7	10.3	5.0

[a] Mulling was done in an intensive high-speed muller.

happen in montmorillonite clay-bonded sands because this type of clay breaks down almost completely with very little mulling. Long or intensive mulling tends to narrow the gap between the strengths of the different types of clay.

Bulk Density

A curve of the general type shown in Fig. 4-1 results when the weight per unit volume of rammed green sand is plotted against the amount of tempering water. The curve indicates that with increasing amounts of tempering water the bulk density first increases slightly, then decreases to a minimum value, and then increases in weight per unit volume. Based on the concept of the bonding action of clays presented herein, the following explanation seems warranted.

Water added up to the amount A in Fig. 4-1 penetrates the clay, but the amount is not enough to permit the clay mineral particles to be broken apart and plastered to the quartz grains. With less water than amount

A, there is little clay actually coating the quartz grains; consequently, the clay and water are present in pore spaces between the grains. The tempering water is, therefore, a net addition to the weight per unit volume of the mixture. As point *A* is passed, the quantity of water becomes adequate to permit the clay mineral particles to break up and to develop the clay-water coating around the quartz grains. As the coating becomes thicker and more perfect with increasing amounts of tempering water, the packing of the grains becomes more difficult under the action of the rammer.

The quartz grains have the greatest resistance to packing at the point of minimum weight per unit volume (*C*) and hence the greatest pore space after ramming. This would also be the point of greatest permeability. Point *B*, at which maximum green compression strength is developed in sands bonded with montmorillonite- and kaolinite-type clays, is at a lower moisture content than that required for minimum weight. In sands bonded with illite- and halloysite-type clays, points *B* and *C* almost coincide.

With moisture contents higher than *C*, the coating on the quartz grains gradually becomes soft, permitting some of the coating to be squeezed into the interstitial space and thereby increasing bulk density.

Sands bonded with sodium montmorillonite clay develop minimum bulk density with 1 molecular layer of water on each basal surface of montmorillonite in excess of that held with maximum rigidity (i.e., at maximum green compression strength). Minimum bulk density develops when the clay-water coating is slightly on the wet side of its maximum rigidity or when some rigidity has been lost. It seems logical that a condition in the coating would prevail just beyond maximum rigidity and before there was enough water to greatly soften the coating, when it would offer the greatest resistance to packing. The same statements can be made for the calcium montmorillonite clay-bonded sands.

Sands bonded with halloysite and illite clays develop minimum density at about the same moisture content as maximum green compression strength. This suggests that for halloysite and illite, water is held in a rigid condition to a given thickness and that additional water is completely nonrigid, whereas for montmorillonites the additional water merely reduces rigidity. If the additional water is completely nonrigid, it cannot be expected that it will increase the resistance to packing over that prevailing when all the water is completely rigid.

Sands bonded with kaolinite develop minimum bulk density with an amount of water appreciably in excess of that necessary for maximum green strength, which suggests a considerable tapering off of rigidity beyond the maximum point.

The general shape of the curves in Figs. 4-10 to 4-14, shows that the relation of bulk density to tempering water is the same, within the limits of experimental error, for all types of clay except halloysite. The halloysite clay curves are steeper, indicating very rapid changes in bulk density with the amount of moisture. There is no satisfactory explanation for this characteristic. Perhaps it is related to the elongate tubular nature of halloysite.

The weight per unit volume at minimum bulk density increases sharply as the amount of kaolinite or illite clay in the sand-clay mixture increases. There is a slight increase for sands bonded with the sodium montmorillonite clay, and for sands bonded with only as much as 8 per cent halloysite or calcium montmorillonite clays there is a very slight increase in weight. Sands bonded with small amounts of kaolinite or illite clay are slightly heavier per unit volume than those bonded with the other types of clay, whereas sands bonded with 8 per cent or more of these clays are considerably heavier than those bonded with equal amounts of either halloysite or montmorillonite clays. The explanation for the variation of weight per unit volume for varying amounts of the different types of clay is not clear.

Flowability

It has been indicated that minimum flowability develops at about the point of minimum bulk density. This is expected because at this point there is the maximum resistance to packing by ramming. The addition of water beyond the minimum density point provides water which is less rigid and therefore can possibly act as a lubricant between the coated grains rather than strictly as a bonding force. In other words, as the nonrigid water develops plasticity, the flowability would be expected to increase. Dietert and Valtier (1931) define *temper point* as the point of minimum weight per unit volume. However, practical foundrymen place it just on the wet side of minimum bulk density, which is very logical from the foregoing discussion.

Dunbeck (1942) listed flowability in relation to clay mineral composition as follows, in decreasing order: calcium montmorillonite, illite, kaolinite, and sodium montmorillonite. The concept of rigid water provides an explanation for this sequence. It has been shown that calcium montmorillonite develops rigid water layers to a given thickness and that with more water there is little tapering off in degree of water-molecule orientation but rather an abrupt change to liquid water. Thus in calcium montmorillonite clay-bonded sands with water in some excess of that held rigidly there is completely liquid water to provide good lubrication and good flowability. On the other hand, an abundance of evidence shows that for sodium montmorillonite the rigidity of adsorbed water is gradually lost above the maximum rigidity point. Therefore water in addition to that held with maximum rigidity would not provide much lubrication, and the sands bonded with this clay would have low flow-ability. Sands bonded with sodium montmorillonite clay on the wet side of maximum green compression strength would be expected to be sticky, and this is the case.

The data indicated that also for illite and halloysite the water held beyond that of maximum rigidity abruptly changes to liquid water which is in accord with the good flowability properties of illite clay-bonded sands.

The condition for kaolinite clay-bonded sands is less clear because the irregular coating and the presence of large particles of wide size distribu-tion with a small proportion of total surface available to water also must influence flowability as well as the nature of the adsorbed water.

Air-set Strength

Air-set strength means in general that the wedge-blocks holding the sand grains in place in a rammed sample become stronger in a short period of time after ramming while a large amount of the tempering water is still retained. In sands bonded with halloysite or kaolinite clays, many of the basal surfaces capable of fixing water in a rigid condition are on the interior of larger particles where water cannot easily reach them. As a consequence, immediately after ramming only a part of the tem-pering water is rigid. Within a short period of time after ramming, some of this originally nonrigid water penetrates to clay mineral surfaces and is fixed. There is, therefore, a gradual change of some of the fluid water to a rigid condition accompanied by an increase in the strength of the wedge-blocks and, consequently, of the rammed sand. While some of the originally liquid water is being fixed, some is also being lost by evaporation, so that in a short time there is no liquid water in the rammed specimen. This is the condition at maximum air-set strength.

Air-set strength develops because a certain amount of time (Grim and Cuthbert, 1945), measured in minutes, is required for some of the tem-pering water to penetrate masses of halloysite or kaolinite and to become fixed in a rigid condition. Sands bonded with these types of clay have a wet feel immediately after mixing because of the presence of liquid water. The wet feel disappears after air-set strength develops.

In the process of allowing sand-clay mixtures to temper before testing, there is time for the water to penetrate to many of the clay mineral surfaces. However, when mixtures are rammed the relation between various masses of clay and the individual clay mineral flakes is changed so that new interfaces develop. The actual ramming operation probably disrupts some of the particles of clay, and additional surfaces are ul-timately available to water. Further, the equilibrium between the flake surfaces and the water attained during tempering is probably disturbed by the ramming. After ramming, water penetrates to new surfaces and becomes rigid to develop a new equilibrium.

In montmorillonite clays, water penetrates easily and rapidly to about all of the clay mineral surfaces. As a consequence the water becomes rigid at once without a time lag, and there is no air-set strength. Such clays develop all the strength they will ever have in the presence of water immediately on ramming. With equivalent amounts of water, sands bonded with montmorillonite clays, unlike those bonded with halloysite or kaolinite clays, do not have a wet feel immediately after mixing unless the amount of water is large.

In illite there seems to be no appreciable penetration of the tempering water into the clay mineral particles. There is, therefore, practically no water that requires a time lag after ramming in order to develop a rigid condition—consequently there is no air-set strength.

Dry Strength

The following theory of dry compression strength seems to fit best with the experimental data and agrees with the facts and theories of green strength.

Wedge-block–shaped masses at the junctions of the sand grains hold the grains in place and give rise to dry compression strength. The homogeneity and uniformity of the wedge-block determine its strength and therefore the amount of dry compression strength. A relatively small, completely homogeneous wedge-block composed of uniformly sized and arranged flakes will provide greater dry compression strength than a larger one composed of an aggregation of large and small particles with a random arrangement, because in the latter case planes of weakness must be present.

The function of the tempering water is to separate the clay mineral particles and to act as a lubricant so that, on ramming, movement can take place between them. Dry strength in general increases with the amount of tempering water, because more water gives more separation and lubrication of the clay particles and consequently results in a more homogeneous wedge-block. The K value is a measure of the speed of the separating and lubricating effect of the water.

There is, of course, a limit to the perfection the wedge-block can develop with increasing amounts of tempering water. As the amount of water is increased, a point is reached where all possible separation of the clay particles is attained and they are completely lubricated. Obviously, more water cannot lead to the formation of a stronger wedge-block. There is, therefore, a maximum dry strength for a given amount of clay —a strength which is not increased by further addition of tempering water.   Since dry strength requires adjustment between the grains, more tempering water is required for the maximum value than for maximum green strength.

In the presence of water, sodium montmorillonite clay breaks down easily into clay mineral flakes approaching unit-cell dimensions.   This character of the clay leads to the formation of a uniform and homogeneous wedge-block with a minimum number of planes of weakness. The wedge-block is therefore strong, and very high dry strength results. Because water penetrates between about all the individual units that make up this clay, it follows that the amount of water necessary to start the development of dry strength (M) should increase with the amount of clay.   The M value (Table 4-3) for sodium montmorillonite indicates that a minimum amount of water is required to get sufficient lubrication of flakes so that adjustments can take place between them leading to homogeneity in the wedge.   It is shown in Table 4-3 that the M value increases in such a way that the water per unit of clay is about the same for all amounts of clay.   It is also shown that this minimum thickness is about equal to the thickness at which the rigidity of the water begins to decrease.   This is in accord with expected conditions, since more water would be required than that held with complete rigidity before there could be any lubricating action.   The high K value for the sodium montmorillonites indicates that, once there is enough water separating each flake so that there is the possibility of adjustment of the flakes, small increments of water cause great increases in dry strength.

Calcium montmorillonite clay also breaks down in water into extremely small units approaching unit-cell dimensions; as a consequence, the observed increase in the M value with an increase in the amount of clay would be expected.   It also would seem to follow that a homogeneous, uniform wedge-block would develop providing high dry strength.   Yet, unlike the sodium montmorillonite, this is not the case because the calcium montmorillonite clay has much lower dry strength.   A considerable body of evidence suggests that when sodium is the exchangeable cation the adsorbed water may not be completely rigid even at low moisture contents, whereas in the case of calcium montmorillonites the adsorbed water is completely rigid up to a given value and then further water is fluid.   It is conceivable that with calcium the clay-water coating would be too rigid on the dry side and too fluid on the wet side to develop a homogeneous wedge-block.   With sodium the lesser rigidity of the orientation of the water molecules over an appreciable moisture range would permit easy adjustment within the coating to develop a strong wedge-block on drying.   A striking characteristic of calcium montmorillonite clay-bonded sands is that clay contents above about 8 per cent cause no further increase in dry strength, which means that wedge-blocks larger than a certain size cause no further increase in strength. A satisfactory explanation for this last characteristic is not at hand.

In halloysite clays, there seems to be some penetration of water between the individual laths of the mineral, and, therefore, the increase in M value with increasing amounts of clay is expected. Halloysite clays do not break down to individual units, and the wedge-blocks that develop are composed of larger units with the result that dry strength is relatively low. Halloysite clays are unique in that maximum dry compression strength is not attained abruptly but gradually with increasing amounts of tempering water. Halloysite also develops outstanding air-set strength, and the two characteristics go together. Because the reaction between water and halloysite is rather slow, a sharp point would not be expected at which there is no further increase in strength. By the same line of reasoning, the slow reaction between halloysite and water may be at least partially responsible for the low K value.

The M value of illite and kaolinite clays is the same and does not vary with the amount of clay. In the illite clay, water does not seem to penetrate between the individual units. All the tempering water is around and outside the particles of the clay, and some of it, not on basal surfaces, is probably not completely rigid even when the amount of water is very small. Therefore, from the start of the addition of tempering water, there is probably some liquid water, and this situation prevails regardless of the amount of clay. It would be expected as a consequence that the M value would be the same for about all amounts of illite clay. The same situation prevails in kaolinite clays except that some slight penetration of water into the kaolinite particles is indicated by the air-set strength. The K factor is small for illite and kaolinite clays because the clay aggregates are comparatively large and irregular, requiring a large amount of water for a small amount of adjustment. Because illite and kaolinite clays do not break down to very small units, resulting wedge-blocks would have less homogeneity, and the dry strength would not be very high. Such relatively imperfect wedge-blocks should increase in strength as they increase in size; consequently, the increase in maximum attainable strength with increasing clay contents is to be expected.

Hot Strength

When clay minerals are heated to elevated temperatures, they lose their hydroxyl water between 900 and 1200°F depending on the type of clay mineral. Between 1500 and 1700°F their crystalline structure is destroyed, and at slightly higher temperatures new crystalline phases begin to form. The formation of the new phases generally is not abrupt but rather is a stepwise development (Grim and Kulbicki, 1957) with the first change being one in bonding between the component units of the structure of the new phase, i.e., a nucleation; this is followed by the growth of the new phase, which involves a movement of ions within the bonded network.

It is interesting that the maximum hot strength develops at the temperature of the nucleation of the new high temperature phase. This nucleation is at a higher temperature for kaolinite than for illite and montmorillonite, and this explains the difference between the temperatures of their maximum hot strength. The bonding shift is a change from face-sharing to edge-sharing octahedral units which are more stable, and it is reasonable that this would create momentarily a strongly bonded wedge-block of high strength. At higher temperatures immediately following the bonding shift there must be considerable migration of ions within the structure as the new nuclei begin to grow—again it seems reasonable that this would be accompanied by a loss of strength. As the temperature is increased liquid phases would appear which would still further lower the strength.

The great difference between the hot strength of the sodium and calcium montmorillonite clays is probably to be explained by the difference in the exchangeable cations. Grim and Kulbicki (1957) have shown that the nature of the cation carried by a montmorillonite greatly changes the characteristics of its high-temperature-phase reactions. Thus, sodium favors the nucleation and calcium retards it, which is in accord with the theory devoloped above. Potassium also retards the formation of high temperature phases, and this fact is in accord with the relatively low hot strength of illite. Structural variations within the montmorillonites themselves also cause variations in the high temperature phase devolopment (Kulbicki and Grim, 1957) which should effect hot strength. Thus, all montmorillonite clays carrying sodium would not be expected to have exactly the same hot strength.

In kaolinite the development of mullite at about the temperature of maximum strength is a vigorous change, and the relatively high hot strength of clays composed of this mineral would be expected. Many kaolinite bonding clays carry a small quantity of other clay minerals, e.g., illite, and the presence of such components might well lower the hot strength considerably. Halloysite experiences about the same high temperature reactions as kaolinite and would probably have the same hot-strength properties.

It has been pointed out that cooling of the test specimens following heating to the temperature of maximum hot strength causes the loss of the strength. This is probably due to slight volume changes which would weaken the wedge-block. It must be remembered that there is very little if any vitrification at the temperature of maximum hot strength. Specimens cooled following heating to higher temperatures (in the vitrification range) may have very high strength.

Hofmann (1958) has shown that, on heating to temperatures below about 1100°F, the calcium montmorillonite clays lose their strength more rapidly than the sodium montmorillonite clays. Hofmann does not give an explanation for this phenomenon, but it probably resides in the fact that the monovalent sodium ion would provide little bond between the montmorillonite flakes from which interlayer water was removed and thereby permit easy penetration of water again. The divalent calcium ion would tend to hold the flakes together so that penetration of water between the dried flakes was more difficult. That is, at these temperatures all the adsorbed water is driven from between the flakes; with sodium, tempering water would again penetrate between the flakes, but with calcium it would not. Hofmann and Endell (1939) have shown that the maximum temperature following which a montmorillonite will rehydrate is dependent on the nature of the cation adsorbed, and that the temperature is higher for sodium than for calcium clays. Hofmann (1958) has also shown that this property is not the same for all calcium montmorillonite clays, which means that variations in the montmorillonite structure itself, as well as the adsorbed cation, also exert an influence.

Durability

In sands bonded with illite or kaolinite clays, some of the larger particles which cause the irregular coating and low strength are broken down each time the sand is mulled. There is, therefore, a tendency in the successive use of such a sand to increase the uniformity of the clay coating and hence its strength. As sands are used, the high temperature of the metal burns out some of the clay and thereby reduces its strength. The strength of a sand during use is determined by the relation between the destruction of the bond by heat and the development of a new bond by mulling. The larger clay particles are in effect a reserve bond that is released as the sand is used. The strength of sands bonded with kaolinite clays may actually increase for several heatings after they are first used. In contrast, sands bonded with montmorillonite clay may break down completely during the first mulling so that there is no reserve of bond to be released when the sand is reused.

Among the other factors important to durability is the resistance of the clay to heat, i.e., its refractoriness. This is not merely the fusion temperature of the clay, but the temperature at which vitrification begins. In considering the effect of heat on clays in molding sands, the vitrification temperature is important rather than the fusion temperature. Illite and montmorillonite clays have both low vitrification and fusion points. Halloysite has very high vitrification and fusion points. Kaolinite has a very high fusion point, but most kaolinite clays begin to vitrify at temperatures considerably below this point. Another factor of importance is that small particles of a clay fuse more quickly at a given temperature than larger particles. Other things being equal, therefore, clays yielding extremely minute units in the mulled mixture would be more likely to undergo changes as a result of the heat of the casting process.

OIL-BASE FOUNDRY SANDS

Recently, foundry-sand mixtures have come into use which are made up of quartz sand, clay prepared so that it is wettable in oil, and an oil instead of tempering water. It is claimed that the use of oil instead of water eliminates steam when metal is poured, which in turn reduces porosity and surface pinholing in castings. It is further claimed that it makes possible the use of very fine sands resulting in smooth surfaces and close tolerances, since the high permeability of coarser sands is no longer needed for the escape of steam. Aluminum, magnesium, bronze, and iron have been cast in such sands. At present, perhaps for economic reasons, castings made in this way have been small.

Montmorillonite and attapulgite clays have been used and made oil-wettable by a chemical treatment that coats the particle surfaces with organic molecules rendering the surfaces oleophilic and hydrophobic. The organic compound used and the means of coating the clay particles have not been revealed publicly.

REFERENCES

Anonymous, "Technical Data Sheet 958-A," Minerals and Chemicals Philipp Corp., Menlo Park, N.J. (1959).

Briggs, C. W., and R. E. Morey, Synthetic Bonded Steel Molding Sand, *Trans. Am. Foundrymen's Assoc.*, **47**, 653–724 (1939).

Casberg, C. H., and C. E. Schubert, An Investigation of the Durability of Molding Sands, *Univ. Illinois Eng. Expt. Sta. Bull.* 281 (1936).

Davidson, S., and J. White, Effect of Heat on Clays and Its Bearing on the "Life" of Clay Bonds, *Foundry Trade J.*, **95**, 165–174, 235–245 (1953).

Davies, W., The Fundamental Characteristics of Molding Sands, *J. Iron Steel Inst.*, pp. 9–46 (1947).

────── and W. J. Rees, Hot Strength Characteristics of Molding Sands, *J. Iron Steel Inst.*, pp. 61–70 (1946).

Dietert, H. W., and F. Valtier, Grain Structure Control Insures Mold Permeability Control, *Trans. Am. Foundrymen's Assoc.*, **39**, 175–192 (1931).

Dunbeck, N. J., American Synthetic Sand Practice, *Trans. Am. Foundrymen's Assoc.*, **50**, 141–164 (1942).

Grim, R. E., and F. L. Cuthbert, The Bonding Action of Clays: Part I, Clays in Green Molding Sand, *Illinois State Geol. Survey Rept. Invest.* 102 (1945).

────── and ──────, Some Clay-Water Properties of Certain Clay Minerals, *J. Am. Ceram. Soc.,* **28,** 90–95 (1945).

────── and ──────, The Bonding Action of Clays: Part II, Clays in Dry Molding Sand, *Illinois State Geol. Survey, Rept. Invest.* 110 (1946).

────── and W. D. Johns, Compaction Studies of Molding Sands, *Trans. Am. Foundrymen's Assoc.,* **59,** 90–95 (1951).

────── and G. Kulbicki, Etudes des réactions de hautes températures dans les minéraux argileux au moyen des rayons-X, *Bull. soc. franç. céram.,* **36,** 21–28 (1957).

────── and C. E. Schubert, Mineral Composition and Texture of the Clay Substance of Natural Molding Sands, *Trans. Am. Foundrymen's Assoc.,* **48,** 935–953 (1940).

Hendricks, S. B., and M. E. Jefferson, Structure of Kaolin and Talc-Pyrophyllite Hydrates and Their Bearing on Water Sorption of Clays, *Am. Mineralogist,* **23,** 863–875 (1938).

Hofmann, F., Beitrag zur Kenntnis und zur Untersuchung der Eigenschaften von Bentoniten, *Giesserei,* **16,** 857–864 (1956).

──────, Investigations on the Effect of Heat on the Bonding Properties of Various Bentonites, *Trans. Am. Foundrymen's Assoc.,* **66,** 305–320 (1958).

──────, Modern Concepts on Clay Minerals for Foundry Sands, *Brit. Foundryman,* pp. 161–170, April (1959).

Hofmann, U., and J. Endell, Die Abhandigkeit des Cationaustausches und der Quellung bei Montmorillonite von der Vorerhitzung, *Ber. deut. chem. Ges.,* **35** (1939).

Jones, D. R., and R. E. Grim, Pinhole Occurrence in Malleable Castings, *Modern Castings,* pp. 397–400 (1959).

Middleton, J. M., and J. White, Metal and Mould Research on Steel Castings: II, Mould and Core: Bonding Agents, *Foundry Trade J.,* **99,** 59–70 (1955).

White, W. A., Allophanes from Lawrence County, Indiana, *Am. Mineralogist,* **38,** 634–642 (1953).

CHAPTER 5

Clay Mineralogy in Relation to the Engineering Properties of Clay Materials

INTRODUCTION

The objectives of this chapter are to consider the relation of the clay mineral composition to the properties of clay materials as determined in soil mechanics studies and to consider the fundamental way in which the clay mineral composition influences these properties. The literature reports only a few investigations into the relation of specific clay minerals to such properties. Nevertheless, the studies are adequate for an initial summation of the data and for its use in these considerations.

In addition to the clay mineral composition, other factors, such as particle-size distribution, nonclay mineral composition, organic material, and geologic history, control the engineering properties of soils and clays. Therefore, it is not possible to classify all soils and clays or to predict their properties solely on the basis of clay mineral composition. However, in very cohesive soils the clay mineral composition is likely to be the most important controlling factor for many properties, and a knowledge of the clay mineral composition may thus provide an understanding of empirical test data which will simplify problems and perhaps avoid construction failures. For other properties, for example, compressibility and shear strength, the previous stress history (geologic history) is likely to be the controlling factor.

The construction engineer is frequently required to build structures on, through, or with clay materials. The usual procedure is to obtain core samples of the clay materials and determine their properties by a series of laboratory tests. The results of such tests and experience gained in using similar materials aid in designing and building the structure. It is not to be expected that the clay mineral determinations will give a full evaluation of soil properties, nor can they be substituted for the laboratory tests. There has been a growing feeling in recent years that it is a matter

204

of good judgment to have clay mineral analyses made of the soils involved in construction projects for two reasons. In the first place, they should explain and provide a concept of the fundamental causes of the particular soil properties involved and, therefore, make any conclusions based on empirical data much more secure. In the second place, they should serve to warn the engineer if there is anything unusual about the clay material which might make special handling necessary or make the test data somewhat misleading. For example, construction activities may change the environment of the soil by causing a cation-exchange reaction. A knowledge of the fundamental causes of properties should indicate to the engineer how such a change would alter these properties.

Since, as will be shown presently, very small amounts of certain clay mineral constituents may greatly influence physical properties, clay mineral analyses must be complete, if they are to be of value, and not limited to the identification of only the major constituents. Actually, a poor or incomplete analysis is worse than none, as it may be misleading and cause great difficulties.

ATTERBERG LIMITS

Engineers have found it convenient to express the plastic properties of soil materials in terms of plastic limit (Pw), liquid limit (Lw), and plasticity index (Ip) as first proposed by Atterberg (1911). Teraghi in 1925 first noted that Atterberg's work might have significance in soil mechanics. Allen (1942) defines these terms as follows:

> Liquid limit is the moisture content expressed as a percentage by weight of the oven dried soil at which the soil will just begin to flow when jarred slightly.
>
> Plastic limit is the lowest moisture content expressed as a percentage by weight of the oven dried soil at which the soil can be rolled into threads 1/8 inch in diameter without breaking into pieces. Soils which cannot be rolled into threads at any moisture content are considered non-plastic.
>
> Plasticity index is the difference between the liquid limit and the plastic limit. It is the range of moisture content in which a soil is plastic. When the plastic limit is equal to or greater than the liquid limit, the plastic index is recorded as 0.

Standard procedures have been developed for determining limit values, and they are fully described in the literature (for example, see Casagrande, 1932). According to Skempton (1953) a clay-water system at the liquid limit has a shear resistance of the order of 0.1 psi. Although the limit values are based on simple empirical tests, they have been found to be very useful as index properties which may be correlated with more fundamental properties, such as shear strength and compressibility. Also, as will be shown, they reveal some fundamental attributes of clay materials.

Values for the plastic limit and liquid limit for several samples of most of the clay minerals saturated with various exchangeable cations are given in Tables 5-1 and 5-2.

Plastic Limit

It is obvious from the data in Tables 5-1 to 5-3 that there is no single plastic-limit value that is characteristic of a particular clay mineral. Indeed the range of values for a particular clay mineral may be large, for example, in halloysites and montmorillonites. This variation is due not only to the variations in the exchangeable-cation composition and the presence of nonclay mineral components, but also to inherent variations of structure and composition within the lattice of the clay mineral itself. This point is shown especially by the substantial variation in the plastic limits for the lithium-saturated montmorillonites.

In general the plastic limits for the clay minerals decrease in the order attapulgite, montmorillonite, halloysite $4H_2O$, illite, halloysite $2H_2O$, and kaolinite. Nontronite, the iron-rich variety of montmorillonite, appears to have a much lower plastic limit than the aluminous varieties (Table 5-2). The value for halloysite $4H_2O$ depends greatly on whether or not the interlayer water is considered in the computation of the limit values (Table 5-2).

In the case of the montmorillonites, exchangeable sodium and lithium cause high plastic limits. There is little difference between the values for samples of this mineral carrying calcium, magnesium, potassium, and ammonium; although ammonium appears to provide slightly higher values than calcium, and potassium and magnesium slightly lower ones. The aluminum, hydrogen, ferric iron and thorium ions appear to produce still lower plastic limits. Based on the work of Williams et al. (1953), it would be expected that montmorillonites carrying sodium mixed with a divalent cation, for example, calcium, would show a considerable variation in plastic limits, with the relative abundance of such ions. It would also be expected that a higher plastic-limit value than that shown for either the sodium or calcium form might be obtained at some particular ratio of calcium to sodium, such as 40:60.

In the case of the other clay minerals the nature of the exchangeable cations causes relatively insignificant variations in the plastic limit; this is to be expected because of their low cation-exchange capacity. In natural materials composed of clay minerals other than montmorillonite, other factors, such as the presence of nonclay mineral materials, would probably cause greater variations in the plastic limits than any differences in the exchangeable-cation composition. An important exception is that

TABLE 5-1

ATTERBERG LIMIT VALUES

(After White, 1955)

Clay	Ca++			Mg++			K+			NH4+			Na+			Li+		
	Pw	Lw	Ac	Pw	Lw	Ac	Pw	Lw	Ac	Pw	Lw	Ac	Pw	Lw	Ac	Pw	Lw	Ac
Montmorillonite (1)	65	166	1.26	59	158	1.24	57	161	1.30	75	214	1.74	93	344	3.14	80	638	6.98
(2)	65	155	1.20	51	199	1.97	57	125	0.91	75	114	0.52	89	443	4.72	59	565	6.75
(3)	63	177	1.34	53	162	1.24	60	297	2.79	60	323	3.09	97	700	7.09	60	600	6.35
(4)	79	123	0.44	73	138	0.65	76	108	0.32	74	140	0.66	86	280	1.12	82	292	2.10
Attapulgite	124	232	1.08	109	179	0.70	104	161	0.57	97	158	0.61	100	212	1.12	103	226	1.23
Illite (1)	40	90	0.50	39	83	0.44	43	81	0.38	42	82	0.40	34	61	0.27	41	68	0.27
(2)	36	69	0.33	35	71	0.36	40	72	0.32	37	60	0.23	34	59	0.25	38	63	0.25
(3)	42	100	0.58	43	98	0.55	41	72	0.31	39	76	0.37	41	75	0.34	40	89	0.49
Kaolinite (1)	36	73	0.37	30	60	0.30	38	69	0.31	34	75	0.41	26	52	0.26	33	67	0.34
(2)	26	34	0.08	28	39	0.11	28	35	0.07	28	35	0.07	28	29	0.01	28	37	0.09
Halloysite (2H2O)	38	54	0.16	47	54	0.07	35	39	0.04	32	43	0.11	29	36	0.07	37	49	0.12
(4H2O)	58	65	0.07	60	65	0.05	55	57	0.02	56	61	0.05	54	56	0.02	47	49	0.02

Activity (Ac) values of montmorillonites (1), (2), and (3) are greater than ($Lw - Pw$)/100 because they contain nonclay minerals.

KEY: Montmorillonite: (1) Pontotoc, Miss.; (2) Cheto, Ariz.; (3) Belle Fourche, S. Dak.; (4) Olmsted, Ill. (contains about 25 per cent illite in mixed layers).

Attapulgite: Quincy, Fla.

Illite: (1) Fithian, Ill.; (2) Jackson County, Ohio; (3) Grundy County, Ill. (contains about 5 per cent montmorillonite in mixed layers).

Kaolinite: (1) Anna, Ill.; (2) Dry Branch, Ga.

Halloysite: (2H2O) Eureka, Utah; (4H2O) Bedford, Ind.

TABLE 5-2

ATTERBERG LIMIT VALUES

Clay	Natural		Al^{+++}		H^{+}		Th^{++++}		Fe^{+++}		Ca^{++}		Mg^{++}		K^{+}		Na^{+}	
	Pw	Lw	Pw	Lw	Pw	Lw	Pw	Lw	Pw	Lw	Pw	Lw	Pw	Lw	Pw	Lw	Pw	Lw
Montmorillonite[a]	41	623	47	149	49	367	48	138	51	138								
Nontronite[b]									25	48	23	37	19	41	27	38	24	72
Kaolinite[a]	42	87	44	105	41	113												
Allophane, undried[c]	131	207																
Allophane, air-dried[c]	78	85																
Allophane, undried[d]	136	231																
Halloysite (2H$_2$O)[b]	47	58					Interlayer water considered in limit values											
Halloysite (4H$_2$O)[b]	56	70																
Halloysite (4H$_2$O)[b]	42	55					Interlayer water not considered in limit values											
Clinochlore[b]	36	47																
Prochlorite[b]	40	44																
Thuringite[b]	not plastic																	

[a] After Samuels, 1950. [b] After Lambe and Martin, 1955. [c] After Birrell, 1952. [d] After Gradwell and Birrell, 1954.

TABLE 5-3

ATTERBERG LIMIT VALUES

(After Grim, 1950)

Clay		Natural		H_3PO_4[a]		H_2SO_4[a]		$Na_6(PO_3)_6$	
		Pw	*Lw*	*Pw*	*Lw*	*Pw*	*Lw*	*Pw*	*Lw*
Montmorillonite	(1)	97	700	54	340	50	250	48	395
	(2)	72	124	63	119	77	142		
	(3)	82	118						
Illite	(4)	25	36	23	35	26	36	21	31
	(5)	24	29						
Kaolinite	(6)	30	35						
	(7)	37	58	35	68	32	68		
Illite +10% Mont.	(8)[b]	26	58	27	52	28	61	25	48
Illite +5% Mont.	(9)[b]	36	61	34	61	35	62		
Kaolinite +10% Mont.	(10)[b]	33	65	31	65	31	74	39	67

[a] Chemical added to tempering water in quantity that acid radical equaled cation-exchange capacity.

[b] Natural mixtures.

KEY: (1) Belle Fourche, S. Dak.; (2) Cheto, Ariz.; (3) Aberdeen, Miss.; (4) La Salle County, Ill.; (5) Fithian, Ill.; (6) Dry Branch, Ga.; (7) Anna, Ill.; (8) Greene County, Ill.; (9) Grundy County, Ill.; (10) Dry Branch, Ga.

sodium causes a slight decrease in the plastic limits for these clay minerals, whereas it increases this value in montmorillonites.

Adequate samples of pure clay mineral chlorite have not been obtained for limit-value measurements, but it would be expected on structural grounds that they would be similar to those for the illites or kaolinites. Lambe and Martin (1955) have presented data for a chlorite ground from a large crystalline sample, and their data suggest that the mineral would have plastic limits in the range of the well-crystallized kaolinites (Table 5-2).

Too few data are available for allophanes to permit any positive conclusions. Gradwell and Birrell (1954) have shown that this mineral may have a high plastic limit particularly in its natural state before drying. Birrell (1952) has shown that air drying may greatly reduce the limit values (Table 5-2). Based on unpublished data obtained in the author's laboratory it appears certain that the plastic limits of some soil materials are enhanced by the presence of poorly crystalline or amorphous material, whereas in other soils they reduce the plastic limits. Probably such materials are not actually amorphous but have too low a grade of organization to be revealed by X-ray diffraction. Where the plastic limits are enhanced, the allophane material perhaps has a crude organization approaching that of montmorillonite. Where the limits are reduced, the crude organization probably approaches that of the two-layer clay minerals.

An inspection of the values for two kaolinite samples (Table 5-1) shows the influence of the degree of crystallinity and particle size, with the relatively poorly crystalline sample composed of smaller particles (kaolinite 1) having a substantially higher plastic limit than the sample composed of relatively coarse well-organized particles (kaolinite 2).

The data for the halloysite samples are somewhat misleading in that they give values only for the pure $2H_2O$ and $4H_2O$ forms and not for samples with intermediate states of hydration. It is known from investigations of the bonding properties of halloysite clays (Grim and Cuthbert, 1945) that samples showing an intermediate state of hydration have very different physical properties from those of either the $2H_2O$ or $4H_2O$ forms. This variation is of great practical significance because it means that laboratory tests on samples with carefully preserved moisture contents may have little significance in depicting the character of a natural material where there is a chance for even a slight change in moisture content. Because halloysite soils are likely to give misleading empirical test data, it is important that the presence of this mineral be taken into consideration in the interpretation and evaluation of such data.

The data in Table 5-1 show the importance of montmorillonite on the plastic limits. Montmorillonite 4 contains about 25 per cent illite without any reduction in plastic limit, indicating that montmorillonite is the controlling factor. Illite 3 contains a small amount of montmorillonite (5 to 10 per cent), which is adequate to cause an increase of the plastic limit in the sodium-saturated sample. The data in Table 5-3 show that the presence of very small amounts of montmorillonite in kaolinite or illite samples has only a slight tendency to increase the plastic limit, but as will be shown presently, causes a substantial increase in the liquid limit and, therefore, the plasticity index.

According to White (1955) the boundary between the plastic and nonplastic state is not as sharp for montmorillonite samples carrying sodium and lithium as for those with other cations. This means that there is no narrowly defined moisture content at which the sodium and lithium montmorillonites become plastic. In samples with other cations at about the plastic limit very small changes in moisture content cause relatively large property changes so that the plastic limit is a sharply defined, easily reproducible value.

Liquid Limit

As in the case of the plastic limit, the data in Tables 5-1 to 5-3 show that there is no single liquid limit that is characteristic of a particular clay mineral. The range of liquid limits for a particular group of clay minerals is much greater than the range for the plastic limits. Even in the case of kaolinite, which has relatively low plasticity, the range is in excess of 100 per cent.

The liquid limits for the various clay minerals in the order of decreasing values is about as follows: lithium and sodium montmorillonite; attapulgite; calcium, magnesium, potassium, ammonium montmorillonite; illite; poorly crystallized kaolinite; halloysite $4H_2O$; halloysite $2H_2O$; and well-crystallized kaolinite. The data in Table 5-2 show that nontronite has a much lower liquid limit than the aluminous montmorillonites.

The data in Table 5-1 show the tremendously high liquid limits for sodium- and lithium-saturated montmorillonite samples. The liquid limit of these materials is difficult to determine, and in fact there is no accurate value for them because of the high degree of thixotropy of such materials. A further complicating factor is that the gelation or development of thixotropy takes an appreciable amount of time which varies from one montmorillonite sample to another, so that the liquid limit may change with increasing time following the preparation of the sample. The values given, therefore, simply represent an order of magnitude. The values for the montmorillonite samples saturated with calcium, magnesium, ammonium, and potassium show no substantial difference and are all about 50 per cent or less those of the sodium- and lithium-saturated montmorillonites. The various montmorillonite samples saturated with the same cation show differences in liquid limit which may be in excess of 100 per cent, indicating again that the character of the cation is not the sole factor influencing this value but that the structure and composition of the silicate lattice is also important. The data in Table 5-3 indicate that hydrogen montmorillonites have liquid limits intermediate between those of the sodium variety and those of the other cations indicated above, and that montmorillonites saturated with aluminum, ferric iron, and thorium have relatively low liquid limits.

Liquid limits for attapulgite are equal or a little higher than those for the calcium, magnesium, potassium, and ammonium montmorillonites. The values for the calcium-, sodium-, and lithium-saturated attapulgite are substantially higher than those for this mineral saturated with potassium, magnesium and ammonium.

The liquid limits for illites fall in the range from about 60 to 90.

There is no significant variation due to particular cations except that the sodium- and lithium-saturated samples appear to be slightly lower. This is opposite from the effect that these cations have on the montmorillonite samples.

The liquid-limit values for kaolinites vary from about 30 to 75. A comparison of kaolinite 1 and 2, Table 5-1, shows a very much larger value (often over 100 per cent) for the poorly crystalline fine-grained samples as compared to the well-crystallized variety. Clearly the crystallinity of the kaolinite lattice and particle-size variations are the controlling factors for the liquid limit of this clay mineral.

The values for halloysite fall in the same range as those for kaolinite, and similarly there is no significant variation with the nature of the cation. As in the case of the plastic limit, the value obtained for the $4H_2O$ variety depends to a considerable extent on whether or not the interlayer water is considered in the computation of the limit value (Table 5-2). Also, as in the case of the plastic limit, it must be emphasized that these values for liquid limit may be misleading because a value for an halloysite in an intermediate stage of hydration would probably be very much greater than the values in Table 5-1 for the $2H_2O$ and $4H_2O$ forms.

Liquid limits for pure clay mineral chlorites are not available, but based on structural considerations they would probably be similar to those for illites and kaolinites. They would be expected to show no significant variation with exchangeable cation composition but to show large variations with the perfection of crystallinity and particle size. Lambe and Martin (1955) have presented values (Table 5-2) for a sample prepared by grinding well-crystallized chlorite, and they are about equal to those for well-crystallized kaolinite.

In the case of allophane, the presence in a clay material of a component amorphous to X rays in some cases is associated with low liquid limits and other cases with very high values. Thus Gradwell and Birrell (1954) have found very high values for allophane samples from New Zealand, if the values are obtained without air drying the sample prior to making the determination (Table 5-2). In the allophane samples producing high liquid limits, variations in the exchangeable-cation composition would probably have substantial influence on the values. Probably, in some cases at least, the allophanes giving the high values have a montmorillonite nucleation, whereas materials giving low values are either more truly amorphous or have a two-layer type of nucleation.

The values from montmorillonite 4 (Table 5-1) indicate that illite in substantial amounts, i.e., about 25 per cent, mixed with the montmorillonite causes a large decrease in the liquid limit, whereas it has much less effect on the plastic limit. In the case of illite 3, which contains about 5 per cent montmorillonite, the presence of this mineral serves to increase the liquid limits, particularly of the sodium- and lithium-saturated samples. It appears to have no effect on the potassium- and ammonium-saturated samples. A comparison of the liquid limits for samples 8 and 9 as compared with samples 4 and 5 in Table 5-3 show that the presence of 5 to 10 per cent montmorillonite in an illite sample can cause a substantial increase in the liquid limit. Similarly a comparison of the values for sample 10 and samples 6 and 7 in Table 5-4 shows that the presence of about 10 per cent montmorillonite in a kaolinite sample can also cause a large increase in the liquid limit. These data serve to emphasize the extremely important point that small amounts (±5 per cent) of montmorillonite associated with other clay minerals may greatly increase the limit values and also cause the nature of the exchangeable cation to become a significant controlling factor. It follows that to be of significance in evaluating properties, clay mineral analyses must be sufficiently complete to reveal the presence of small quantities of all constituent minerals.

Plasticity Index

The plasticity indices of the clay minerals range from higher than 600 for some sodium montmorillonites to 1 for some sodium kaolinites in about the following decreasing order: montmorillonite, attapulgite, illite, poorly crystalline kaolinite, halloysite 2H$_2$O, well-crystallized kaolinite, halloysite 4H$_2$O.

Sodium and lithium montmorillonites give tremendously high values of about 300 to 600. Montmorillonites with other cations give values ranging from about 50 to 300 with most of them in the range of 75 to 125; there is no systematic variation with cation composition. Again the data show a large variation for a particular cation with different montmorillonites (for example, the values for ammonium-saturated samples). Further, a montmorillonite showing a particularly high value for one cation does not necessarily show a particularly high value for another cation. Nontronite has a much lower plasticity index than the aluminous montmorillonites (Table 5-2). According to the values presented by Lambe and Martin (1955), it is in the range of the values for kaolinite.

The plasticity indices for attapulgite vary from 57 to 123, with the potassium, ammonium, and magnesium varieties at the lower end of the range and the calcium, sodium, and lithium varieties at the higher end. The plasticity indices for illites range from 23 to 50 with the ammonium-, sodium-, and lithium-saturated samples being generally lower than the samples saturated with other cations. The presence of montmorillonite in illite 3 (Table 5-1) substantially increases the index particularly in the sodium- and lithium-saturated samples. The data in

Table 5-3 also show that the presence of small amounts of montmoril-lonite in illite and kaolinite samples substantially increases the plasticity index by increasing the liquid limit.   In the case of montmorillonite 4 (Table 5-1), the presence of about 25 per cent illite serves to reduce the index very greatly, because of a great reduction in liquid limit with only a slight reduction in plastic limit.   The plasticity index of montmoril-lonite 4 is similar to that of the illites, whereas its plastic limit is much higher than that of the illites.

The plasticity indices for kaolinite vary from 1 to about 40 with usual values about 25.   The data show the extremely low values for well-crystallized coarse kaolinites, which are almost nonplastic.   The data also show the generally low values for sodium-saturated kaolinites.   The values for halloysite vary from 2 to 16 depending in part on whether the interlayer water of the $4H_2O$ form is considered in computing the limit values.   Samples in an intermediate state of hydration, for which there are no pertinent data, would probably show considerably higher values than those given in the tables.   The plasticity index of the sample of chlorite prepared by grinding well-crystallized material is very low (Table 5-2).   It is probable that clay mineral chlorite would have values in the range of those for kaolinite and that the values would vary considerably depending on the perfection of crystallinity of the mineral.

The plasticity indices of allophane presented in Table 5-2 and ob-tained on undried samples are quite large being in the range of 76 to 95. As indicated previously, unpublished data obtained in the author's laboratory indicate that the indices of some allophanes are quite low.

Effect of Particle Size

White (1949) has presented data (Table 5-4) to show the relation of the particle size of the clay minerals to their limit values.   The limit values increase with a decrease in particle size, and the liquid limit tends to increase somewhat more than the plastic limit.   Among the factors, therefore, determining the limit values of a clay or soil are the fineness of its particles in its natural state and the degree to which the particles and aggregates are cleaved or dispersed during the preparation of the sample and the determination of the values.   The latter point is illustrated by some bentonite samples which are seen by microscopic examination in their natural state to be composed of montmorillonite particles at least several microns in diameter.   When these bentonites are mixed with water, the water penetration between particles and into aggregates is so great that the mass is effectively split into particles substantially less than 1μ in diameter.   Since montmorillonite particles are easily broken up in making particle-size analyses, a determination of the particle-size distribu-tion may indicate only the degree of disaggregation and not represent the

TABLE 5-4

ATTERBERG LIMIT VALUES IN RELATION TO PARTICLE SIZE

(After White, 1947)

Clay mineral and particle size	P_w	L_w	I_p
Illite, Grundy County, Ill.			
$<1\,\mu$	39.6	83	43.4
$<0.5\,\mu$	52.3	103.7	51.4
Illite, La Salle County, Illinois			
$<1\,\mu$	46.2	85.6	39.4
$<0.5\,\mu$	53	111.2	58.2
Kaolinite, Anna, Illinois			
$<1\,\mu$	37.1	64.2	27.1
$<0.5\,\mu$	39.3	71.6	32.3
Montmorillonite, Pontotoc, Mississippi			
Whole	81.4	117.5	36.1
$<1\,\mu$	109.5	177.6	66.1

particle-size distribution of the original material. As the degree of disaggregation is important, particle-size distribution determinations may still correlate with limit values of montmorillonite clays.

Frequently the particle-size distribution of a clay is related to the perfection of crystallinity of the clay mineral components, with the smaller particles being less well ordered. For example, in comparing the limit values for two kaolinites or two illites carrying the same cation but with different particle-size distributions, the higher limit values of the sample with the smaller particles are to be explained by the presence of these smaller particles and *also* because the smaller particles are less well ordered.

Another factor is that poorly ordered clay minerals break down into smaller particles more easily than well-ordered minerals. Thus, for poorly ordered minerals, a small amount of working will suffice to disperse the clay. As a result there would be relatively less difference in limit values with variations in particle-size and in the amount of work put into dispersing the clays.

A decrease in particle size would be accompanied by an increase in total surface, and therefore an increase in plasticity index would be expected. Platen and Winkler (1958) have shown that the kind of surface as well as the amount is important (Fig. 5-1). Thus, the plasticity index increases much more rapidly with an increase in total surface for montmorillonites than for kaolinites, with illites and halloysites being intermediate.

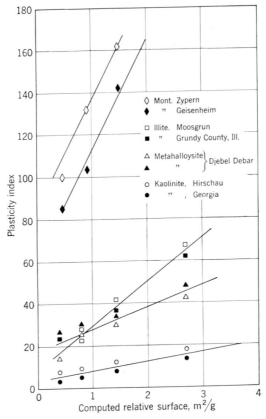

Fig. 5-1. Plasticity index versus surface area for various clay minerals, after Platen and Winkler (1958).

Effect of Drying

Casagrande (1932) pointed out that drying could alter the plasticity of a soil, and numerous investigators since then have confirmed this finding. Lambe and Martin (1953), for example, presented data to show the reduction in limit values following drying for a variety of soils, some of which were calcareous marls with substantial organic contents, and others were red lateritic soils containing free hydrated ferric iron and alumina. Soils composed of these components perhaps are prone to show, on air drying, the greatest decrease in limit values. Thus, slight oxidation of the organic components and dehydration of the R_2O_3 components would be expected to develop a bond between the particles which would be resistant to penetration by water. Gradwell and Birrell (1954) have shown the great reduction in the liquid limit produced by air drying soils containing allophane (Table 5-2).

Drying of soils is accompanied by shrinkage, which tends to bring the particles so close together that attractive forces become so strong that water can no longer penetrate between them.   It is known in the case of montmorillonites that removal of substantially all of the water between the particles, causing complete collapse of the structure, effectively prevents water from again entering between the particles.   That is to say, complete removal of adsorbed water destroys the colloidal properties and the swelling capacity of this mineral.   It generally takes more than air drying to cause such complete dehydration.   Nevertheless, drying with any degree of vigor tends to cause an irreversible change in clays of any composition tending to lower the limit value.   To be representative of natural properties, therefore, limit values must be determined on undried samples.

It is interesting to point out in this connection a fact well-known to ceramists, namely, that repeated wetting and moderate drying frequently tend to increase the plastic properties of clay material.   This seems to be particularly true of clays composed of illite, chlorite, and kaolinite.   The explanation seems to be that the repeated penetration of water between the particles followed by subsequent partial removal tends to so weaken the bond between the particles that the effective particle size is thereby reduced.   In addition, such treatment may serve to change the exchangeable-cation composition of the clay material and thereby also influence the plastic properties.

Effect of Miscellaneous Additives

Some clays, for example Ball clays (see Chap. 3, Ceramic Properties), have high plastic properties which have been attributed in part, at least, to the relatively small amount of organic material which they contain. On the other hand, treatment with certain polar and ionic organic compounds (Grim et al., 1947; Jordan, 1949) tends to make the clay minerals hydrophobic.   This fact has been used extensively in the numerous investigations in recent years on soil stabilization using organic additives. The varying effect of the organic compounds on the plastic properties of clays and soils undoubtedly depends on the nature of the compound, as well as on the clay mineral composition, and also on the geologic history, e.g., whether the soil has at any time been dried.

In the case of inorganic additives the effect of additives causing variations in the adsorbed-cation composition has already been considered, and there are little other data available.   Grim (1950) has shown (Table 5-3) that sulfate and phosphate additives seem to reduce the limit values of a montmorillonite from Wyoming carrying sodium as the exchangeable cation, but they have little effect on these values for a calcium montmorillonite from Arizona.   These anions seem to have no effect on the limit values of an illite sample but serve to increase the liquid limit of a poorly ordered kaolinite sample.

Investigations of the effect of many treating agents on the plastic properties of the clay minerals is difficult to evaluate because the silicate lattices are easily attacked. Thus, in studying the effect of anions using an acid, the effect noted may be caused by the attack of the proton on the silicate structure freeing aluminum, iron, and/or magnesium, which in turn react with the anion. Also the effect may be the result of the reaction of the anion with small amounts of these same elements which are present in the sample as impurities; i.e., they are not present in the structure of the clay minerals. The effect of such additives on the plastic property of clays is an important matter and merits further research. Further consideration is given to this subject in Chap. 3, Ceramic Properties.

Activity

Activity (Skempton, 1953) is the ratio of the plasticity index to the abundance of the clay fraction defined as the per cent dry weight of the minus 2 μ fraction of the sample. Activity is a very useful value indicating the plasticity index of the clay-size fraction of the soil.

Activity values for many of the clay minerals with different exchangeable cations are given in Table 5-1. The activity of montmorillonites ranges from about 0.5 to 7; of attapulgite, from 0.57 to 1.23; of illite, from 0.23 to 0.58; of kaolinite, from 0.01 to 0.41; and of halloysite, from 0.02 to 0.16. Values for clay mineral chlorite would probably be similar to those for kaolinite or illite, and for allophane they might well be either high or low. Gradwell and Birrell (1954) have given a value for allophane of more than 3 for a New Zealand sample, and Yamanouchi (personal communication) has given values of 0 to 2 for samples from Japan.

Skempton (1953) gives the following values for the clay minerals: sodium montmorillonite, 7.2; calcium montmorillonite, 1.5; illite, 0.9; and kaolinite, 0.33 to 0.46. These values are generally higher than those given by White (1955), because in Skempton's work natural clays were used containing some material coarser than 2 μ. The components coarser than 2 μ are likely to produce some activity which is added to that of the minus 2 μ fraction. Activity values of natural clays and soils, therefore, tend to be higher than values which would be anticipated from their clay mineral composition based on data for pure clay minerals. This is particularly true when montmorillonite is not a component and when the minus 2 μ fraction is very small.

Grim, Bradley, and Vargas (1959) have recently studied a kaolinitic soil with only 2 per cent of minus 2 μ fraction where the activity is 10 (Fig. 5-31). The activity values as defined consider that for a given mineralogical composition of the clay-size fraction, the plasticity index of the material increases in simple proportion as the clay size increases in per cent of the total weight. This is likely not to be quite true in clays with small percentages of the clay-size material. In other words, the diluting effect of the nonclay minerals decreases as the percentage of the nonclay minerals increases in the range of high nonclay mineral compositions.

In 1953 Skempton suggested three classes of activity (active, normal, and inactive) and later (1953) subdivided these classes into five groups as follows:

Group 1. Inactive with activity less than 0.5
Group 2. Inactive with activity 0.5 to 0.75
Group 3. Normal with activity 0.75 to 1.25
Group 4. Active with activity 1.25 to 2
Group 5. Active with activity greater than 2

An inspection of the data in Table 5-1 shows that there is only a general correlation between clay mineral composition and Skempton's classification. This is to be expected since particle size, soluble salts, and organic material are other factors influencing activity. Kaolinite, halloysite, illite, chlorite, and some allophanes would be in the inactive classes, usually in group 1. Some few attapulgites, montmorillonites are in group 2. In group 3 one would expect attapulgites, some montmorillonites, and illite and chlorite mixed-layer assemblages with montmorillonite. Montmorillonites other than those with substantial sodium as exchangeable cation would be expected in group 4, whereas sodium montmorillonites would be in group 5.

In general one would expect that active clays would have relatively high water-holding capacity, high compaction under load, high cation-exchange capacity, and, therefore, properties varying greatly with the nature of the exchangeable cation. They would also be highly thixotropic, have low permeability, and low resistance to shear, with cohesion largely responsible for the strength. With very low activity there would be little cohesion, and internal friction would be largely responsible for strength. Very active soils, therefore, would be expected to cause problems for the engineer. It should not be concluded that inactive soils, as will be shown later, may not also cause problems for the engineer.

Discussion

It has been pointed out in the consideration of ceramic properties (Chap. 3) that the property of plasticity involves a combination of attractive forces between particles and the lubricating action of a liquid between the particles; the shape and size of the particles, the distance of their separation, the strength of the attractive force, and the physical state of the liquid, therefore, are the controlling factors. Further, in the case of water, it was pointed out that the first few molecular layers of water adsorbed immediately on the available surfaces consist of oriented molecules, so that at very low moisture contents the fluid state did not exist and there would be no lubricating action.   The lubricating action and hence the plastic state would develop only after the adsorbed water layers became sufficiently thick that the outermost ones were not composed of well-oriented water molecules and hence had lubrication properties.   It is not necessary to postulate that the outermost layers are completely unoriented but only that their organization would yield under the application of slight force.

In the light of the above concept, the *plastic limit* is a measure of the water content which the particle surfaces can adsorb just slightly in access of that which can be fixed in a highly rigid condition and which does not separate the particles too much to greatly reduce the attractive forces between them.   In addition to the oriented water directly adsorbed in the surfaces, there would be some pore water in a liquid or semiliquid condition enclosed in pores in such manner that it had little lubricating effect.   It is difficult to estimate the thickness of the water layers and the amount of pore water at the plastic limit, because the amount of adsorbing surface cannot be determined.   However, the amount of oriented water is probably of the order of 5 to 10 molecular layers, and the pore water probably ranges from about 20 per cent of the plastic limit value in the case of montmorillonite to a major part for some kaolinite clays.

The *liquid limit* is the measure of the water which can be held with any substantial rigidity and which does not separate the particles, so that there is substantially no bonding force between them, plus the water at least in part in the liquid state, enclosed within the pores.   The relative abundance of fixed water decreases and the pore water increases at the liquid limit as compared to the plastic limit.   However, this change would be expected to be less for the montmorillonites, particularly those carrying sodium and lithium, than for the other clay minerals.

The *plasticity index* is a measure of the range of moisture that can be held in excess of that with a high degree of rigidity and without the separation of the particles beyond that essential for a definite attractive force between them.   It indicates something of the range of the moisture content with a relatively low degree of rigidity and which yields with slight applied force.

The high limit values for montmorillonites are a consequence of their ability to disperse into extremely small particles with a tremendous amount of potent adsorbing surface.   The extremely high values for sodium and lithium montmorillonites are a consequence of the great dispersing action of these cations which permits the breakdown to flakes approaching unit-cell thickness.   These cations exert little attractive force between the particles and, while they may not actually enhance the development of oriented water, permit it to develop to a very great thickness. The oriented-water layers going out from opposing montmorillonite surfaces must unite to develop some cohesive force. However, as Hofmann and Hausdorf (1945) have shown, at the high moisture contents of the liquid limit there is still considerable touching of the edges of particles so that the water need not be the sole binding force.

The lower limit values for the montmorillonites carrying the other cations are a consequence of the greater bonding action of these cations and the fact that they favor the development of rigid oriented water to only a limited thickness. These cations, therefore, do not disperse the montmorillonite particles so much because the cations tend to hold them together and the water layers do not tend to develop great thicknesses pushing the flakes apart.

In the case of montmorillonites the effect of the adsorbed cations is a combination of the dispersing effect and the water-orienting effect. In the case of the other clay minerals, the particles are more firmly tied together (for example, by potassium in the case of illites). The variation of the exchangeable cation can have little tendency to split particles and increase surface. The effect of the cations, therefore, is largely on the attractive force between the existing particles and on the nature of the adsorbed water. As a consequence, lithium and sodium have the opposite effect on the limits of clay minerals other than montmorillonites. In the case of illites, for example, sodium as compared with calcium decreases the attractive force between the particles, so that the particles must remain close together to maintain an adequate attractive force, and, further, the sodium reduces the thickness of *well-oriented* water; the net result is that sodium tends to reduce the limit values of the illite.

Since sodium and lithium exert little influence on the development of oriented water and the structure of the clay mineral surface is the cause of the orientation, the degree of orientation would be expected to gradually taper off with increasing distance from that surface. As a consequence, there is no sharp boundary between the oriented and nonoriented water, and, as a result, the limit values are not sharply delineated when sodium and lithium are the adsorbed cations.

In the case of the other cations, the cation itself influences the development of the oriented water as well as the clay mineral surface. The cation may tend to develop a firm hydration net about it with the result that well-oriented water goes only to a fixed and sharply bounded thickness. The limit values for clays with these other cations, therefore, tend to be sharply delineated.

The effect of montmorillonite when interlayered with the other clay minerals is essentially a dispersing one. Its presence in particles and aggregates permits them to be split apart easily. It permits sodium and lithium to have their dispersing effect and, therefore, changes their influence on the limit values. The interlayering of illite with montmorillonite has the opposite effect. It would be expected that the presence of illite with the montmorillonite would reduce the liquid limit relatively more than the plastic limit because the dispersing effect is more important for the high moisture content value. It should be emphasized that the influence of montmorillonite in an interlayer assemblage is not necessarily the same as it is in a synthetic mechanical mixture of discrete particles of another clay mineral and montmorillonite the reason being that in the interlayer mixtures the montmorillonite not only itself disperses but causes planes of weakness within the host clay mineral, so that the host is split into more and smaller particles. Limit values obtained on prepared mixtures of pure clay minerals are not likely to give the same values obtained with natural clays and soils of the same clay mineral composition.

Since the limit values for the pure montmorillonites with the same adsorbed cation may be very different, it is clear that factors within the silicate unit are also important. It is probably a matter of the substitutions within the lattice which result in variations in the ease of dispersion, in the ionizability of adsorbed cations, and in the strength and distribution of the attractive forces at the surface of the clay mineral particles. It seems clear, from information based on the work of Foster (1955), that maximum swelling and probably maximum dispersion take place when lattice substitutions give the structure a net residual negative charge in the range of 0.7 to 1.10 meq per g. With larger values the attractive force is great enough to hold the particles together; with smaller values the number of cations is too small to permit their hydration to have an appreciable separating effect. Foster (1953) reported that swelling decreased in the montmorillonites she studied with an increase in the substitution of iron and magnesium for aluminum and also with an increase in the ferric iron content. However, as Foster pointed out, much further work is necessary to obtain precise knowledge of the relation of the cation population of the lattice to the swelling and dispersion characteristics of the montmorillonites.

With regard to the other three-layer clay minerals, nothing is known of the possible effect of variations in composition on limit values. It would be expected that variations in composition would have little effect unless they were large enough to approach a change in clay mineral species (for example, vermiculite versus chlorite) or to cause a change in the morphology of the particles. Thus, illite in elongate units has been reported by Weaver (1953); as compared to the usual equidimensional flake-shape units it would be expected that the elongate particles would provide a mass with greater water-holding capacity.

The relatively high limit values for attapulgite are accounted for by its fibrous nature that provides a mass with high water-holding capacity. In the natural state, attapulgite occurs in bundles of many fibers in which the individuals are fairly tightly held together. As work is applied to a mass of such bundles more and more of the individual fibers are separated. The limit values for attapulgite, therefore, vary a great deal depending on the preparation of the samples for the determinations.

It is well known that weathering tends to increase the limit values of clays. A change in the character of the adsorbed cations or even the development of different clay mineral composition, such as montmorillonite from illite, may be the explanation for this increase. It may also be a purely physical effect, in that the continual alternate wetting and drying may so weaken the bonds between particles and aggregates that they are more easily dispersed. Exposure at the earth's surface may, of course, have other effects, such as the development of organic material or the oxidation of the iron, which would be important in changing limit values.

The relatively high limit values for halloysite in an intermediate state of hydration as compared with either the $2H_2O$ or the $4H_2O$ form is probably to be explained by a nonequilibrium condition that develops when all of the surfaces of the halloysite units are not coated by a uniform thickness of water layers. In an intermediate state, when the thickness of the water layers is not the same between all particles, the particles are more easily separated. The same situation prevails in the case of montmorillonite; with a certain proportion of sodium and calcium being more dispersible than one containing only sodium or calcium as the adsorbed cation.

Hogentogler (1937) pointed out that the liquid limit is about equal to the moisture content of freshly sedimented clays. In this connection the data of White (1955) and White and Pichler (1959), obtained from measurements of the variation in the rate of water adsorption for the clay minerals, are pertinent (see Figs. 5-2 to 5-4). They found that in general the water pick-up of a dry clay is rapid up to, or slightly in excess of, the liquid limit and that there is usually little further water adsorption except when sodium and lithium are the adsorbed cations. When sodium and lithium are present there is generally no sharp break in the adsorption rate in the range of the liquid limit, i.e., water adsorption continues far beyond the liquid limit. The break is particularly pronounced for calcium clays, and, since many, perhaps most, natural clays carry this cation, the liquid limit often approximately marks the upper limit of

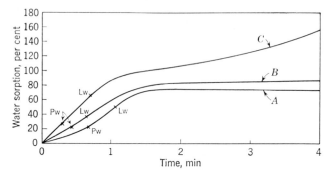

Fɪɢ. 5-2. Water-sorption curves for illite (*A*), kaolinite with calcium (*B*), and sodium (*C*), after White (1955).

water-holding capacity. This is not true for sodium clays, and hence a change from sodium to calcium in a clay could greatly change its water-holding capacity.

In Fig. 5-5, the plasticity index is plotted against the liquid limit for a series of the commonest clay minerals. These clay minerals exhibit variations in particle-size distribution, exchangeable cations, and crystallinity; hence Fig. 5-5 serves to show the range that can be expected for materials whose composition is that of a substantially pure clay mineral. The presence of nonclay minerals in most natural clays and soils would place the values in the lower end of the ranges shown.

The data in Fig. 5-5 also serve to emphasize that for kaolinite, illite, and attapulgite clays the liquid limits increase more rapidly than the plastic limits. This relationship, illustrated by the slope of the lines in Fig. 5-5 does not appear to hold for montmorillonite clays. The zone appears to be steeper; i.e., for montmorillonite there is relatively less difference between the variation in the plastic limit and the liquid limit than there is for kaolinite and illite. This seems reasonable in view of the large capacity of montmorillonite for holding rigid water, which would seem to make relatively little more than this amount essential for lubricating action.

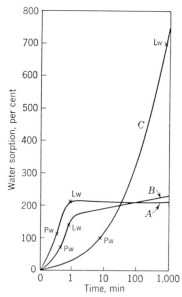

Fɪɢ. 5-3. Water-sorption curves for attapulgite (*A*), calcium montmorillonite (*B*), and sodium montmorillonite (*C*), after White and Pichler (1959).

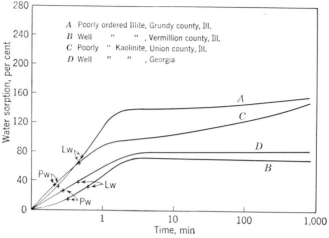

FIG. 5-4. Water-sorption curves for kaolinites and illites, after White and Pichler (1959).

The foregoing concept of the nature of clays and soils in the plastic state seems to the author to account for the limit values adequately. It is not to be construed that it is universally accepted. Some investigators believe that the charges on the particles are the essential element and that

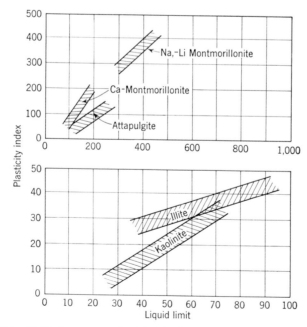

FIG. 5-5. Liquid limit versus plasticity index for the common clay minerals.

plastic properties can be explained solely by the "double-layer" concepts of the colloid chemists (Lambe, 1958). In such concepts the water in the system is often assigned no major role and, in fact, is considered by some to play a passive role, serving only to separate the particles and thereby to influence the charge effects (Michaels, 1958). The influence of the physical state of the water is not considered to have any significance.

In the writer's opinion, the adsorption of water on the clay mineral surfaces composed of oriented molecules has been established unequivocally (Low, 1958; Rodebush and Buswell, 1958). Such water would have different physical properties from those of liquid water. Since this is true, it seems equally certain that layers of water molecules between particles in an oriented condition could serve as a binding force between the particles; consequently water cannot be assigned simply to a passive

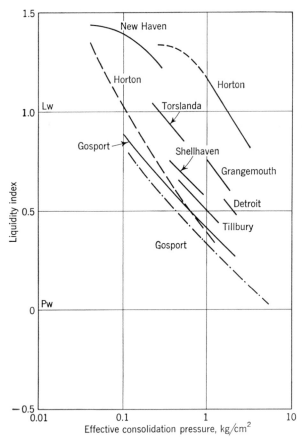

Fig. 5-6. Relation between liquidity index and consolidation pressure, after Skempton and Northey (1952).

role. The nature of the adsorbed water, *in addition to the charge on the particles,* must enter into any satisfactory concept explaining plastic properties. Further, the consideration of the effect of the nature of the water provides a simple explanation for many of the attributes of clays and soils in the plastic state that are otherwise difficult to understand, for example, the effect of time on the development of plastic characteristics and the relatively gradual change in the plastic properties with water content for sodium and lithium clays as compared to the abrupt change for those carrying other adsorbed cations.

LIQUIDITY INDEX

The liquidity index of a soil is defined as the ratio of the natural water content of the soil minus the plastic limit to the plasticity index. It is, therefore, a way of expressing the natural water content of a soil or clay in relation to its limit values. If the water content is equal to the liquid limit, the liquidity index is 1. At water contents greater or less than the liquid limit the liquidity index is greater or less than 1.

On the basis of the previous discussion of limit values one would theorize that sodium and lithium when present as exchangeable cations would favor the existence of high liquidity indices. In the case of the clay minerals themselves, montmorillonites, allophanes, and the clay minerals composed of elongate units, such as attapulgite and possibly halloysite, would favor a high liquidity index. In addition, regardless of the clay mineral composition, a concentration of particles in a narrow silt-size range or an open, loose texture in which there was a large amount of small pore space, such as might be developed in a clay deposited in a flocculated condition, would favor a high liquidity index.

Figure 5-6 illustrates the reduction in liquidity index with increasing consolidation pressure for a group of soils which are composed largely of illite. It would be expected that kaolinite and chlorite soils would show the same type of curves and that such curves for soils composed of montmorillonite and attapulgite would be steeper because of the high water-adsorbing capacity of such minerals. One would expect extremely variable results for halloysite soils depending on the state of hydration of the mineral.

Figure 5-7 shows a frequent relationship of liquidity index with depth of burial in a nor-

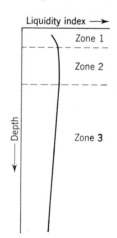

Fig. 5-7. Variation of liquidity index with depth with surface drying zone, after Skempton and Northey (1952).

mally consolidated sediment with a surface drying zone. It is seen that, after a low value at the surface due to drying, the liquidity index increases until a depth zone is reached wherein the index remains constant (zone 2). Below zone 2 the liquidity index gradually decreases with depth. The constant value in zone 2 represents an equilibrium moisture content which is stable throughout an appreciable range of over-burden pressures. Only with a pressure greater than that at the base of zone 2 is the equilibrium structure of the water destroyed thereby permitting the moisture content to decrease. No data are at hand for the possible relations of the clay mineral composition of soils and the development of a zone of constant liquidity index below the surface. One might guess that soils containing some montmorillonite would especially favor its development because of the high water-adsorbing capacity of such soils. However, other factors, such as texture and organic material, might outweigh the effect of the clay mineral composition.

Terzaghi (1955) pointed out that the liquidity index of the top layers of a freshly deposited clay is commonly close to 1; sediments on deposition commonly quickly arrive at a moisture content equal to their liquid limit. This is understandable on the basis of the concept that the liquid limit is the moisture content at which the adsorbing surfaces are coated by the maximum thickness of rigid water plus some pore water. In general this conclusion would not apply when sodium was the dominant adsorbed cation (see pages 220–221); hence, under some conditions of accumulation, liquidity indices in excess of unity would be expected.

Clay particles on settling in water would be expected to come together easily until their envelopes of adsorbed rigid water came in contact. In the sediments deposited rapidly and in a flocculated condition, the water envelopes would be expected to touch only in a few places, so that much pore water would be present and the liquidity index would perhaps be somewhat larger than for sediments deposited slowly. Under slow deposition there is time for the particles to adjust to each other, and hence there is less pore space.

UNCONFINED COMPRESSION STRENGTH

Cohesive soils are often classified on the basis of the compressive force required to cause failure of an undisturbed sample tested under unconfined conditions as follows:

Very soft: less than 0.25 kg per sq cm
Soft: 0.25 to 0.5 kg per sq cm
Medium: 0.5 to 1 kg per sq cm
Stiff: 1 to 2 kg per sq cm
Very stiff: 2 to 4 kg per sq cm
Extremely stiff: greater than 4 kg per sq cm

The unconfined compression strength depends on the clay mineral composition, nonclay mineral composition, particle-size distribution, shape of the particles, and the arrangement of the particles with respect to each other (for example, parallel versus random arrangement of flake-shaped clay minerals). The stress history (geologic history) of a clay material may in some cases exert a greater control on compression strength than the foregoing factors of composition. Mielenz and King (1955) have shown that the introduction of small proportions of clay minerals to a sand or silt greatly increases the compression strength and that the maximum strength of such mixtures may exceed the strength of either the sand, or silt, or the clay alone. Table 5-5, giving data for prepared mix-

TABLE 5-5

COMPRESSIVE STRENGTH OF SYNTHETIC SAND AND CLAY MIXTURES
(After Mielenz and King, 1955)

Mixture, % by weight			Moist specimens		Air-dried specimens		
Sodium montmo-rillonite[a]	Kaolin-ite[b]	Sand	Water content,[c] %	Com-pressive strength, psi	Water content, % Initial	Final	Com-pressive strength, psi
100			17.1	55.5	20	7.0	195.2
25		75	14.4	42.0	18.1	1.3	541.0
25	25	50	13.9	85.8	19.6	2.6	533.5
	25	75	13.6	9.1	17.8	0.1	76.5
	100		14.2	100.3	17.8	0.4	65.6

[a] Sodium montmorillonite from Osage, Wyo.
[b] Kaolinite from Bath, S.C. (well crystallized and fine grained).
[c] Optimum moisture content for strength.

tures of sand, kaolinite, and montmorillonite, illustrates these conclusions. The data also show that montmorillonite, which yields lower strength than kaolinite when not mixed with sand, yields higher strengths than kaolinite when mixed with sand. Strength determinations of the pure clay minerals, therefore, have little significance.

The largest relative amount of clay mineral required in mixtures to give maximum strength is not known, and it would obviously not be a finite value as the particle-size distribution and the shape and texture of the nonclay mineral particles would play an important role. It seems likely that the amount of montmorillonite required to develop maximum strength in such a mixture would be less than that required of the other clay minerals. For the other clay minerals the strength would probably increase with increasing percentages of clay minerals in the mixtures to a very high clay content. For all the clay minerals, but especially for the montmorillonites, small additions of clay mineral, say 5 to 10 per cent, to pure nonclay minerals would add relatively more strength than the addition of the same amount of clay to mixtures already containing about 50 per cent clay minerals. These statements are in accord with concepts of activity, which show a tendency for a straight-line relationship between the plasticity index and the amount of minus 2 μ material in a soil except in examples where the amount of minus 2 μ material is very small.

Compressive strength of sands with various amounts of different clay minerals are given in Chap. 4 on bonding clays. These data show that the strength increases with increasing amounts of clay minerals in the following order: montmorillonite, illite, kaolinite, in mixtures with small amounts of clay minerals (5 to 15 per cent). In the case of montmorillonite the strength varies greatly with the water content and the nature of the exchangeable cation. Chlorite would be expected to give values similar to those for kaolinite. Halloysites would also be expected to give values similar to those for kaolinite if the mineral was in an intermediate state of hydration. In the case of either the $2H_2O$ or the $4H_2O$ form, strength values would be expected to be very low. Some attapulgite clays give strength values about equal to those of the calcium montmorillonites. Unpublished data indicate that when attapulgite is the clay mineral constituent of the soil the strength values are likely to be relatively insensitive to changes in moisture content. For allophane no values permitting general conclusions are available, but it seems likely that strengths of undisturbed material would show considerable variation from one sample to another.

The data given in Chap. 4 on bonding clays illustrate that, for each sand-clay mineral mixture, the compression strength increases with increasing moisture contents up to a maximum value. At higher moisture contents there is a sharp decrease in strength. The moisture content at highest strength decreases in the following order: calcium montmorillonite, sodium montmorillonite, illite, and kaolinite, with chlorite and halloysite probably about equal to kaolinite. The sharpness of the decrease of strength at moisture contents above the optimum is greatest for the montmorillonite clay minerals. The presence of appreciable amounts of nonclay minerals, particularly if they exhibited a considerable particle-size range, would be expected to reduce the sharpness of the decrease in strength.

The data in Table 4-2 show that maximum green compression strength is attained at considerably lower moisture contents than the plastic limit for montmorillonite clay-bonded sand and that the difference increases as the clay content increases. For sands bonded with illite, kaolinite, and halloysite clays, the moisture content for maximum green compression strength is slightly larger than the plastic limit in low-clay-content (4 per cent) sands and equal or slightly less in high-clay-content (15 per cent) sands.

For a discussion of the theory of unconfined compression strength see the discussion of bonding clays in Chap. 4.

SHEAR STRENGTH

Shear strength is measured by the shearing stress at maximum displacement before failure. It is usually determined under conditions of increasing load pressure. The shear strength of a soil varies with the

TABLE 5-6

PROPERTIES OF SOME SOILS
(After Skempton and Northey, 1952)

Clay	Mineral composition of clay fraction, in order of abundance	Clay fraction $<2\,\mu$, %	Activity	Undisturbed shear strength, lb/sq ft	Sensitivity
St. Thuribe	Quartz, mica, montmorillonite (trace)	36	0.33	800	150±
Detroit I	Mica, illite, calcite, quartz, montmorillonite	36	0.36	360	2.5
Horten	Mica, quartz, illite, montmorillonite	40	0.42	850	17
Beauharnois	Mica, illite, calcite, quartz, montmorillonite	79	0.52	380	14
Gosport	Illite, halloysite	55±	0.88	600	2.2
Shellhaven	Illite, kaolinite, some organic colloids	41	1.33	760	7.6
Mexico City	Montmorillonite (mainly)	90±	4.5	960	5.3

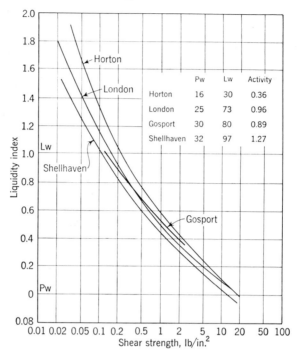

Fig. 5-8. Relation between liquidity index and shear strength of molded clays, after Skempton and Northey (1952).

factors given in the discussion of unconfined compression strength and also with the load placed on the soil.

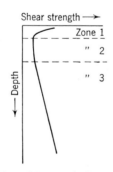

Fig. 5-9. Variation of shear strength with depth in normally consolidated clays with surface drying zone, after Skempton and Northey (1952).

Winterkorn and Moorman (1941) found that the shear resistance of cohesive soils is approximately a logarithmic function of the moisture content in the lower part of the moisture range. This relationship would not be expected at higher moisture contents where the nature of the clay mineral and the exchangeable cation play a very important role. Further, a time factor is involved. For example, in montmorillonite soils, particularly those with sodium as the exchangeable cation, the very low permeability requires a long time for the attainment of equilibrium moisture content following load-pressure changes. In tests performed under drained conditions, different results are obtained in quick tests as compared to those carried to equilibrium conditions.

The data in Table 5-6 show undisturbed shear strength values for a series of soils of different compositions. Figure 5-8, showing the relationship of liquidity index to shear strength for several molded clays, illustrates the kind of relationship frequently existing between these values. Shearing strength varies with depth and consequently with increased effective overburden pressure (Fig. 5-9). With increasing depth there may be a zone (zone 2 of Fig. 5-9) in which the shearing strength remains constant even though the load pressure increases. In this same zone the liquidity index also remains constant (Fig. 5-7). Skempton (1948 and 1953) and Bjerrum (1954) have shown that strength increases relatively more rapidly with depth for clays with higher plasticity-index values. Thus, relatively rapid increases would be expected for montmorillonite clays.

Samuels (1950) has shown that in a sample of montmorillonite (Wyoming bentonite) shearing resistance in relation to exchangeable-cation composition increases in the following order: sodium, calcium, and aluminum (Fig. 5-10). He has also shown that the shear resistance of sodium, calcium, and aluminum modifications of kaolinite is essentially identical to the shear resistance of the montmorillonite containing aluminum as the exchangeable cation. By replacing naturally occurring hydrogen, calcium, and sodium with potassium in a soil composed of a mixture of montmorillonite and illite, Winterkorn and Moorman (1941) increased the angle of friction from 19 to 22°. The effect of the exchangeable cation upon the angle of friction of kaolinites was negligible.

The shearing resistance of a soil in an undisturbed condition may be considerably greater than its strength after being remolded at the same moisture content. The shearing strength of the remolded sample frequently increases considerably with time after the remolding without any change in moisture content. These matters will be considered presently in a discussion of sensitivity.

The data in Table 5-6, showing the shear strength of undisturbed samples of a series of soils with varying clay mineral compositions, show that there is no clear-cut relationship in these soils between clay mineral composition and shear strength. In view of the many factors which control shear strength no

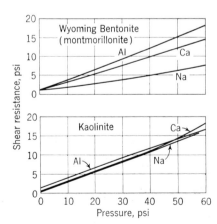

FIG. 5-10. Effect of exchangeable cation on shear resistance, after Samuels (1950).

precise correlation is to be expected in natural soils. However, as will be shown presently, variations in the clay mineral composition do cause substantial differences in the shear strength of soils.

The shear strength of a clay is made up of two parts, cohesion c_r and the coefficient of internal friction $\tan \varphi_r$ according to the expression $t_f = c_r + \sigma_n' \tan \varphi_r$ (Hvorslev, 1937) where σ_n' is the effective pressure normal to the shear plane. The cohesion is independent of the loading pressure and caused by a cementing or gluing force between particles. It is the shearing resistance after the removal of any loading pressure. In silts and sands with substantially no clay mineral content cohesion is zero. The factor of internal friction is due to the movement of one particle over another and in general increases with increasing loading pressure. Skempton (1953) has pointed out that

If a clay is normally consolidated from a slurry under a pressure σ_n', and is then sheared sufficiently slowly for all of the pore water pressure to be fully dissipated (a 'drained' shear test) then $t_f = \sigma_n' \tan \varphi_d$ where φ_d is the angle of shearing resistance in the 'drained' state. If, moreover, c_r is the cohesion of the clay at the water content at failure in the drained shear test, then the proportion of shear strength due to cohesion is $\dfrac{c_r}{\sigma_n' \tan \varphi_d}$, and the proportion due to internal friction is $\dfrac{\tan \varphi_r}{\tan \varphi_d} = 1 - \left[\dfrac{c_r}{\sigma_n' \tan \varphi_d} \right]$. (In Fig. 5-11) the components of shear strength in 8 normally consolidated materials are plotted against their activity. It is not to be expected that there would be an exact correlation, but the results show beyond doubt that the greater the activity the greater the contribution of cohesion to shear strengths.

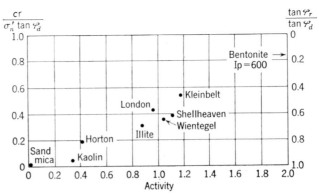

Fɪɢ. 5-11. Relation between components of shear strength and activity of normally consolidated clays, after Skempton (1953).

The data show that in the bentonite sample cohesion contributed 80 per cent of the shear strength; in the illite samples, from 40 to 60 per cent of the shear strength; and in the kaolinite sample, less than 20 per cent of the shear strength.

Figure 5-12 shows the relationship between the angle of internal friction and the plasticity index. The angle given for kaolinite is 20°; for illite, 10 to 15°; and for montmorillonite the angle approaches 0°.

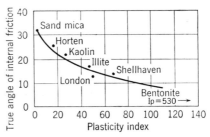

Fɪɢ. 5-12. Relation between plasticity index and true angle of internal friction, after Gibson (1953).

Discussion

The large amount of cohesion yielded by the montmorillonites cannot be explained solely on the basis of its high water-holding capacity or on the basis of its very small particle size. It seems more logical to account for it on the basis of its ability to orient the adsorbed water. It also seems logical that liquid water would have little cohesive strength but that oriented water would have considerable cohesive power. In the case of montmorillonites, the increased shearing resistance with variable cation composition, in the order sodium, calcium, aluminum, seems logical also, in that, at moisture contents frequently found in soils, the thickness of the water films would be such that calcium would develop a considerably better orientation of water molecules than would sodium.

The contributions of the other clay minerals to cohesion would be smaller than that of montmorillonite because they would tend to orient a relatively smaller percentage of the water present in a given soil than would montmorillonite. This would be a consequence of their larger particle size and probably also of their inherent structural characteristics. The larger particle size of the non-montmorillonite clay minerals and their relatively poorer cleavage would permit them to develop some appreciable internal friction.

The zone of uniform shear resistance and liquidity at some depth beneath the surface shown in Figs. 5-7 and 5-9 indicates that an equilibrium moisture condition prevails which is unaffected by large variations in loading pressure and also that a certain threshold loading pressure is necessary to break this equilibrium moisture condition, which probably involves the destruction of some of the oriented water. The destruction of some water orientation would favor a reduction in moisture content which in turn would cause an increase in shear resistance. It seems to the author that this relationship with depth can best be explained by including the state of the adsorbed water in the concept rather than solely by interparticle bonding forces. The soil represented in Figs. 5-7 and 5-9 contains illite and montmorillonite. It would be interesting to obtain such data for a kaolinitic soil, i.e., one which had a lesser amount of water-adsorbing power. One would expect that in a kaolinitic soil such a zone of uniformity below the surface would be less well developed.

SENSITIVITY

Sensitivity was defined by Terzaghi (1944) as the ratio of the strength of the soil in an undisturbed state to the strength of the remolded material at the same moisture content. A classification of the sensitivity of clays is given in Table 5-7, and stress-strain curves for a typical sensitive clay are given in Fig. 5-13.

TABLE 5-7

CLASSIFICATION OF SENSITIVITY OF CLAYS
(After Skempton and Northey, 1952)

Insensitive clays	<1
Low-sensitive clays	1–2
Medium-sensitive clays	2–4
Sensitive clays	4–8
Extra-sensitive clays	>8
Quickclay	>16

Clays which have been heavily overconsolidated during their geologic history are insensitive. Clays and soils with high sensitivity values are obviously ones with very little or no strength after being disturbed. Instances are known (Peck et. al., 1951) in which only a slight disturbance will cause an initially fairly strong material to behave as a fluid. Sensitive clays generally have high moisture contents, frequently with liquidity indices considerably in excess of unity. A sharp change in moisture content may cause a great increase in sensitivity, sometimes with disastrous results.

Some clays with moderate to high sensitivity show a regain in strength when the remolded sample is allowed to stand without the loss of moisture. These materials are thixotropic, and their sensitiv-

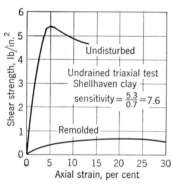

FIG. 5-13. Stress-strain curves for typical sensitive clay, after Skempton and Northey (1952).

ity is to be explained on the basis of thixotropy. The amount of strength regained varies from soil to soil and with the moisture content. Skempton and Northey (1952) have shown (Fig. 5-14) that the regain in strength is considerable for montmorillonites, moderate to small for illites, and practically nil for kaolinites. That is to say, soils composed largely of montmorillonite, and consequently with high activity, are very thixotropic and have moderate to high sensitivity. The thixotropic regain in strength seems to be at a maximum in these clays when the moisture content is about equal to the liquid limit. As the moisture content decreases below the liquid limit the thixotropic regain decreases. Above the liquid limit the relationship is not quite clear but probably would depend on the nature of the exchangeable cation carried by the montmorillonite. With sodium as the exchangeable cation there probably would be more regain above the liquid limit than when other cations were present. Boswell (1949) has presented data indicating the moisture content for various types of clay necessary to develop this thixotropic effect.

There are numerous examples of soils with extremely high sensitivities, frequently in the range of "quick" clays, which do not show any appreciable regain in strength on standing after remolding and consequently for which thixotropic hardening does not provide an explanation. The clay mineral composition of these clays is variable and complex, and there seems to be no definite correlation between the clay mineral components and the sensitivity. Skempton and Northey (1952) have suggested that there is also no correlation between the particle-size distribution and the extreme sensitivity of these clays, which also have low activity, but in some cases at least, they show a considerable concentration of particles in a fine-silt-size range. In every case these soils have liquidity indices considerably in excess of unity.

Gradwell and Birrell (1954) have described a soil composed of allophane with a sensitivity of 7. It would be expected that allophane soils would

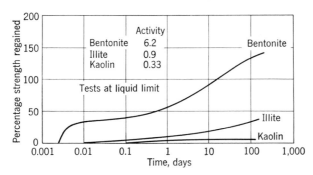

Fig. 5-14. Regain of strength versus time, after Skempton and Northey (1952).

have in general fairly high sensitivity, because it is likely they would have textural characteristics in their natural state which would be quite different from those in a remolded state with consequent substantial differences in strength. Also it seems likely that halloysite soils might be very sensitive because a disturbed sample would not have the same moisture relationships as the natural soil. Working such a soil might well cause a change in the state of hydration with a consequent change in properties. Further, the original state of hydration would not be regained if the dehydration loss was replaced.

Discussion

The amount of thixotropic regain of strength is greatest, as would be expected, in clays with high activity, that is, in clays containing montmorillonite as a major component. This is a consequence of the extremely small particle size of the montmorillonite and its high water-adsorbing capacity favoring the development of oriented water on the clay mineral surfaces. Also, it would be expected that sodium as the exchangeable cation would particularly favor such regain of strength, particularly at high moisture content, because the sodium ion favors the development of thick layers of oriented water on the montmorillonite particle surfaces. At lower moisture contents the nature of the cation probably would make little difference. According to this concept the effect of the adsorbed cation is essentially its effect on the development of oriented water and only indirectly, through the water bond, on the interparticle bonding forces.

Lambe (1958) has attempted to explain the thixotropic regain of strength in remolded soils on the basis of the effect of interparticle bonding forces without considering the role of adsorbed water. It seems to the author that the character of the adsorbed water is probably the major factor. In clay with a high liquidity index, the bonding between the particles is probably oriented molecules of water in the natural state of the clay. On reworking, the orientation of molecules is destroyed, and the bond is broken or at least reduced in strength. That is to say, on reworking, liquid water develops between the particles and the strength is lost. When the remolded sample is allowed to stand the water orientation gradually develops again and the strength is regained. This is a crystallization phenomenon, and some time would be required for the water to recrystallize and, therefore, for the strength to be regained. At low moisture contents the amount of water serving as a bond is small; hence, there would be very little water to recrystallize, and there would be little thixotropic regain. The effect of time and moisture on the regained strength are very easy to explain on the basis of a concept which attributes a major role to the nature of the adsorbed water.

It has been pointed out that extremely sensitive materials with low activity may have any clay mineral composition. It appears that such highly sensitive clays have a loose, open texture, permitting a large amount of pore water with relatively weak bonds at the particle junctions. If the bond is broken there may be enough liquid water released to cause the entire mass to flow as a liquid. In some cases the load is probably carried in the undisturbed state by a loose skeleton of solid grains. If the skeleton is ruptured the load is transferred to the soft interstitial material of low or no bearing power with a consequent abrupt change from relatively high strength to no strength. In some cases the interparticle bond is probably oriented water layers which are fluidized in the rupturing. One would expect that such sensitive clays would have been deposited in a flocculated condition to produce the loose, open texture and that there has been little diagenesis to increase the interparticle bond. Also such clays would be expected to have undergone little compaction. These latter statements apply particularly to clays with appreciable amounts of clay minerals.

Rosenquist (1946) has described some interesting "quick" clays from Norway in which the high sensitivity has been developed by the leaching of the sodium content without a change in the moisture content. As Skempton and Northey (1952) explained, the water content before the leaching was largely in an oriented state because of the presence of the sodium ion. Leaching of the sodium ion served to remove much of the orienting force of the water, with the result that the orientation of much of the water was reduced or destroyed. In other words, the leaching of the sodium ion changed some of the adsorbed water to pore water—it reduced the liquid limit but not the moisture content and, therefore, increased the liquidity index. It weakened the interparticle water bond. The net result is the loss of remolded strength and the probability of a sudden rupture of the bond with an abrupt transition from considerable strength to no strength. Bjerrum and Rosenquist (1957) have produced clay materials in the laboratory with similar properties of sensitivity by leaching experiments. Their data support the conclusion that the primary effect of adsorbed cations in interparticle bonding is through their action in the development of oriented water. It should be emphasized that this effect on water orientation would be significant only within a certain moisture range. It would be relatively unimportant at low moisture contents in the range of the plastic limit where direct interparticle contact is important. It would be expected to be of relatively great importance in moisture contents in the range of the liquid limit and slightly above.

Although Rosenquist (1953) has shown the effect of leaching which removes cations, it should be emphasized that an exchange of cations without leaching might well have a similar effect. Thus, if an exchange of calcium for sodium ions took place in the clays described by Rosenquist, as is conceivable by the emplacement of masses of concrete accompanied by suitable ground-water movements, the change in the amount of oriented water might follow with a consequent change in liquid limit, liquidity index, and sensitivity. The general conclusion is that since the character of the water is greatly influenced by the nature of the cation present *any* change in the cation composition might greatly alter the sensitivity.

A further factor which may be significant is that, with time, clays with a given moisture content develop an equilibrium condition which may give them considerable strength. Apparently the moisture content becomes uniformly distributed throughout the clay with an attendant increase in strength. A very slight decrease in moisture content may cause a great reduction in strength. A uniform distribution of moisture content favors the development of oriented water layers. A slight reduction in moisture tends to break some of the water layers with a consequent substantial reduction in strength. Engineers are aware of this phenomenon, as indicated by the great care exerted in collecting core samples with their natural moisture content retained, but the magnitude and abruptness of the change is not always appreciated. An example of this phenomenon is shown by some bentonites. Samples with moisture contents in excess of 40 per cent carefully collected to preserve their natural moisture may be immersed in large volumes of water without any change in the dimensions or character of the core. However, if the moisture content is changed by drying only a very small amount, the core is likely to slake down rapidly when placed in a large volume of water and the clay expands.

PERMEABILITY

Permeability has a decisive influence on many engineering properties of sediments, for example, on the rate at which the void ratio decreases with an increase of the load on the sediment and on the relationship between shearing stress and the rate of application of the shearing force.

The coefficient of permeability k of a sand composed of more or less equidimensional grains depends almost entirely on the effective grain size, D_{10} and the void ratio e. Therefore, the value k of such sand can be roughly estimated by means of semiempirical equations. For instance, $k = 200\ D_{10}{}^2 e^2$ (Terzaghi, 1955).

In a usual occurrence, clay minerals in earth materials are exceedingly fine and, consequently, tend to fill void spaces between grains of silt, sand, and gravel. Consequently clay minerals characteristically decrease perme-

TABLE 5-8

PERMEABILITY OF CLAYS AND SAND-CLAY MIXTURES
(After Endell et al., 1938)

Clay and mixture	Permeability k in cm/min at 65 kg/sq cm
Quartz sand	1×10^{-3}
Quartz sand : mica	
9 : 1	4.6×10^{-4}
1 : 3	4.2×10^{-4}
1 : 1	5.8×10^{-4}
0 : 1	4.9×10^{-4}
Quartz sand : kaolin	
9 : 1	9.5×10^{-5}
7 : 3	8.9×10^{-6}
1 : 1	2.5×10^{-6}
0 : 1	3.0×10^{-6}
Quartz sand : Ca-Mont.	
9 : 1	4.3×10^{-5}
7 : 3	2.1×10^{-6}
1 : 1	5.5×10^{-7}
0 : 1	2.0×10^{-7}
Quartz sand : Na-Mont.	
9 : 1	1.6×10^{-7}
7 : 3	3.0×10^{-8}
1 : 1	Impermeable
0 : 1	Impermeable

ability of earth materials, especially of remolded clays in which structural features, such as shrinkage cracks, joints, stratification, or shear zones, are absent.   If a sand contains more than a few per cent of mica flakes the equation given above loses its validity, and no substitute is available. The factors that affect permeability are mineral composition, particle-size distribution, texture, void ratio, exchangeable-cation composition, characteristics of the fluid, and degree of saturation.   Because of the great variety of factors that determine permeability, the k value of sediments other than clean sand and the relation between this value and the void ratio can only be determined by experiment.   There is, however, a definite correlation between clay mineral composition and the order of magnitude of the permeability.

The data in Table 5-8 show the substantial reduction in permeability on the addition of mica to a quartz sand.   The addition of 10 per cent mica reduces the permeability of the quartz sand essentially to that of pure mica. The data in Table 5-8 also show that the replacement of mica by kaolinite further reduces the permeability and that when montmorillonite is the clay mineral the permeability is still further reduced. In the

TABLE 5-9

COMPACTION PERMEABILITIES OF NONTRONITE
(After Lambe and Martin, 1955)

Exchangeable cation	Load, lb/cu ft	k, cm/sec
Sodium.....................	117.2	9.3×10^{-9}
Potassium..................	104.2	9.9×10^{-9}
Calcium....................	114.9	9.8×10^{-8}
Magnesium.................	114.2	5.0×10^{-8}
Ferric iron................	109.2	1.1×10^{-7}

case of montmorillonite, the sodium form causes considerably less permeability than the calcium form, and when more than about 30 per cent sodium montmorillonite is present the sand becomes essentially impermeable. In all cases the maximum reduction in permeability is attained when the clay minerals make up about one-half or less of the total mixture.

The data in Table 5-9 show that nontronite yields about the same coefficient of permeability as aluminous montmorillonites. These data further show that for nontronite with various exchangeable cations the permeability decreases in the following order: iron, magnesium, calcium, sodium, and potassium. These same authors present data for halloysite indicating that both the $2H_2O$ and $4H_2O$ forms have about the same permeabilities as kaolinite.

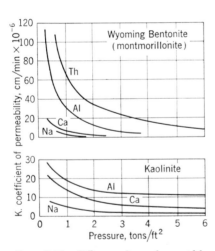

FIG. 5-15. Effect of exchangeable cations on permeability of kaolinite and montmorillonite under load, after Samuels (1950).

Gradwell and Birrell (1954) have pointed out that allophane soils have rather high permeability in spite of the extremely small particle size of the allophane.

Samuels (1950) has shown that for montmorillonite the permeability decreases in the order: thorium, aluminum, calcium, and sodium, and that with an increasing load the permeability of the sodium and calcium varieties is essentially zero at pressures in excess of about 1 ton per sq ft (Fig. 5-15). This same author has shown that the permeability of kaolinite with various exchangeable cations decreases in the order: aluminum, calcium, and sodium, and that for such clays the decrease in permeability with increasing load is much more gradual than with montmorillonites. In the case of the kaolinite samples, some permeability persists to loads of the order of 6 tons per sq ft (Fig. 5-15).

Winterkorn and Moorman (1941) found the permeability approximately equal for the hydrogen, calcium, and magnesium modifications of a soil composed of illite and montmorillonite and distinctly less than that of the potassium modification at a void ratio less than 1.3, but at void ratios greater than 1.3 the permeability of the the magnesium modification rises rapidly and greatly exceeds that of the calcium soil.

In Fig. 5-16, the data of Samuels (1950) are plotted to show the variation of the coefficient of permeability with the void ratio. As expected permeability increases as the void ratios increase. The increase is relatively small when sodium is the exchangeable cation (about nil for sodium montmorillonite).

It is well-known from drilling-mud data (Chap. 6) that attapulgite clays are quite permeable. Their k values would probably approach those of kaolinite.

Quirk and Schofield (1955) have shown that there is a threshold concentration of electrolytes specific for each ion below which the permeability of soils decreases. This is to be expected since it is known that the replacement of one ion by another does not have to be complete before the maximum influence of the replacing ion becomes effective. Also it is known that the presence of an excess of various ions may have the opposite effect on physical properties from the presence of small amounts of the same ion.

The permeability of kaolin can be decreased greatly by a decrease in particle size and an increase in surface area (Harman and Fraulini, 1940). With an increase of apparent surface area from about 30 sq m per g to 240 sq m per g, the permeability of kaolin decreased by a factor of 3.5.

Michaels and Lin (1954) and later Wardlich (1959) have pointed out that the permeability of clay materials varies with the nature of the fluid and that the permeabilities substantially decrease as the polarity of the liquid increases.

Discussion

It would be expected that the very small particle size of the clay minerals would act to reduce the permeability of granular materials. It would also be expected that for clay minerals with similar particle sizes those with a flake shape would reduce the permeability to a greater degree than those with an elongate fibrous shape or a granular shape. Thus attapulgite would be expected to be more permeable than montmorillonite, halloysite more permeable than kaolinite, and allophane with a granular shape relatively permeable, even though exceedingly fine grained. It would be expected that kaolinite with a relatively low order of crystallinity would be less permeable than well-crystallized kaolinite because of the ease with which the poorly organized material breaks down into extremely small particles.

The variation caused by the nature of the exchangeable cation can in part be explained by the dispersing effect of the cation. Thus, the reduction in permeability attained when sodium is the exchangeable cation is partly a consequence of the dispersing effect of this cation reducing the particle size of the clay minerals.

It is suggested that, in addition to the dispersing effect, the exchangeable cations influence permeability by their influence on the nature and thickness of water adsorbed on the clay mineral surfaces. It seems likely that the thick water layers adsorbed on the surface of sodium-saturated

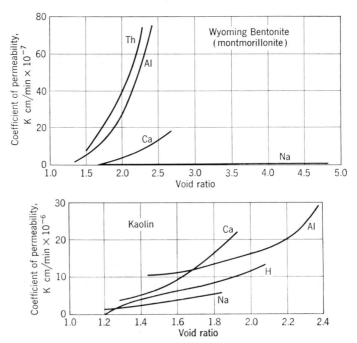

Fig. 5-16. Permeability versus void ratio, after Samuels (1950).

montmorillonites would serve to impede the flow of water for two reasons: (1) because of a reduction in pore diameter, and (2) because of the physical interference of the movement of fluid water against a surface of moderately oriented water such as would exist in the outermost molecular layers of the adsorbed water.

Michaels and Lin (1954) suggest that the decreased permeability accompanying an increase in the polarity of the fluids can be explained solely on the basis of a dispersing effect.   The tendency of polar liquids to be adsorbed on the surface of the clay mineral particles is well-known. Any such adsorption would unavoidably tend to reduce the size of the pores which in turn would reduce the permeability.   For further discussion of permeability see Chap. 4.

It seems worthwhile to point out that the extremely high impermeability of montmorillonite clays, particularly of the sodium variety, makes such clays useful to the engineer as additives when he needs to develop high impermeability in a structure, such as a dam.   The much higher permeability of sodium as compared with calcium varieties gives the engineer a means by cation exchange of treating a montmorillonite soil to enhance its impermeable character.   This was done in the preparation of the lake on Treasure Island at San Francisco (Lee, 1940).

FROST HEAVING

Frost heaving is raising of the ground surface by the development of bodies of ice within the soil.   The magnitude of the uplift depends upon the capillarity and transmittancy of the soil, the rate of freezing, surcharge or loading, and the ground-water conditions.   Taber (1929) has demonstrated conclusively that frost heaving is caused by movement of water into the freezing zone in an amount equal to the uplift.   Expansion of water with freezing is virtually insignificant in the process.   Indeed, heaving can be produced by freezing of soils saturated with liquids which contract on freezing, such as nitrobenzene and benzine.

Beskow (1935) demonstrated the importance of the particle-size distribution and the texture of the soils.   He concluded that heaving will not develop in soils containing less than 30 per cent by weight of fractions passing the 0.062-mm sieve or less than 55 per cent by weight of fractions passing the 0.125-mm sieve.   For most soils, heaving will not develop if fractions passing the 0.062-mm sieve constitute less than 50 per cent of the material.   Plank and Drake (1947) have shown that with the addition of 5 per cent of plastic clay to a sand frost heaving can occur, and with the addition of 10 to 20 per cent of such clay frost heaving is well developed. However, with larger additions of plastic clay, for example, 40 per cent, frost heaving decreases virtually to zero.   Mielenz and King (1955) have stated that the fabric most conducive to frost heaving lies intermediate between fine sand or coarse silt and stiff clays.   The latter inhibit ice-lense formation because of their extremely low permeability.

Endell (1935 and 1941) demonstrated the relative effect of kaolinite, sodium montmorillonite, and calcium montmorillonite upon the rate of frost heaving in synthetic mixtures of quartz dust and the clay minerals (Fig. 5-17).   The rate of heaving is reduced the most with sodium mont-morillonite and the least with kaolinite.

Lambe (1953) showed that, at low concentrations of clay in mixtures with sand, the frost heaving ability decreases in the order illite, kaolinite, montmorillonite and that at higher concentrations the decreasing order is kaolinite, illite, and montmorillonite (see Fig. 5-18).   An exception is the iron form of montmorillonite, which is more prone to frost heaving than kaolinite.   In the presence of small amounts of montmorillonite with varying exchangeable cations, the tendency to produce frost heaving with exchangeable cations decreases in the order: iron, magnesium, potas-sium, calcium, and sodium.   The tendency to frost heaving with mont-morillonite clays varies more than a hundred-fold with variations in the nature of the exchangeable cations.   According to Lambe (1953) chlorite is about equal to kaolinite, and attapulgite has a tendency to large amounts of frost heaving.

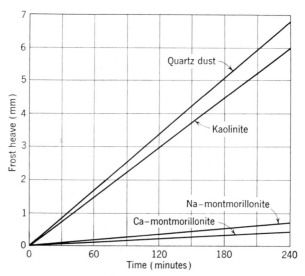

Fig. 5-17.   Relation of clay mineral composition and fabric to rate of frost heave, after Endell (1935 and 1941).

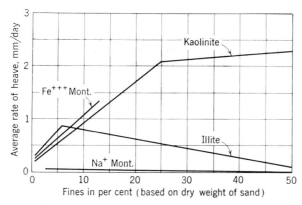

Fɪɢ. 5-18.   Effect of clay minerals on frost heave, after Lambe (1953).

Lambe (1953) also investigated the effect of chemical additives on frost heaving and concluded that dispersive additives tend to reduce frost heaving and that additives which are aggregants have little effect on frost heaving.

Discussion

The data indicate clearly that the clay mineral components which permit a high degree of permeability are those which permit a large amount of frost heaving.   This is to be expected since the necessary movement of water through the soil that permits the growth of ice lenses could not take place with low permeability.

It must be remembered that the presence of fractures permitting the movement of water through soils might effectively eliminate the influence of all of the other factors on the tendency to produce frost heaving.

WATER ADSORPTION AND SWELLING

Figures 5-2 to 5-4 show the amount and rate of water adsorption for a series of clay minerals in which the samples were composed of air-dried, uncompacted material of minus 200-mesh particle size.   The data show the very high water adsorption of sodium montmorillonite, which begins slowly and then after about 10 min increases very rapidly.   Initial slow adsorption is probably due to the low permeability of the material.   The amount of water adsorbed by the other samples increases in the order attapulgite, calcium montmorillonite, poorly ordered illite, poorly ordered kaolinite, well-ordered kaolinite, and well-ordered illite.   Halloysite values are in the range of those for kaolinite. The data show that for these clay minerals water adsorption is very rapid in the first few minutes with slow, if any, adsorption with greater lengths of time. The rate is relatively less for the clay minerals with the lower amounts of water adsorption.

Mielenz and King (1955) have pointed out that the adsorption of water by clays leads to expansion or swelling and that its magnitude varies widely depending upon the kind and the amount of clay minerals present,

TABLE 5-10

FREE-SWELLING DATA FOR CLAY MINERALS
(in Per Cent)
(After Mielenz and King, 1955)

Ca-Mont.:

Forest, Mississippi..................	145
Wilson Creek Dam, Colo.............	95
Davis Dam, Arizona................	45–85
Osage, Wyoming	
(prepared from Na-Mont.)..........	125
Na-Mont., Osage, Wyoming...........	1,400–1,600
Na-Hectorite, Hector, California........	1,600–2,000

Illite:

Fithian, Illinois.....................	115–120
Morris, Illinois.....................	60
Tazewell, Virginia..................	15

Kaolinite:

Mesa Alta, New Mexico.............	5
Macon, Georgia....................	60
Langley, N. Carolina................	20
Halloysite, Santa Rita, New Mexico......	70

their exchangeable ions, electrolyte content of the aqueous phase, particle-size distribution, void size and distribution, the internal structure, water content, superimposed load, and possibly other factors.

Data for synthetic mixtures of Wyoming bentonite (sodium montmorillonite), kaolin, and sand (Fig. 5-19) reveal the expansive potential of sodium montmorillonite. Under load of 1 psi with lateral restraint sodium montmorillonite expanded 66 per cent during 33 days of water adsorption and was apparently still expanding at the conclusion of the test. A mixture of 25 per cent sodium montmorillonite and 75 per cent sand expanded 24 per cent under the same conditions. In a test of a mixture of 25 per cent montmorillonite, 25 per cent kaolinite, and 50 per cent fine sand the specimen expanded 33.5 per cent in the same period. The expansion of the latter mixture is greater than that of the first mixture because of the more dense fabric and, hence, greater effectiveness of a given expansion of the montmorillonite constituent. The data demonstrate similar relationships for the mixtures containing 10 per cent bentonite.

Data in Table 5-10 (Mielenz and King, 1955) show the amount of free swelling of various clay minerals and that this swelling decreases in the order: montmorillonite, illite, halloysite, and kaolinite. These same authors point out that with clays of the montmorillonite type the swelling decreases greatly when sodium is replaced by other univalent ions or by divalent and trivalent ions. For Wyoming bentonite (sodium montmorillonite) Baver and Winterkorn (1935) observed decreased swelling in the sequence sodium, lithium, potassium, calcium, magnesium, and hydrogen. For a soil composed of a mixture of illite and montmorillonite these same authors observed the following order of decreased swelling: lithium,

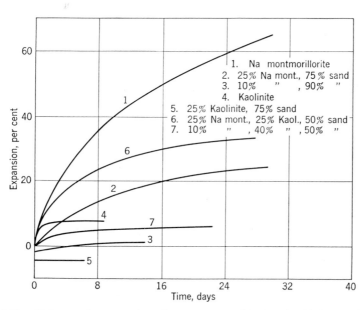

Fig. 5-19. Volume changes of sodium montmorillonite, kaolinite, and sand mixtures, after Mielenz and King (1955).

sodium, calcium, barium, hydrogen, and potassium.   Mielenz and King (1955) report that using sodium montmorillonite and various liquids the swelling tended to increase with an increase in the dielectric constant of the liquids.

Hendricks, Nelson, and Alexander (1940) showed that the expansion of a montmorillonite with various exchangeable cations differed somewhat depending on the relative humidity to which it was subjected.   At a relative humidity of 5 per cent the order of decreasing expansion is magnesium, calcium, lithium, strontium, barium, hydrogen, sodium, cesium, and potassium.   With a relative humidity of 40 per cent the order is calcium, strontium, magnesium, hydrogen, lithium, barium, sodium, potassium, and cesium.   With a relative humidity of 90 per cent the order is calcium, hydrogen, lithium, strontium, magnesium, barium, sodium, potassium, and cesium.   These data indicate the avidity for water of magnesium, calcium, lithium, strontium, and barium montmorillonites at very low humidities.   These data do not indicate the very important fact that in the presence of an excess of water, lithium and sodium montmorillonites swell to a larger extent than do montmorillonites with other cations (see Fig. 5-2).

The change in bulk volume taking place in earth materials when wetted is influenced considerably by original density, the expansion decreasing with decreasing original density, other factors of texture, structure, and composition being equal.   For example, in tests reported by Mielenz and King (1955) a soil composed of montmorillonite showed a total volume increase from a dry to a saturated condition ranging from 2 to 21.6 per cent with variations in dry density from 74.1 to 96.5 lb per cu ft.   The pressures developed in maintaining the constant volume range from 5.1 to 146.6 psi in the same series.   These authors point out that if expansive clay is subjected to initial loads of high magnitude, tremendous swelling pressures are developed.   They give values as high as 540 psi developed in sodium montmorillonite that was originally compressed at 5,000 psi and subsequently wetted following a period of unloading sufficient to permit relaxation of the specimen.   Initial loading of the clays at 3,000 psi, instead of at 5,000 psi, produced lesser swelling pressures. Consolidometer tests of undisturbed clays and shales containing illite- or montmorillonite-type minerals in the clay fraction indicate potential hydration pressures as high as 15 tons per sq ft.   Dawson (1953) reports that expansive pressures exerted by confined bentonite clays have been observed to reach 15 tons per sq ft with the usual range being from 1 to 6 tons per sq ft.   This investigator reports that the swelling pressure is greatly reduced if such clays are permitted to swell a little, which indicates that the initial adsorption of the water produces the very high swelling pressures.   Holtz and Gibbs (1953) have stated that the uplift pressure is greatly reduced with slight expansion of clays and shales and, further, that expansion is reduced greatly by even a slight increase in loading.

Extensive investigations by the Missouri River Division of the U.S. Army, Corps of Engineers (Anon., 1954) have shown that the expansive properties of clays of high cation-exchange capacity can be radically changed by the chemical nature of the seepage waters. Goldberg and Cline (1953) demonstrated a reduction of swelling pressure from about 9 to 5 psi by the admixture of 8 per cent calcium hydroxide to a sodium montmorillonite and from about 7 to 1.5 psi by a similar admixture to a soil composed of montmorillonite and illite.

Discussion

According to Mielenz and King (1955) two mechanisms are involved in the swelling of soils: (1) a relaxation of effective compressive strength related to enlargement of capillary films, and (2) osmotic imbibition of water by clay minerals with an expanding lattice. The high swelling of the montmorillonite-type clays is the result of the property of this mineral to adsorb water between the individual silicate layers. Sodium montmorillonite with its property of adsorbing extremely thick water layers between all of the silicate layers would be expected, and it is the case, to have the potential of the greatest amount of expansion.

Terzaghi (1955) has pointed out that moisture heave sometimes takes place in heavily preconsolidated clays with a high plasticity index. In many cases this is a matter of the reswelling of montmorillonite which has been reduced to a relatively low moisture content by consolidation pressures. However, there seem to be cases in which such moisture heave takes place in soils which do not have any expandable clay minerals. Such soils seem to be composed essentially of illite and chlorite with very little nonclay mineral material. Apparently such soils may have a texture which does not come to equilibrium when under consolidation pressures so that it reswells when the pressure is removed and additional water becomes available. The added moisture does not expand the lattice of the clay minerals but perhaps serves as a lubricant between the particles so that strains may be relieved. Such expanding preconsolidated soils deserve detailed study.

COMPRESSIBILITY AND CONSOLIDATION

The term compression refers to the relationship between the increase of unit load on a laterally confined specimen of a sediment and the corresponding decrease of its void ratio. Void ratio e is defined as the ratio of the total volume of voids to the volume of solid constituents of the

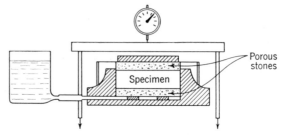

FIG. 5-20.   Compression apparatus, after Skempton (1944).

soil.   In running consolidation tests the normal procedure is to use undisturbed core samples.   Frequently tests are also made with a sample of
clay mixed with water to form a slurry at its liquid limit.   A commonly
used form of such an apparatus is shown in Fig. 5-20.   The clay is held
in a brass ring between two porous stones, and the load is applied to the
upper stone.   The clay is therefore compressed vertically with no op-
portunity for lateral displacement, which is the condition prevailing in a
bed of clay during deposition.   As the test is rather lengthy, the stones
are kept in contact with water to prevent drying of the clay by evaporation.   A load is applied, and the clay at once starts consolidating; the
extruded pore water flows out through the porous stones.   It is found
that the rate of consolidation decreases with increasing time after application of the load, and for the usual sample thickness of 2 cm equilibrium is
reached after approximately 24 hr with most clays.   The clay is then at
equilibrium with some definite water content or void ratio under the
pressure p.   The pressure is then increased, and after 24 hr the clay again

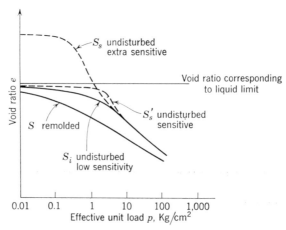

FIG. 5-21.   Principle types of relationships between unit load and void ratio for
cohesive sediments, after Terzaghi (1955).

reaches equilibrium at a new void ratio. By applying a series of loads the relation between pressure and void ratio is obtained.

Application and subsequent removal of a load p on a sediment permanently reduces its compressibility under loads that are smaller than p. Normally consolidated sediments are those that have never been subjected to a load reduction, such as removal of superimposed sediments by erosion. Precompressed or preconsolidated sediments are those which apparently have been subjected to a greater load than those under which they are presently buried.

The relation between unit load and void ratio for a sediment can be conveniently represented by plotting the void ratio e against the logarithm of the unit load p (Fig. 5-21) or against the pressure plotted arithmetically. For every sediment the e-log p curve starts with the horizontal tangent and at certain unit loads joins an inclined straight line with the equation

$$e = -C_c \log_{10} p + C \qquad (5\text{-}1)$$

where C_c represents the *compression index* and C is a constant. The value C_c is equal to the decrease of the void ratio produced by an increase of the unit load from p to 10 p. The value of C_c ranges between approximately 0.15 for lean sandy clays to more than 1 for highly colloidal clays. According to Skempton (1944), the compression index increases with increasing liquid limit (Lw) approximately in accordance with the empirical equation

$$C_c = 0.007 \ (Lw - 10 \text{ per cent}) \qquad (5\text{-}2)$$

Skempton (1944) has shown the relationship between the increase in the compression index and the increase in the percentage of clay fraction in natural sediments (see Fig. 5-22). As will be shown presently, this relationship would be expected to vary somewhat, depending on the mineral composition of the clay fraction.

If the compression test is performed on an undisturbed specimen of clay with low sensitivity, a e-log p curve such as s_i of Fig. 5-21 is obtained which is like the e-log p curve s of the same clay in a remolded state, except that the inclined straight part of the curve is steeper, i.e., the compression index is greater. The C_c values of the undisturbed specimens exceed those of the specimens in the remolded state by amounts up to about 30 per cent.

If the consolidation test is performed on an undisturbed specimen

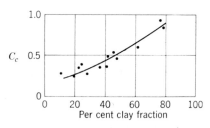

FIG. 5-22. Correlation of compression index with per cent clay fraction, after Skempton (1944).

of a highly sensitive clay, the e-log p curve has the characteristics of curve s_s in Fig. 5-21. Since the liquidity index of such clays is commonly much greater than unity, the horizontal part of the curve is located high above the similar part of the curve for sediments in the remolded state. At some given load, representing the load at which the structure is broken, the curve descends abruptly.

In a natural clay deposit the load on the sediment increases with increasing depth below the surface. Therefore, the relation between the depth and void ratio should be determined by the same laws as those represented by the e-log p curves in Fig. 5-21. Skempton (1944) has confirmed this relationship from field data.

As the thickness of the sedimentary deposit increases, both pressure and temperature increase at any given point in simple proportion to the depth of the overburden. As a consequence of such increase of pressure and temperature, chemical and mineralogical changes may take place which invalidate the e-log p curve. For example, Terzaghi (1955) has pointed out that in the Wilmington oil field in California the compressibility of the clay strata located between the oil-sand layers decreases rather abruptly at a depth of about 4,000 ft corresponding to an effective overburden pressure of about 150 kg per sq cm and a temperature of about 180°F. Yet the void ratio of the sediments decreases to a depth of 6,000 ft in accordance with Eq. (5-1).

The sudden application of a load on a layer of cohesionless sediment (i.e., essentially without any clay) composed of sound equidimensional particles produces an instantaneous compression followed by slight additional compression at a decreasing rate. If the load on a saturated layer of clay is increased, the corresponding compression takes place gradually and at a decreasing rate. The compression is associated with a decrease of the water content of the clay and the rate at which the excess water drains out of the clay, which may be very slowly.

The degree of consolidation of a sediment at time t can be represented by the ratio U_c between the decrease of void ratio at time t and the ultimate decrease of the void ratio at time infinity. Terzaghi has developed the theory of consolidation, and the following is quoted from his work (1955).

> At a given thickness H of the clay layer, the degree of consolidation at time t depends exclusively on the coefficient of consolidation c_v

$$c_v \ (\text{cm}^2/\text{sec}) \ = \ \frac{k(\text{cm/sec})}{\gamma_w(\text{gm/cm}^3) \ m_v(\text{cm}^2/\text{gm})} \tag{5-3}$$

> wherein k is the coefficient of permeability of the clay for the load p to $p + \Delta p$, m_v the coefficient of compressibility for the same load interval (decrease of void ratio per gram of increase of the unit load) and γ_w the

unit weight of water. With increasing values of p, both k and m_v decrease. Therefore, c_v is fairly independent of p. It decreases for normally consolidated clays from about 10^{-2} cm²/sec for very lean clays to about 10^{-6} cm²/sec for highly colloidal clays. At a given value c_v the time at which a given degree of consolidation U_c is reached increases in simple proportion to the square of the thickness H of the layers.

If c_v is known, U_c can be computed for any given time t by means of the theory of consolidation (Terzaghi, 1925 and 1943). According to this theory, the value U_c should increase with time t as shown [in Fig. 5-23]. The theory is based on the assumption that the time lag between increase in unit load and the corresponding decrease in void ratio is exclusively due to the low permeability of the clays. According to the theory the slope of the curve representing the relation between U_c and the logarithm of time should steadily increase until the time t becomes approximately equal to

$$t_1 = \frac{H^2}{c_v} \tag{5-4}$$

when the corresponding degree of consolidation is about 95 percent. Then the slope should rapidly become flatter and approach the value zero.

In reality the U-log t curve continues to descend after time t as indicated [in Fig. 5-23 by the dashed line]. In the semi-log plot [Fig. 5-23b] this line can either be straight or slightly convex downward. Its average slope is very different for different clays. For organic clays its initial slope can be almost equal to that of the adjacent section of the plane curve. The consolidation represented by the plane curve for time $t < t_1$ is commonly referred to as *primary consolidation*. The consolidation represented by the dashed curve is the *secondary consolidation*.

Samuels (1950) has presented excellent compression and consolidation data for montmorillonite and kaolinite clays and Figs. 5-24 to 5-26 are from his publication. The tests were started on samples at liquid-limit consistency with increments of load from almost 0 pressure to approximately 9 tons per sq ft with each increment being allowed to act until all primary consolidation had taken place and the rate of secondary compression had been reasonably established. The data show that for the natural montmorillonite, which is the sodium variety, there is a very large reduction in volume with the application of small pressure and that

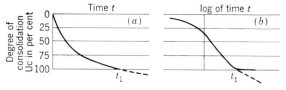

FIG. 5-23. Relation between time and degree of consolidation: (*a*) arithmetic and (*b*) logarithmic scale, after Terzaghi (1955).

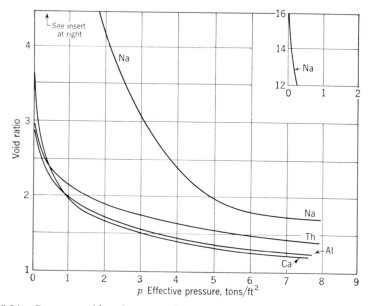

Fɪɢ. 5-24.   Pressure-void ratio curves for montmorillonite, after Samuels (1950).

further increments of pressure cause a relatively slight reduction in volume.   For the calcium montmorillonite the amount of compression is reduced, but there is also a large reduction in volume at low applied pressures, and further applications of pressure cause relatively small reductions in volume.   For the aluminum and thorium montmorillonites the amount of compression is less, and there are relatively small decreases in volume with increasing pressures.

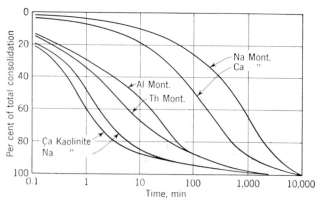

Fɪɢ. 5-25.   Rate of consolidation of montmorillonite and kaolinite at 4 to 8 tons per sq ft, after Samuels (1950).

The rate-of-consolidation curves (see Fig. 5-25) for the montmoril-lonites are particularly interesting in that they show a slow initial rate of consolidation with the rate increasing with increasing time. The plot is logarithmic, so that the actual rate of consolidation is more rapid at the beginning than the curves might suggest. The slow initial rate is par-ticularly small for the sodium variety and somewhat more rapid for the aluminum and thorium varieties; the calcium variety is intermediate.

The compressibility of the kaolinite samples (Fig. 5-26) is considerably less than that of the montmorillonite samples. The difference between samples with different exchangeable cations is relatively small, but the compression is seen to decrease in the order aluminum, calcium, hydrogen, and sodium. In each case there is an initial large reduction in volume at small loads and small, rather uniform decreases in volume with increasing loads. The rate of consolidation varies little depending on the nature of the exchangeable cation—it is in the decreasing order calcium, hydrogen, and sodium. The rate is similar to that for the aluminum and calcium varieties of montmorillonite shown in Fig. 5-25.

With increasing loads on montmorillonite the rate of consolidation decreases somewhat initially, but after short periods of time the increase in pressure has little effect on the rate. Therefore, the coefficient of consolidation decreases as the load increases (Fig. 5-27). For kaolinite, on the other hand, increasing pressure increases the rate of consolidation throughout the time of its application, and consequently the coefficient of consolidation increases as the amount of load increases.

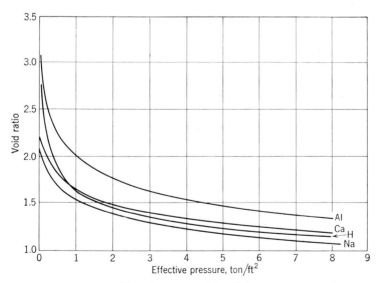

Fig. 5-26. Pressure-void ratio curves of kaolinites, after Samuels (1950).

The data shown in Fig. 5-28 from experiments performed at Cornell University in 1951 show e-log p curves for the hydrogen form of montmorillonite, kaolinite, illite, and attapulgite. Attapulgite shows somewhat less compressibility than montmorillonite, and kaolinite is seen to vary considerably depending on the particle-size fraction. The data for illite are substantially the same as those for kaolinite. It would be expected on theoretical grounds that illite, kaolinite, and chlorite would have somewhat the same compressibility and consolidation characteristics, probably fairly well represented by the data given by Samuels (1950) for kaolinite. These characteristics would be expected to show substantial variations depending on the particle size and perfection of crystallinity of the clay mineral particle as indicated by the Cornell University investigation.

Few data are available for allophane, but Gradwell and Birrell (1954) have shown that the sample that they investigated had a high compression index (1.53 to 1.73). Data are not available for halloysite; Lambe and Martin (1955) have shown, however, that compacted samples have relatively low density. It would be expected that the consolidation properties of halloysite clays would be quite variable depending on the state of hydration of the mineral.

Winterkorn and Moorman (1941) have shown that the compressibility of a soil composed of a mixture of illite and montmorillonite varies with

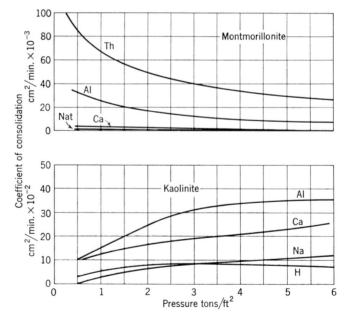

Fig. 5-27. Coefficient of consolidation versus pressure, after Samuels (1950).

the exchangeable cation in the following decreasing order: sodium, calcium, magnesium, potassium, and hydrogen. It appears that in such a mixture, montmorillonite exerts the controlling influence.

Discussion

At the liquid limit, montmorillonite clays contain large amounts of water, and the individual montmorillonite particles are very small. The water is present in two states: (1) oriented water surrounding the clay mineral particles, and (2) nonoriented liquid water in the interstitial pores. It can be considered that a small amount of pressure is adequate to remove the pore water and that considerable pressure is probably necessary to remove the oriented water. In montmorillonite clays relatively much of the water is oriented and this is particularly true in the sodium form; therefore, it would be expected that there would be only a moderate loss of water at small pressures and a considerable loss as the pressure was increased. The smaller particle size of the sodium forms would augment this effect. Also the envelope of oriented water around

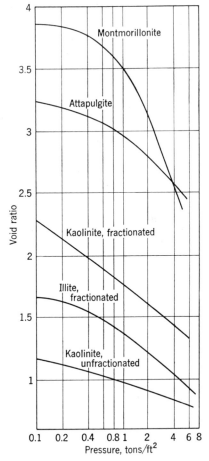

Fig. 5-28. Pressure-void ratio curves for hydrogen clay minerals, after Cornell University data (1951).

the montmorillonite particles would make it relatively difficult to adjust them in space one to the other with the application of pressure. This would be much more the case than when the water was in the liquid form and could act as a lubricant. The calcium form would differ from the sodium form in that it would have relatively more pore water and relatively less oriented water which, however, would have a higher degree of orientation than in the sodium form. Therefore, it would be expected that there would be a relatively high reduction in volume with the application of small pressure and small reductions in volume with increases in pressure. The data show this to be true.

In the case of kaolinite clays the amount of water at the liquid limit is small, and a relatively large part of it is pore water. There would be less oriented water than in the case of montmorillonite clays, and perhaps the orientation would be less perfect. As a consequence, the water would be more easily removed and the particles would find it easier to adjust themselves one to the other, so that on the application of pressure there would initially be a large reduction in volume and a continuing small loss as the pressure increased.

The different effect of sodium in the kaolinite and montmorillonite clays is of interest. It perhaps can be explained by the presence of the small amount of oriented water in the kaolinite clay where the effect of the sodium ion would be to destroy substantially any orientation, whereas in the case of montmorillonite with the large amount of oriented water the effect of the sodium would be only to reduce somewhat the degree of orientation. Also in the case of montmorillonite the dispersing effect of sodium would be important in developing smaller particles, whereas in the case of kaolinite clays the dispersing effect of sodium in the plastic state would be small or nil.

The montmorillonite clays consolidate relatively slowly at the start and then increase in rate with time; the increasing rate changes very little as the pressure is increased. This can be explained as the result of the slowness with which the oriented water breaks up and the resistance of interparticle adjustment due to the rigid water envelopes, the fine particle size, and low permeability, all adding up to a very slow loss of water. Stated another way, the small size of the pores, the character of the water, and the frictional resistance of particles to mutual adjustment would make it difficult to squeeze the water out of the clay, and increasing pressures would have relatively little effect on such squeezing action.

In the case of kaolinite the loss of water and the reduction in volume is rapid from the start of the application of load, and the rate of volume reduction increases with increasing load. Also there is little difference due to variations in the cation composition. This would be expected because of the increased permeability, increased amount of liquid as compared to oriented water, and increased pore size as compared to montmorillonite.

Waidelich (1959) has attempted to correlate the dipole moment and dielectric constant of a series of organic liquids on the compression index of kaolin and bentonite. His data show that the nature of the fluid has considerable influence on the compression index of these clays and that the effect is not the same for the kaolinite and the montmorillonite clays. He was not able to arrive at any general correlation between these characteristics of the fluid and the compression index, and perhaps none is to be expected since, as the author points out, other factors, such as size and structure of the fluids, would also be expected to exert an influence on compressibility.

Lambe (1958) has attempted to explain compressibility on the basis of the charge on the particle. It is not meant to deny that the charge on the particles is important, but it is desired to emphasize that the nature of the fluid is also important and that the effect of the adsorbed cations is important in their relation to the structure of the fluids, at least as much as because of their effect on the charge on the particles.

Secondary consolidation, that is the reduction in volume which takes place very slowly following the primary consolidation, would involve mostly slippage between grains, whereas primary consolidation probably is the simple squeezing out of water with relatively little slippage between grains. As the water content is reduced the reduction in distance between particles would increase the bonding force between them, and the prevalence of rigid water would make the slippage between grains increasingly difficult. Therefore, a slow reduction in volume would be expected.

As secondary consolidation continues it would be expected that chemical and mineralogical changes would take place in the clay. One would expect, for example, the development of a higher degree of crystallinity in the micas and perhaps the development of a completely new mineral species as the applied pressure passed into the range of metamorphic processes.

Studies by Skempton (1953) of cores taken at considerable depths show that to depths of about 3,000 ft with maximum pressures of about 100 to 150 kg per sq cm there is a regular decrease in void ratio with an exponential increase in pressure. The void ratio of the cores is about that expected from laboratory test results. At greater depths frequently the void ratio decreases more in the natural material than would be expected from laboratory data. Apparently at pressures in excess of 100 to 150 kg per sq cm different processes are at work, and one might speculate that these are possibly changes in the crystallinity of the clay minerals and perhaps the development of new mineral species.

The relation of secondary consolidation to clay mineral composition is a subject that merits considerable investigation. One would expect in the case of the three-layer clay minerals that the effect of secondary consolidation would be greater than for the two-layer clay minerals. In the case of the two-layer clay minerals one would expect greater effects for halloysite than for kaolinite, and perhaps halloysite would approach values obtained by the three-layer clay minerals. As to attapulgite one can only guess, but it seems that secondary consolidation effects would be substantial. The presence of alkalies and alkaline earths in attapulgite and the three-layer clay minerals would make them relatively more susceptible for the development of new mineral phases than kaolinite.

PRECONSOLIDATION UNDER LOAD

If the load on a sediment is reduced from p to p_1, for instance, by the melting of an ice sheet or the removal of superimposed sediments by erosion, its void ratio increases. The relation between the decrease of the void ratio resulting from a load application (curve AB) and its increase owing to subsequent load reduction (curve BC) is shown in Fig. 5-29 in which both the unit load and the void ratio have been plotted on an arithmetic scale. If the load reduction is again followed by a load increase, the void ratio decreases as indicated by the dashed curve CDE.

The relation of preconsolidation to clay mineral composition is not well-known, and only theoretical considerations can be given. The effect of preconsolidation in relation to the clay mineral composition would be expected to vary depending on the amount of preconsolidation. For example, in the case of montmorillonite, if the preconsolidation was carried to the place where the individual particles are brought substantially in contact by almost complete removal of interlayer water, the effect would be relatively permanent, and there would be little possible expansion if the load was reduced and the clays were wetted. On the other hand, if the preconsolidation caused only the partial dehydration of the montmorillonite particles, very large volume changes would be expected if the load was reduced and the clays were again wetted. The effect of wetting on preconsolidated clays composed of other clay minerals would be much less.

One would expect that the variation in the strength of preconsolidated clays as compared with normally consolidated clays would be somewhat different. It would also be expected to be considerably greater where montmorillonite was the dominant constituent as compared with those with a prevalence of nonexpanding clay materials.

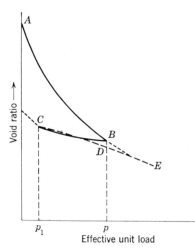

Fig. 5-29. Influence of reduction of load on relation between unit load and void ratio of a sediment, after Terzaghi (1955).

DRYING

It is well known that evaporation at the surface of clay or soil exposed to the atmosphere results in an increase of strength if the clay or soil is cohesive. Evaporation is accompanied by a decrease in void ratio; that is to say, the particles are closer together. The increase in strength would be expected because the shorter distance between particles would serve to increase the attractive forces between them. Also the adsorbed water layers would be thinner and hence stronger. The strength increase may be considered as resulting from negative pore-water pressure caused by capillarity. The increase in strength from drying may also be due to a chemical effect, such as the precipitation of salts between the particles which may serve to bond them together.

In soils composed almost wholly of clay minerals, drying is accompanied by shrinkage, which is likely to develop cracks and hence an over-all reduction in strength. This is particularly true when montmorillonite is the clay mineral. In soils with appreciable amounts (more than 25 per cent) of nonclay minerals, shrinkage disruptions are unlikely to overcome the strength developed on drying, and in such soils montmorillonite carrying sodium is likely to cause the highest dry strength.

There are instances known in which repeated wetting and drying at an exposed surface causes a loss of strength of clay material. For example, the slight wetting and substantial drying of outcrops of some bentonites in the Wyoming area cause the development of a granular, porous material which has little or no strength. The large change in volume, which is unique to sodium montmorillonites, seems to account for this phenomenon.

For further consideration of drying see Chap. 3 on ceramics and Chap. 4 on bonding clays.

PENETRATION RESISTANCE

Penetration resistance means here the resistance of the soil to the penetration of an object, such as a pile, by a driving force. Penetration resistance may be a consequence of many things, such as the amount and particle-size distribution of the nonclay minerals, cementation of the particles, density, or moisture content, and the resulting variation in compressive strength. It may vary with the clay mineral content, which is the sole factor to be considered here.

In an analysis of a series of deep cores from the Sao Paulo area of Brazil, Grim, Bradley, and Vargas (1959) have shown that the penetration resistance is relatively higher in soil zones containing montmorillonite than those composed of kaolinite and micas. Except in cases where the amount of clay mineral is very low and the activities are fictitiously high, penetration resistance increases with increasing activity (Figs. 5-30 and 5-31). These authors attribute this increased penetration resistance to

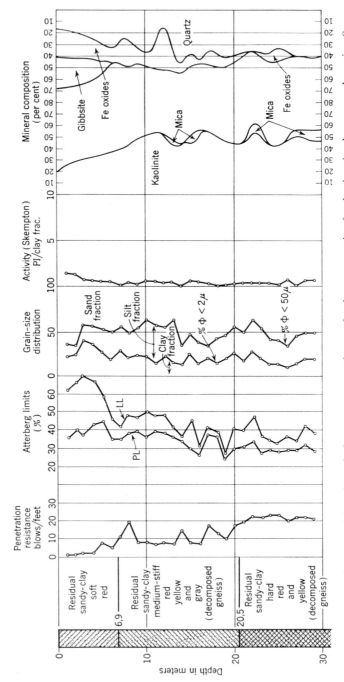

FIG. 5-30. Mineral composition in relation to penetration and other properties for boring in decomposed gneiss, Sacoman, Brazil, after Grim, Bradley, and Vargas (1959).

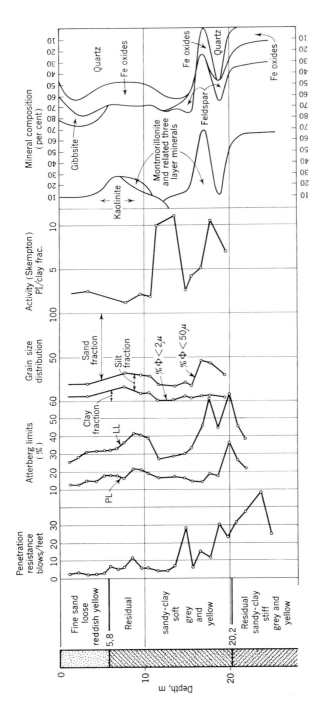

Fig. 5-31. Mineral composition in relation to penetration and other properties for boring in decomposed sandstone, San Carlos, Brazil, after Grim, Bradley, and Vargas (1959).

the greater impermeability of the montmorillonite soils.   They show also
that, where the permeability is low because of the accumulation of ferric
hydroxides, the penetration resistance increases.   In Figs. 5-30 and 5-31,
the difference between the sum of the percentages for clay minerals and
nonclay minerals and 100 per cent represents material too poorly organized to diffract X rays.

DENSITY

The true density of all the clay minerals is much the same, with values
in the range from about 2.5 to 2.8.   The higher values are to be found
in the iron-rich clay minerals.   The true density is difficult to measure
for attapulgite and halloysite, because of the indefinite penetration of
liquids into the elongate channels between the particles.   Values reported for these clay minerals are likely to be somewhat lower than those
given above.

The bulk density of soils and clays in their natural state depends on
their mineral composition, the particle-size distribution of their components, their texture and resulting void ratio, and their moisture contents.   Clays composed largely of attapulgite with low moisture contents
have very low bulk density.   Similarly, montmorillonite clays and those
with the lower hydration form of halloysite are likely to have low bulk
density.   The random arrangement of elongate particles and of extremely
small particles causes a relatively high void ratio.   Few data are available
on the bulk density of soils composed of different clay minerals after reworking.   Martin and Lambe (1957) have shown (Fig. 5-32) that the
maximum compacted density of kaolinite-sand mixtures occurs at a mixture of about 70 per cent sand and 30 per cent clay and that this maximum density exceeds that of the pure components.

Lambe and Martin (1955) have shown that halloysite soils have relatively low compacted dry-density values (65 to 80 lb per cu ft) and that

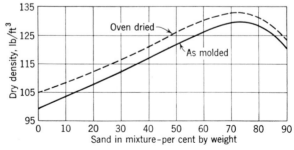

Fig. 5-32.   Optimum dry density of kaolinite sand mixtures, after Martin and
Lambe (1957).

the maximum density is obtained with unusually high moisture contents. Their tests show maximum dry densities less than 70 lb per cu ft and optimum moisture contents as high as 50 per cent. One would expect that the compacted density of attapulgite clays would also be very low and that montmorillonitic soils would show a wide range of compacted densities depending on the composition, particle shape, size, and the nature of the cation present. These values, however,

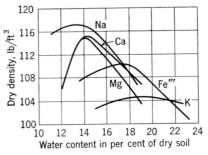

FIG. 5-33. Compacted dry density of nontronite with various exchangeable cations, after Lambe and Martin (1955).

would rarely be as low as those for attapulgite or as high as those for illites, chlorites, and kaolinites.

Lambe and Martin (1955) have given values for the compacted dry density of nontronite with various exchangeable cations (Fig. 5-33). These data show that at low moisture contents the compacted density decreases in the order sodium, calcium, magnesium, ferric iron, and potassium. At high moisture contents the nature of the cation causes little difference in density. As would be expected, the optimum moisture content for maximum density is less for sodium than for the other cations.

For the clay minerals in general it seems that sodium, as compared with other cations, would give the lowest values for maximum density of reworked materials, because it provides the lowest demand for rigid water thereby reducing interparticle bonding force and decreasing the amount of water required for interparticle adjustments. Compacted density values are not at hand for kaolinite and illite clays, but it seems that they would be in the range of the maximum values attained for nontronite. Also one would expect relatively little influence from variations in the nature of the exchangeable cation, except that sodium probably would tend to reduce the amount of water required for the development of maximum density.

SOIL STABILIZATION

In recent years a vast amount of research has gone into attempts to develop processes and treating media for the stabilization of soils. The object is to bind the soil particles together so that a rigid, nondispersible mass is quickly obtained with high load-bearing strength and resistance to the effects of weathering. A great deal of this work has proceeded without much consideration of the variations in the mineral compositions of the soils investigated. However, sufficient information is now available for an attempt at a correlation of soil stabilization and clay mineral composition.

Lime Soil Stabilization

The discovery that the workability of clay soils is generally greatly improved by the addition of lime, $Ca(OH)_2$, dates from the remote past. Recently highway and airport engineers have found that lime as a stabilizing agent greatly improves subgrade soils containing high percentages of expansive clays by reducing the plasticity indices and by increasing the bearing values. The effect of lime on the soil properties has been explained (Goldberg and Klein, 1952) by aggradation caused by flocculation of dispersed clay, by the exchange of calcium ions for other adsorbed ions such as hydrogen, sodium, and potassium, by pozzolanic reactions which were thought to be the formation of calcium silicates by the reaction of the lime with free silica of the soil, and by the gradual reaction of the lime and carbon dioxide from the atmosphere and the soil to form calcium carbonate, thereby cementing the soil particles together.

Eades and Grim (1960) have investigated the reactions of lime with some pure clay minerals in the soil stabilization processes. According to these authors, there is an actual chemical reaction between the lime and kaolinite, illite, montmorillonite, and some mixed-layer assemblages with an accompanying increase in bearing power. Other clay minerals were not studied, but probably they would also react with lime. The quantity of lime needed to effectively treat a soil to develop increased strength varies with the type of clay mineral present. Thus the optimum amount of lime for maximum strength with the kaolinite that they investigated was from 4 to 6 per cent, and for illite and montmorillonite it was 8 per cent; in some cases an even higher percentage was necessary.

In the case of kaolinite, the increase in strength began with the addition of the first increment of lime (Fig. 5-34). In the case of illite and montmorillonite lime in excess of about 4 to 6 per cent was required before any strength was developed.

The reaction of lime and kaolinite leads to the formation of new crystalline phases, which are tentatively identified as calcium silicate hydrates on the basis of their X-ray-diffraction characteristics. This reaction seems to take place by lime eating around the edges of the kaolinite particles with a new phase forming around the core of unaltered kaolinite. In contrast, the reaction of lime with the three-layered clay minerals begins by a replacement of the existing cations between the silicate sheets with calcium ions. Following the saturation of the interlayer positions with calcium, the whole clay mineral structure deteriorates without the immediate formation of substantial new crystalline phases. Later, and particularly with large lime additions, crystalline-reaction products develop which are difficult to identify specifically but undoubtedly are calcium silicate hydrates and calcium aluminum hydrates. For illite and montmorillonite, there is little strength developed until after the clay is saturated with lime and the destruction of the clay mineral is started. For kaolinite, the strength begins to increase immediately as some of the edges of the kaolinite particles are attacked.

In the case of montmorillonites which have a high cation-exchange capacity, an appreciable amount of lime is required to drive the calcium onto and into the clay. Thus initial increments of lime cause little or no increase in strength. The sodium montmorillonites require more lime to become wholly saturated than the calcium variety, and thus there is a larger lag in the development of strength with lime additions for sodium montmorillonite than for calcium montmorillonite.

The illite sample in Fig. 5-34 contains some sulfate ions as a consequence of the oxidation of pyrite present in the sample. The initial

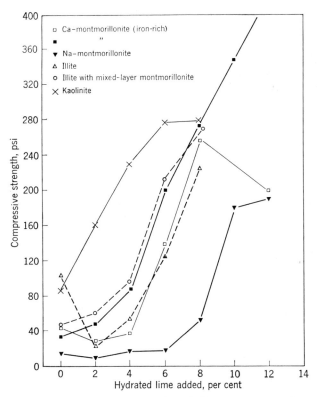

Fig. 5-34. Relation of additions of hydrated lime to compressive strength of various clay minerals, after Eades and Grim (1960).

reduction in strength can be explained by the sulfate ions reacting first with the lime. The sulfate originally present probably contributed some strength to the natural clay which was lost in the reaction with lime. Following the reaction of all the sulfate, the illite became saturated with calcium, and the strength increased.

Eades and Grim (1960) attribute the increase in strength to the reactions noted above. Since the development of strength is accompanied by distinct structural changes in the clay minerals, it is believed that they are relatively permanent. In some cases free lime might remain in the soil and would later become carbonated to add to the strength developed by the reaction with the clay minerals.

Lime-Flyash Soil Stabilization

Mixtures of lime and flyash have been used as additives to soils for the same purpose as additions of lime alone. There seems to be no agreement as to the relative merits of the two processes. Probably the value would depend on the composition of the soil to be stabilized.

It seems generally agreed that lime and flyash react to develop pozzolanic material, i.e., reaction products which have cementitious properties (Miller and McNichol, 1958). This reaction is thought to be slow, so that the mixture in a soil would cause a gradual development of strength over a considerable period of time. Such strength development could take place without the presence of any clay mineral component. Such a development of strength also could be independent, at least in part, of the nature of the clay mineral components. Some reaction of the lime and any clay minerals in the soils would be expected along the lines indicated in discussing lime soil stabilization. Consequently a more rapid development of strength would be expected in kaolinitic soils.

It may be reasoned that the clay minerals exert another influence. Thus, the presence of substantial amounts of montmorillonite in a soil causes relatively high impermeability and stickiness, which could well cause difficulties in adequately mixing the components. Further the high adsorptive capacity of the montmorillonite might serve to fix some of the additions on surfaces so that they would be relatively immobilized and consequently could not adequately develop all their inherent strength. Thus it would seem that highly montmorillonitic clay soils might be relatively less satisfactory for lime-flyash stabilization than kaolinitic soils. Illite and chlorite would probably act the same as kaolinite except if very poorly ordered or if they contained mixed-layer montmorillonite.

Cement Soil Stabilization

Additions of small amounts of portland cement have been used successfully to stabilize and increase the bearing capacity of many soils. As in the case of lime-flyash soil stabilization, cement stabilization would not require the presence of any clay mineral components and, in part at least, would be independent of the nature of the clay mineral composition of the soil. For the same reasons noted above, montmorillonite clays would probably be less satisfactory than kaolinitic clays, and illite and chloritic clays would react like kaolinite except when they are poorly organized and/or contained mixed-layer, expandable material.

Soil Stabilization with Organic Compounds

Organic compounds, such as petroleum fractions and bitumen, have been used for centuries to stabilize earthen roads. There is substantially no information available on the influence of clay mineral composition on the stabilization of soils with such organic compounds.

Winterkorn (1950) has pointed out that soils with exchangeable iron and aluminum provide results superior to soils carrying alkalies and alkaline earths. The presence of sodium causes extremely poor results. A possible explanation is that the iron and aluminum flocculate the soils, whereas sodium disperses the soil particles so that it becomes difficult for them to mix with the stabilizers.

Recently there has been much interest in the possible use of other types of organic chemicals. It has been hoped that chemicals and processes would be found that would develop strength immediately upon their application and, further, that little or no mixing or compacting would be required. There has been much investigation of possible stabilization in which two or more chemicals are added to the soil forming a cementing material in situ by chemical reaction. It seems certain that the effect of such chemical treatment would vary with the clay mineral components and that the relationship would probably vary also with the organics used. Thus montmorillonite might react with relative effectiveness for some organic compounds because of its ability to form complexes with them, whereas for others with which it does not react there might be a less satisfactory result. On the other hand the presence of montmorillonite probably would make the soil difficult to mix with some organics. Also the high water-holding capacity of montmorillonite would provide a soil that might make the addition of organics extremely difficult and retard their reaction. Kaolinite and illite would probably be easy to mix with the organic, and their lower water-holding capacity would also favor their effectiveness. However, their lower reactivity with organic compounds might be more detrimental than their values.

The matter of clay mineral composition and possible organic stabilizing agents is one deserving extensive research and also one on which general conclusions on scant data should be avoided.

FACTORS OF PARTICULAR SIGNIFICANCE
IN CONTROLLING SOIL PROPERTIES

The author attempted some years ago (1950) to list certain factors of composition that are apt to give soils unusual properties. It was noted that these factors of composition make it difficult to predict, on the basis of laboratory tests, the behaviors of a soil in situ, under load, and throughout an interval of time. Also it was pointed out that there undoubtedly are some soils in which these factors do not produce particularly bad soil properties, because other factors might tend to neutralize them. Also soils with the compositional factors indicated are quite likely to change as a consequence of changes of soil environment, such as changes in ground-water circulation or changes due to construction activities. The factors are as follows:

1. High montmorillonite content. Lambe and Martin (1957) pointed out that these soils are characterized by low permeability, slow compression, relatively large secondary compression under load application, high rebound on load removal, and loss of strength in the presence of moisture. These soils also have high cation-exchange capacity, and their properties vary widely depending on the nature of the exchangeable cation that they carry. Changes in environmental conditions, therefore, during and after construction, which would lead to a cation-exchange reaction might well cause great changes in the properties from those determined in laboratory tests.

2. High halloysite content. Perhaps the most significant factor regarding halloysite soils is the great variation in the properties of halloysite with variations in the state of the hydration of the mineral. Thus the $2H_2O$ and $4H_2O$ forms are substantially nonplastic, whereas an intermediate state of hydration is exceedingly plastic. This means that the plastic properties of a worked sample are apt to be quite unlike those of an undisturbed sample if there has been any change in moisture content. Lambe and Martin (1955) have pointed out that halloysite can also cause unusual engineering properties, such as low compacted density, high optimum water content, and high frost susceptibility.

3. High cation-exchange capacity. This is frequently due to the presence of montmorillonite, and the statements made under factor 1 are applicable. High cation-exchange capacity can also be due to the presence of poorly organized and extremely fine-grained clay mineral material and to the presence of organic matter. Such soils are, in general, likely to have the physical characteristics of montmorillonite-rich soils.

4. Sodium as an important exchangeable cation. Sodium tends to disperse the clay mineral particles and thereby decrease permeability. In the case of expandable minerals it tends to produce the maximum amount

of swelling. Its effect on the plastic and compaction properties of soils varies greatly depending on the nature of the clay mineral. In some instances, because of the tendency of the sodium ion to reduce the demand for oriented water, the presence of this cation can be beneficial as, for example, in reducing the amount of water required for the development of maximum compacted density. A further factor is that the sodium cation is relatively very replaceable. It is much easier for calcium to replace sodium than for sodium to replace calcium. In actual engineering practice there is often a chance that a soil naturally containing sodium would have its sodium at least partially replaced by calcium as, for example, in the emplacement of a mass of concrete. The replacement of sodium by calcium would drastically change the properties of the soil. Laboratory tests of natural sodium soils may well not produce the results found in actual engineering use.

5. High soluble-salt content. The presence of relatively large amounts of soluble salts would be a significant factor in determining the physical properties of soils. Changes in the soil environment during and after construction could considerably change the soluble-salt composition with attendant significant changes in physical properties.

6. Allophane and poorly organized clay minerals. The presence of substantially amorphous (allophane) and poorly organized clay minerals might well produce a soil with high cation-exchange capacity. As Gradwell and Birrell (1954) have shown, such soils may have very different physical properties in the natural and remolded conditions. In the natural condition there apparently is frequently some intergrowth of soil particles which is irreversibly broken on reworking. Also such soils are apt to be exceedingly unstable chemically, so that they can experience substantial changes in composition and properties on weathering for very short intervals of time. For example, volcanic-ash debris composed of poorly organized material can show substantial changes on weathering after only a few years under humid, tropical conditions.

7. High content of organic material. The influence of organic material obviously would depend on the nature of such material. Extremely fine-grained, colloidal organic material would have a different influence than detrital, woody material; the following remarks pertain to the former type. Martin and Lambe (1957) state that organic material is likely to cause low permeability, slow compression under load, relatively large secondary compression, high rebound on load removal, and loss of strength in the presence of moisture.

8. Concentration of component particles in fine silt-size grade. Soils of this character would have low activity. It has been pointed out that such clays might, however, have very high sensitivity and consequently might well cause serious difficulties for the engineer.

It perhaps needs to be mentioned again that the prime role of clay mineral studies in the field of soil mechanics is to provide a better understanding of the fundamental nature of the properties of natural cohesive soils. The objective is not to provide a substitute for laboratory tests but to provide a better understanding of the meaning and significance of the test data.

REFERENCES

Anonymous, "Report on Soil Solidification Research," Cornell University, vol. I (1951).

———, Report of Investigation of Expansive Characteristics of Shale and Weak Rocks, *Missouri River Div., Civil Works Investigation* 465, *U.S. Army, Corps of Engineers* (1954).

Allen, H., Classification of Soils and Control Procedures Used in Construction of Embankments, *Public Roads*, **22**, 263–282 (1942).

Atterberg, A., Die Plastizitat der Tone, *Intern mitt. boden.*, I, 4–37 (1911).

Baver, L. D., and H. F. Winterkorn, Sorption of Liquids by Soil Colloids, II, *Soil Sci.*, **40**, 403–419 (1935).

Beskow, G., Soil Freezing and Frost Heaving with Special Application to Roads and Railroads, *Swedish Geol. Soc.*, ser. C., no. 375 (1935).

Birrell, K. S., "Physical Properties of New Zealand Volcanic Ash Soils," Conference on Shear Testing of Soils, Melbourne, pp. 30–34 (1952).

Bjerrum, L., Geotechnical Properties of Norwegian Marine Clays, *Geotechnique*, **4**, 49–69 (1954).

——— and I. T. Rosenquist, Some Experiments with Artificially Sedimented Clays, *Norwegian Geotechnical Inst. Pub.* 25 (1957).

Boswell, P. G. H., A Preliminary Examination of the Thixotropy of Some Sedimentary Rocks, *Quart. Jour. Geol. Soc. London*, **104**, 499–526 (1949).

Casagrande, A., Research on the Atterberg Limits of Soils, *Public Roads*, **13**, 121–130, 136 (1932).

Dawson, R. F., The Design of Building Footings on Expansive Clay Soils, *Proc. Am. Soc. Civil Eng.*, **79** (1953).

Eades, J. L., and R. E. Grim, "The Reaction of Hydrated Lime with Pure Clay Minerals in Soil Stabilization," U.S. Highway Research Board meeting, January (1960).

Endell, K., Beitrag zur chemische Erforschung und Behandlung von Tonboden, *Bautechnik*, **13**, 226–229 (1935).

———, Die Quellfahigkeit der Tone im Baugrunde und ihre bautechnische Bedeutung, *Bautechnik*, **19**, 201–209 (1941).

———, W. Loos, H. Meischeider, and V. Berg, Über Zusammenhänge zwischen Wasserhaushalt der Tonminerale und Bodenphysikalischen Eigenschaften bindiger Böden, *Veröffentl. deut. Forsch. Bodenmech.*, 5 (1938).

Foster, M. D., Geochemical Studies of Clay Minerals: II, Relation Between Ionic Substitution and Swelling in Montmorillonites, *Am. Mineralogist*, **38**, 994–1006 (1953).

———, The Relation between Swelling and the Composition of Clays, *Natl. Acad. Sci. Publ.* 395, pp. 205–220 (1955).

Gibson, R. E., Experimental Determination of the True Cohesion and True

Angle of Internal Friction in Clays, *Proc. Third Intern. Conf. Soil Mechanics,* **I,** 126–130 (1953).

Goldberg, I., and A. Klein, Some Effects of Treating Expansive Clays with Calcium Hydroxide, *Am. Soc. Test. Mat., Spec. Tech. Pub.* 142, 53–67 (1953).

Gradwell, M., and K. S. Birrell, Physical Properties of Certain Volcanic Soils (from New Zealand), *N. Z. J. Sci. & Technol.* 36B, 108–122 (1954).

Grim, R. E., Some Fundamental Factors Influencing the Properties of Soil Materials, *Proc. Second Intern. Conf. Soil Mechanics,* **3,** and *Illinois State Geol. Survey Rept. Invest.* 146 (1950).

———, W. H. Allaway and F. L. Cuthbert, Reaction of Different Clay Minerals with Organic Cations, *J. Am. Ceram. Soc.,* 30, 137–142, (1947).

———, W. F. Bradley, and M. Vargas, "Clay Mineral Composition and Properties of Deep Residual Soils from Sao Paulo, Brazil," manuscript (1959).

——— and F. L. Cuthbert, The Bonding Properties of Clays: Part I, Clays in Green Molding Sands, *Illinois State Geol. Survey, Rept. Invest.* 102 (1945).

Harman, C. G., and F. Fraulini, Properties of Kaolinite as a Function of Its Particle Size, *J. Am. Ceram. Soc.,* 23, 252–258 (1940).

Hendricks, S. B., R. A. Nelson, and L. T. Alexander, Hydration Mechanism of the Clay Mineral Montmorillonite Saturated with Various Ions, *J. Am. Chem. Soc.,* 62, 1457–1464 (1940).

Hofmann, U., and A. Hausdorf, Über das Sediment Volumen und die Quellung von Bentonit, *Kolloid-Z.,* 110, 1–17 (1945).

Hogentogler, C. A., "Engineering Properties of Soils," McGraw-Hill Book Company, Inc., New York (1937).

Holtz, W. G., and H. J. Gibbs, Engineering Properties of Expansive Clays, *Proc. Am. Soc. Civil Engrs.,* 79 (1953).

Hvorslev, M. J., Über die Festigkeitseigenschaften gestorter bindiger Boden, *Ingenirvidenskab. Skrifter, Der.* A, no. 5, Copenhagen (1937).

Jordan, J. W., Alteration of the Properties of Bentonites by Reaction with Amines, *Mineral. Mag.,* 28, 598–605 (1949).

Lambe, T. W., Cold Room Studies, Appendix D: Mineral and Chemical Studies, in U.S. Army, Corps of Engineers, "Frost Investigations" (1953).

———, The Engineering Behavior of Compacted Clay, Paper 1655, and The Structure of Compacted Clays, Paper 1654, *J. Soil Mech. & Foundation Div., Am. Soc. Civil Engrs.* (1958).

——— and R. T. Martin, Composition and Engineering Properties of Soils, (I), *Proc. U.S. Highway Research Board,* 32, 576–590 (1953).

——— and ———, Composition and Engineering Properties of Soils, (III), *Proc. U.S. Highway Research Board,* 34, 566–582 (1955).

——— and ———, Composition and Engineering Properties of Soils, (V), *Proc. U.S. Highway Research Board,* 36, 693–702 (1957).

Lee, C. H., Sealing the Lagoon Lining at Treasure Island with Salt, *Proc. Am. Soc. Civil Engrs.,* 66, 247–263 (1940).

Low, P. F., Movement and Equilibrium of Water in Soil Systems as Affected by Soil-Water Forces, "Water and Its Conduction in Soils," *Natl. Acad. Sci. Publ.* 629, pp. 55–64 (1958).

Martin, R. T., and T. W. Lambe, Soil Composition and Its Influence on the Engineering Behavior of Fine Grained Soils, *Clay Minerals Bull.* 3, pp. 137–150 (1957).

Michaels, A. S., "Remarks on the Mechanical Properties of Soil-Water Systems," discussion at American Society of Civil Engineers meeting, New York (1958).

—— and C. S. Lin, Effect of Counter Electro-osmosis and Sodium Exchange Ion on Permeability of Kaolinite, *Ind. Eng. Chem.*, **47**, 1249–1253 (1955).

Mielenz, R. C., and M. E. King, Physical-Chemical Properties and Engineering Performance of Clays, *Calif. Div. Mines Bull.* 169, pp. 196–254 (1955).

Miller, R. H., and W. J. McNichol, Structural Properties of Lime-Flyash-Aggregate Compositions, *U.S. Highway Research Board Bull.* 193, pp. 12–23 (1958).

Peck, R. B., H. O. Ireland, and T. S. Fry, Studies of Soil Characteristics: The Earth Flows of St. Thuribe, Quebec, *Univ. of Illinois Dept. Civil Eng. Soil Mech. Ser.*, no. 1 (1951).

Plank, C. J., and L. C. Drake, Difference between Silica and Silica-Aluminum Gels; II, A Proposed Mechanism for Gelation and Syneresis of the Gels, *J. Colloid Sci.*, **2**, 413–427 (1947).

Platen, H., and H. G. F. Winkler, Plastizitat und Thixotropie von Fractionierten Tonmineralien, *Kolloid-Z.*, **158**, 3–22 (1958).

Preece, E. F., Geotechnics and Geotechnical Research, *Proc. U.S. Highway Research Board*, **27**, 384–416 (1947).

Quirk, J. P., and R. K. Schofield, The Effect of Electrolyte Concentration on Soil Permeability, *J. Soil Sci.*, **6**, 163–178 (1955).

Rodebush, W. H., and A. M. Buswell, Properties of Water Substance, "Water and Its Conduction in Soils," *Natl. Acad. Sci. Publ.* 629, pp. 5–13 (1958).

Rosenquist, I. T., Om de Norske Kuikkleirers egensnapen og mineralogiske sammensetning, *N.I.M. Forhandlinger,* **10**, 1–15, Stockholm (1946).

——, Sensitivity of Norwegian Quick Clays, *Geotechnique*, **3**, 195–200 (1953).

Samuels, S. G., The Effect of Base Exchange on the Engineering Properties of Soils, *Bld. Research Sta. G. Britain,* Note C176 (1950).

Skempton, A. W., Notes on the Compressibility of Clays, *Quart. J. Geol. Soc. London*, **100**, 119–135 (1944).

——, Vane Tests in the Alluvial Plain of the River Forth, *Geotechnique*, **1**, 111–124 (1948).

——, A Possible Relation between True Cohesion and the Mineralogy of Clays, *Proc. Second Intern. Conf. Soil Mech.*, **7**, 45–46 (1950).

——, The Colloidal "Activity" of Clay, *Proc. Third Intern. Conf. Soil Mech.*, **I**, 57–61 (1953).

——, Soil Mechanics in Relation to Geology: Part I, *Proc. Yorkshire Geol. Soc.*, **29**, 33–62 (1953).

—— and R. D. Northey, The Sensitivity of Clays, *Geotechnique*, **3**, 30–53 (1952).

Taber, S., Frost Heaving, *J. Geol.*, **37**, 428–461 (1929).

Terzaghi, K., "Erdbaumechanik auf bodenphysikalischer Grundlage," Franz Deudicke, Vienna (1925).

——, Undisturbed Clay Samples and Undisturbed Clays, *J. Boston Soc. Civil Engrs.*, **28**, 211–231 (1941).

——, "Theoretical Soil Mechanics," John Wiley & Sons, Inc., New York (1943).

——, Ends and Means in Soil Mechanics, *Harvard Univ. Grad. School Eng. Pub.* 402 (1944).

——, Influence of Geological Factors on the Engineering Properties of Sediments, *Econ. Geol.*, Fiftieth Anniversary Volume, pp. 557–618 (1955).

Waidelich, W. C., Influence of Liquid and Clay Mineral Type in Consolidation of Clay-Liquid Systems, *Natl. Acad. Sci. Publ.* 629, pp. 24–42 (1959).

Weaver, C. E., A Lath-shaped Nonexpanded Dioctahedral 2:1 Clay Mineral, *Am. Mineralogist,* **38,** 279–289 (1953).

White, W. A., Atterberg Plastic Limits of Clay Minerals, *Am. Mineralogist,* 34, 508–512 (1949).

————, "Water Sorption Properties of Homoionic Clay Minerals," Ph.D. thesis, University of Illinois (1955).

———— and E. Pichler, Water Sorption Characteristics of Clay Minerals, *Illinois State Geol. Survey Cir.* 266 (1959).

Williams, F. J., M. Neznayko, and D. J. Weintritt, The Effect of Exchangeable Bases on the Colloidal Properties of Bentonite, *J. Phys. Chem.,* **57,** 6–10 (1953).

Winterkorn, H. F., Engineer Properties of Clay Soils, *Winterkorn Road Research Inst. Bull.* I, Princeton, N.J. (1950).

———— and R. B. Moorman, A Study of Changes in Physical Properties of Putnam Soils Induced by Ionic Substitution, *Proc. U.S. Highway Research Board,* **21,** 415–434 (1941).

CHAPTER 6

Clays in the Discovery and Recovery of Petroleum

INTRODUCTION

Clay mineral studies have wide application in the search for petroleum and in its recovery. This fact has been widely recognized, and as a consequence, large research laboratories of major oil companies have devoted much attention in recent years to clay mineral researches. Fortunately, many of these companies have permitted the results of their researches to be published so that there is a substantial literature on the subject.

SEARCH FOR PETROLEUM

The clay mineral composition can be distinctive for particular horizons of a sedimentary sequence and, hence, be used for correlation. Weaver (1958), for example, has shown such use of clay mineral analyses in a thick, generally nonfossiliferous shale section in West Texas. Clay mineral analyses on a routine basis can be made very rapidly by X-ray diffraction methods or by differential thermal procedures planned so that several samples are analyzed at the same time. The clay mineral characteristics that are valuable for correlation may not be the large variations in composition but the more subtle differences, such as the nature of the mixed layerings. A study to determine if clay mineral data can be used for correlation purposes must, therefore, be thorough and complete.

Clay mineral analyses often prove of value in interpreting the environment of the formation of the sediments and their geologic history. For example, Smoot (1959) has shown that kaolinite is generally restricted to near-shore deposits in a series of Mississippian sediments from Illinois. Clay mineral analyses also provide information on the source area and possible postdepositional changes. This involves the consideration of whether or not the clay minerals experienced diagenetic changes on passing from one environment to another and, hence, whether any clay mineral composition is characteristic of a particular environment. This is a subject that is currently being studied intensively in oil-company and other laboratories and on which there is much difference of opinion. Thus, Millot (1949) concluded that there are particular clay mineral compositions that are characteristic of various environments of sedimentary accumulation, whereas Weaver (1958) and Riviere (1953) have arrived at substantially the opposite conclusions. For further consideration of this matter, the works of Grim (1958), Powers (1954), Milne and Early (1958), and Burst (1958) should be consulted.

It seems to the author that the study of ancient sediments has shown conclusively that in some cases there has been significant diagenetic clay mineral development in marine waters, e.g., in shales composed of a single clay mineral, or in a simple mixture of a few clay minerals for which it is inconceivable that the material supplied could have been so uniform and so simple in composition, and in the formation of glauconite and metabentonites. Undoubtedly there are some ancient marine sediments for which diagenetic changes seem to have been unimportant, for example, thick marine argillaceous rocks which have a complex clay mineral composition including considerable amounts of kaolinite. Any research findings on the factors actively controlling the amount of diagenesis would be most helpful in investigations of the relation of the clay mineral composition to the environment of accumulation. At present, about the only general conclusion that can be given is that the dominance of the three-layer clay mineral, i.e., illite, chlorite, and montmorillonite, rather than kaolinite, suggests marine conditions of deposition, particularly if these three-layer clay minerals are well organized.

It is noted elsewhere (Chap. 7) that the clay minerals have catalytic properties towards hydrocarbons, and it has been suggested (Grim, 1947) that the clay minerals acted as a catalyst in the transformation of organic material to petroleum. This is certainly a possibility, although recent findings (Smith, 1954) that hydrocarbons are present in Recent sediments and generally in living organic material may make it unnecessary to assume that catalysis has played a role in the origin of petroleum. However, the possibility remains, and it seems likely that catalysis due to clay mineral components might well influence the character of the hydrocarbons even though it is not a determinative factor in their genesis. In the catalysis of hydrocarbons, the catalyst frequently becomes coated with carbon, and sulfides may develop in them. The presence of such materials associated with clay minerals in ancient sediments might well provide a clue as to whether or not they have entered into catalytic reactions in the past. This would seem to be a fruitful field for research.

The clay minerals have high adsorbing power for various types of organic molecules (Grim, 1953). Even though the clay minerals may not have acted as catalysts, a knowledge of the kind of organic material carried by them in sediments conceivably could throw light on the history of the sediment in relation to the hydrocarbons in it or near it at some time in the geologic past.   Sedletsky and Yussupova (1943) have concluded that in some cases the *c*-axis dimension in montmorillonites may be correlated with the presence of hydrocarbons in the associated geologic section, the variation in montmorillonite being due to variations in the organic molecules adsorbed.   This again would seem to be a fruitful field for research.

Degens et al. (1957) have shown that there is a relationship between the relative abundance of gallium and rubidium in fresh versus marine sediments, and that the abundance is related to the clay mineral composition.   Gallium is more abundant in kaolinitic fresh-water sediments, and rubidium is more abundant in marine illitic sediments.   This may be explained on the basis that gallium proxies for aluminum and hence is most abundant in the highly aluminous clay mineral, i.e., kaolinite. Rubidium proxies for potassium and is, therefore, most abundant in illite.

Smoot (1959) has shown that the clay mineral composition varies with the permeability of a series of Mississippian sands in Illinois and therefore is a significant factor in exploratory drilling and reservoir evaluation. The permeable sands contain a heterogeneous clay mineral suite composed mainly of illite plus mixed-layer material, degraded chlorite, and kaolinite, with minor amounts of illite and montmorillonite.   The relatively impermeable sands contain proportionately larger amounts of illite and well-ordered chlorite with minor amounts of degraded illite and chlorite; kaolinite and montmorillonite are relatively rare.   The difference in clay mineral composition is attributed by Smoot in large part to postlithification alteration due to the degrading influence of circulating formational fluids.   Where the permeability is low, such circulation is drastically reduced, thereby reducing the possibility of altering the prelithification clay mineral suites.

DRILLING FLUIDS

Introduction

In drilling operations by the rotary method, which is now essentially the only drilling procedure used in the petroleum industry, a fluid is maintained in the hole at all times.   During actual drilling the fluid is circulated continuously to remove cuttings.   The fluid is pumped down through the hollow drill stem emerging at the bottom of the hole through "eyes" in the bit.   It rises to the surface in the annular space between the drill stem and the walls of the hole and flows into a pit for the removal of cuttings and entrained gas.   From the pit it is recirculated down the hole.   According to Larsen (1946) the usual composition by volume of such drilling fluids is as follows: water, 65 to 98 per cent; clay, 2 to 30 per cent; weighting material, 0 to 35 per cent, substances arising from drilling operations, for example, rock cuttings and gas, 0 to 10 per cent. There are some drilling fluids of quite different compositions, used under special conditions, which will be mentioned later.

A vast amount of valuable research, from the point of view of colloid chemistry, has been done on the properties of drilling fluids and the fundamental factors which control them.   These works can be followed from the excellent papers and extensive bibliographies of Larsen (1946 and 1955) and Van Olphen (1950).   No attempt will be made herein to consider this subject in detail, as it is considered beyond the scope of this volume.   Rather an attempt will be made to show how the properties of the clay minerals, especially their structural attributes, are related to the essential properties of drilling fluids.

Functions and Properties of Drilling Muds

The removal of cuttings from the hole is readily facilitated by a fluid with a viscosity greater than that of water.   At the same time the drilling mud must be pumpable, and its viscosity characteristics must be subject to some control.   Viscosities of the order of 15 centipoises are about the usual norm of good drilling practice.

The drilling fluid should be markedly thixotropic, that is, it should show an initial yield point after standing without agitation.   In the parlance of the art, it should have gel strength.   This attribute is necessary so that cuttings do not settle to the bottom of the hole and "freeze" the drill stem when pumping or agitation of the drill fluid ceases temporarily.   On the other hand, the gel strength and viscosity cannot be excessive; otherwise, cuttings and gas are not easily separated in the mud pit.   The drilling fluid serves to keep formation fluids confined to their formations.   Normally such formation fluids are under pressure at least equal to that of a column of water of equal depth so that densities in excess of water alone are required.   Frequently, considerably greater densities are required, so that muds of high weight per unit volume obtained by adding weighting materials, such as finely ground barites, are necessary.   The drilling mud must have sufficient density and gel strength to maintain such weighting material in suspension.

An impervious coating must be built up on the wall of the hole in order to impede the penetration of water from the drilling fluid into the formations.   This coating must be thin in order not to retard the drilling operation.   The high impermeability is particularly important in drilling through formations which are permeable and contain fluids under relatively high pressure, and also it is important when drilling water may soften formations and cause them to cave or heave (heaving shale) into the hole. It is important to keep to a minimum the amount of any argillaceous material added to the drilling fluid from the penetrated formations, because this material tends to increase viscosity. It is also important to prevent water from the drilling fluid from penetrating possible producing sands, as the reaction of the water to any clay in such sands may be to reduce their permeability and, hence, the oil production from them.

It is desirable that the viscosity and gel strength of the drilling fluid be altered relatively little by large variations in the concentration of an electrolyte and that these properties be subject to some control by chemical treatment. Drilling operations in some areas frequently encounter masses of salt or gypsum which suddenly cause a large change in the electrolyte content of the mud. In order to maintain the properties of the mud the specifications must be preserved by suitable chemical treatment or by major variations in composition. The problem of viscosity and gel-strength control is different in drilling muds than in the kaolin-clay slips used in the ceramic industry. A small amount of sodium hydroxide serves to thin the slip, whereas in the montmorillonite clay drilling muds sodium hydroxide in small amounts may cause the opposite effect, i.e., thicken the slip. A variety of chemical agents are used for viscosity and gel-strength control in the drilling mud, for example, complex polyphosphates, such as sodium hexametaphosphate, and organic weak acids generally of high molecular weight, such as tan stuffs like quebracho and humic acids.

High-pH lime muds are also used to maintain viscosity and gel strength in the presence of added clay from penetrated formations and large amounts of electrolytes. Such fluids contain much slaked lime and caustic soda and have pH values in the range of 12 to 13. Essentially, they also contain a protective colloid which may be tan stuffs, humic-acid derivatives, or gelatinized starch; otherwise the system would be completely flocculated. The control of the properties of such high-pH muds is a delicate matter and is a test of the skill of the drilling-mud engineer. The concentration of organic material in these muds is likely to be high, ranging upward from 4 or 5 lb of organic material per bbl of mud. When clay is added, either deliberately as a drilling-mud clay or as ground-up cuttings encountered during drilling, dispersion is at a minimum, even though the clay would normally readily become dispersed in water, and only a slight contribution is made to the consistency of the mud. This effect is of enormous advantage in drilling through intervals of mud-making shale, and, indeed, with proper mud control there seems to be no limit to the footage of normally dispersible shales which can be so drilled. Such muds are characterized principally by very low gel strength, after both agitation or a period of quiescence, and by quite low filter-cake permeabilities. Substantial contamination by salt can occur without harming the mud, particularly when gelatinized starch is present.

In some areas relatively high bottom-hole temperatures and pressures are encountered, and adequate properties of the mud must be preserved under such conditions (Gray et al., 1952). Instances are known in which zeolitic and cementitious products developed in drilling muds under the conditions found at the bottom of the hole with extremely detrimental results. Lime-caustic–high-pH muds would be expected to be most susceptible to this difficulty.

In recent years (Hurdle, 1957; Smith, 1958), muds with additions of gypsum have been used where a high resistance to salt contamination was required. Such muds have a high concentration of calcium and tend also to inhibit the dispersion into the drilling fluid of the shales and clays encountered. Such gypsum muds have a moderate pH and do not tend to form cementitious compounds which cause gelation at the high temperatures sometimes encountered in deep drilling. Until recently it was difficult to control the viscosity and gel strength of gypsum muds, but with the development of lignosulfonates of the chrome-ferro type (e.g., the material sold under the trade name "Q-BROXIN") adequate chemical treating agents are available. The resistance of such muds to salt concentration is illustrated by the fact that sea water can be used as their make-up fluid.

Clays Used in Drilling Fluids

It is obvious from the foregoing discussion that water alone is not a satisfactory drilling fluid and, further, that clays with special characteristics would frequently be required. The qualification of clays for use in drilling fluids is measured primarily by the number of barrels of mud of a given viscosity (usually 15 centipoises) obtained from a ton of clay in fresh water and in salt water; by the gel strength, which is the difference in yield value immediately after agitation and after standing 10 min; and by the wall-building properties as measured by the water lost through a filter paper when a 15-centipoise clay is subjected to a pressure of 100 psi for 30 min (Anon., 1957) and as measured by the thickness of the filter cake produced in the standard API water-loss test. Other tests, such as the influence of electrolytes on viscosity, are frequently used, but the foregoing generally serve to evaluate clays for drilling-mud use. Figures 6-1 and 6-2 and Table 6-1 give the characteristics of a variety of clays as determined by drilling-mud tests.

Clays and soils with more than very small amounts of nonclay minerals, particularly in silt and sand sizes, are not suitable for drilling muds because such materials dilute the desired properties and have abrasive action on pumps and other drilling equipment. Local soils and clays of low nonclay mineral content are frequently used to start a well—in

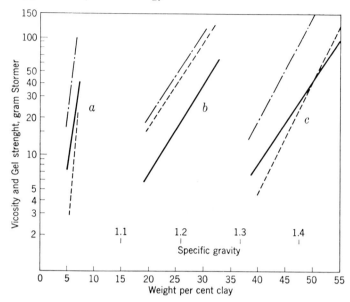

Fɪɢ. 6-1.   Viscosity and gel strength of some clay minerals, after Larsen, (1955).
* As designated in American Petroleum Institute code: (*a*) sodium montmorillonite clay, (*b*) calcium montmorillonite and illite clay, (*c*) impure clay with
montmorillonite and attapulgite.
—·—- shear strength after 10 min
– – – – shear strength immediately after agitation
————— so-called Stormer viscosity at 600 rpm

TABLE 6-1

YIELD AND WATER LOSS DATA FOR VARIOUS TYPES OF CLAY MINERALS
(After Larsen, 1955)

Clay mineral	Yield, bbl, 15 cp mud/ton (fresh water)	Solids in filter cake, % by weight	API water loss at 15 cp	Filter-cake per-meability, microdarcys	pH
Hectorite, California...	160	6.5	7	0.85	8.6
Na-Mont., Wyoming...	125	10	11	1.8	8.2
Ca-Mont., California...	71	16	15	2.1	8.7
Ca-Mont., Texas.....	18	50	11	1.5	7.5
Illite, Illinois.........	13	67	57	38	7.4
Kaolinite, Georgia....	14	70	190	285	7.0
Attapulgite, Georgia..	105	23	105	68	7.1
Halloysite, Colorado..	17	60	35	15	7.7

fact, the well may be started with water if considerable argillaceous material of suitable properties is to be drilled through initially. Local and surface clays frequently require concentrations of 20 to 40 per cent of clay to give adequate viscosity (Fig. 6-2). They are likely to have low gel strength and high water-loss properties. Drilling with such clay-muds is often continued until the penetration of soft formations, saline water, and/or great depths require special mud properties that only can be attained by the use of special types of clays. Frequently, as drilling progresses, such special clays of the types noted below are added to the drilling mud composed of local clay in order to change the properties

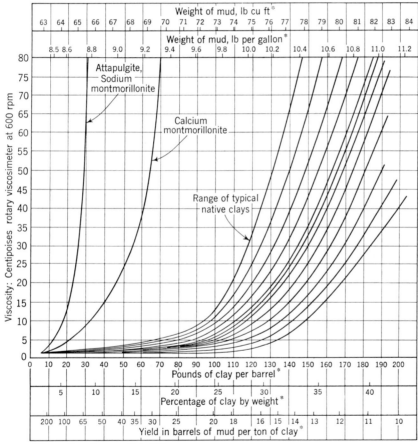

Fig. 6-2. Viscosity and weight of mud in relation to percentage of various types of clay in fresh water, modified from data in "Drilling Mud," Baroid Division National Lead Co. (1953).

in the direction desired. The local and surface clays may be of any composition, although those containing montmorillonite or attapulgite clay minerals are most desirable.

In many parts of the world, for example, the Gulf of Mexico coastal area, England, Germany, and France, clays distinctly superior to generally available local and surface ones are found readily. Ten to fifteen per cent of such clay is frequently adequate to produce the desired viscosity, and yields of 40 to 75 bbl per ton are common. The water loss of these clays is moderately high, and the gel strength is moderately low, but where drilling operations are not severe, for example, at moderate depths in hard nonargillaceous formations, clays of this type are satisfactory. The mineral composition is dominantly montmorillonite with calcium as the exchangeable cation. Bentonites of such composition and properties are found in many parts of the world. Frequently the yield of such clays can be improved by treatment with a sodium compound, but, unfortunately, the water-loss and filtration characteristics are not much improved by such treatment. An example of such a clay is the calcium montmorillonite shown in Fig. 6-2.

The special type of clay used most extensively for drilling muds all over the world is a bentonite from the Wyoming area in the United States composed of montmorillonite carrying sodium as the major exchangeable cation. This clay gives yields in excess of 100 bbl per ton. Only about 5 per cent clay is adequate to produce the desired viscosity. This clay also has very high gel strength but is particularly outstanding for its low filter-cake permeability (Table 6-1). The fact that, even when very thin, this bentonite produces an impervious clay layer on the wall of the hole is a major property which sends it around the world for use in drilling oil wells. Williams et al. (1953) have shown that the montmorillonite making up this bentonite contains calcium in addition to sodium as the exchangeable cation and that the optimum yield is developed when about 40 per cent of the sodium is replaced by calcium. It has been shown also (Williams et al., 1954) that weathering of the clay sometimes increases the yield. The yield of the Wyoming bentonite can be increased sometimes by treatment with soda or lime or other chemicals, such as permanganate (Ratcliffe, 1955), but it is important that no treatment process appears to have been found to improve substantially the water-loss property of the bentonites. That is to say, so far no process has been found for treating bentonites generally to raise the standard of their water-loss characteristics up to that of the Wyoming-type bentonites. It is also interesting that in the Wyoming and Montana area the Cretaceous section contains many beds of bentonite, but only a few of these beds have the desired properties for drilling muds or will yield such properties following chemical treatment (Knechtel and Patterson, 1956).

The importance of clays for drilling fluids with the properties of the Wyoming bentonite has caused a world-wide search for such clays. Many bentonites have been found that give desired viscosity characteristics but none that duplicate the extremely low water loss. In the Mostaganem area of northwest Algeria a sodium bentonite is produced which closely approaches the Wyoming material in drilling-fluid properties.

A clay with properties even superior to those of the Wyoming bentonite has been produced at Hector, California (Table 6-1). This clay, known as hectorite, is composed of a unique magnesium-rich montmorillonite clay mineral of the same name. The properties of hectorite are such that even with natural dilutions of as much as 50 per cent of very fine carbonate minerals a satisfactory mud can be produced. Unfortunately, the deposits of this clay are small, so that it has never been able to supply an appreciable amount of the drilling-mud requirements.

Considerable tonnages of clays composed of attapulgite are used in the industry, because muds containing it have characteristics showing small variations in viscosity and gel strength with large variations in electrolyte content. Such clays have only moderate thixotropic properties and unfortunately have very high water loss. In practice the high water loss is corrected frequently by the addition of gelatinized starch, ferro-chrome lignosulfonate, or quebracho. The yield of such clay has been about equal to that of Wyoming bentonite, that is, about 100 bbl per ton in fresh water (Table 6-1). Recently attapulgite clays have been placed on the market with yields reported to be 150 bbl per ton (Anon., 1959). The yields of attapulgite clay are higher than those of montmorillonite clays in highly saline waters.

Attapulgite tends to release its viscosity rather slowly so that it increases the viscosity of an agitated drilling fluid for some time after its addition. Attapulgite clay in the United States is produced from a unique deposit in beds of Miocene age in northwestern Florida and southwestern Georgia. Some of these beds are quite pure attapulgite. Others contain varying amounts of montmorillonite and sepiolite. Clays of similar clay mineral composition, except for a somewhat lower attapulgite content, are found in southern France, central Spain, western Australia, western India, and perhaps elsewhere in the world.

Chambers (1959) has claimed that a substantially pure sepiolite from the Vallecas area near Madrid, Spain, has drilling-mud properties similar to those produced by attapulgite clays but that "this sepiolite has proven even more resistant to flocculation by electrolytes than attapulgite."

DISCUSSION

It is interesting to consider possible reasons for the unique properties of the bentonites from the Wyoming area which make them outstanding for use in drilling fluids. The high viscosity and thixotropy of clay-water suspensions at very low clay contents can be largely explained by the fact that this montmorillonite is easily dispersed into flakes approaching unit-cell thickness which have relatively very large areal dimensions. That is, a given amount of this bentonite disperses in water into a relatively much larger number of larger, thinner flakes than other bentonites and clays. Plastering of such large, thin flakes on the walls of the bore hole would cause the development of a thin and very impervious clay layer.

There is abundant evidence to indicate that the water adsorbed directly on the surfaces, particularly on the basal-plane surfaces of the clay minerals, is composed of oriented water molecules and does not have the character of liquid water (see Chap. 2). The possible thickness of the adsorbed layers of oriented water molecules is a matter of some dispute, but it is suggested that such water layers can develop to relatively great thicknesses on the montmorillonite flakes of the Wyoming type. This would in effect increase the size of the flakes and make the very high viscosity and thixotropic characteristics of the clay more understandable. It would also help to explain the impervious nature of the wall layer, because water first penetrating the clay would be oriented and immobilized and would thereby effectively seal the clay against further water penetration. In the writer's opinion, the development of thick oriented water layers on the montmorillonite surfaces permits a more satisfactory explanation of the effect of polyphosphate additions on viscosity and gel strength than any other concept. Such phosphates have structural attributes which would permit them to *almost* perfectly fit into the water net. They probably could fit with some slight disruption of the water orientation. It would be anticipated that extremely small amounts of such phosphates, therefore, would have a large modifying effect on the viscosity and gel properties. The inherent advantage of this concept is that it provides a mechanism whereby the viscosity and gel properties can be modified only slightly and with extremely small amounts of additives.

The problem now is to find an explanation for the dispersibility of the montmorillonite of this Wyoming bentonite and its water-orienting properties. Also it is necessary to explain why other montmorillonites cannot be chemically treated to match the properties of the Wyoming material. It is probably significant that the Wyoming material carries exchangeable sodium but also has an appreciable amount of adsorbed calcium (25 to 40 meq per 100 g). The tendency of these cations to develop different thicknesses of adsorbed water under the same conditions would tend to develop nonequilibrium conditions between the montmorillonite layers that would permit them to split easily. McAtee (1958) has shown that the sodium and calcium ions are not uniformly distributed between the montmorillonite flakes; i.e., there is a kind of mixed-layer structure in this montmorillonite. This author has reasoned that this variability of cation distribution reflects a variability within the silicate layers themselves. Again, it would be expected that such variability would cause an instability of the montmorillonite in water that would enhance its dispersibility. Chemical-treatment processes could not be expected to develop the variability of the cation distribution and could not develop the variability within the silicate sheets themselves; they could not, therefore, be expected to reproduce in other montmorillonites the properties of the Wyoming type.

The high water-orienting ability of the Wyoming montmorillonite is difficult to explain. The presence of adsorbed sodium would in part favor it because of the probable nonhydrating characteristic of this cation when adsorbed on montmorillonite surfaces (Hendricks et al., 1940). This, however, cannot be a very significant factor because of the inability to duplicate the Wyoming material synthetically by treating other bentonites with sodium compounds. Perhaps the large areal dimensions of the montmorillonite flakes is significant in enhancing water development. Grim and Kulbicki (1959) have provided data suggesting that a characteristic of the Wyoming-type montmorillonite is that there is relatively little inversion of the tetrahedrons in the silica layers as compared with that in other montmorillonites. The presence of inverted tetrahedrons on the surface of the silica sheets would be expected to retard the development of oriented water. It is entirely conceivable that some feature of the silicate structure itself may be important. Thus the population of cations in tetrahedral and octahedral positions may not only be responsible for the charge distribution on the surface but also may provide a structure resistant to curling, so that the flatness would favor thick oriented-water layers.

All this is highly theoretical and, beyond the variability of the adsorbed-cation composition, there is little real knowledge of the cause of the peculiar attributes of the montmorillonite in the Wyoming bentonite. Further, there is no explanation as to the conditions of formation of these bentonites that might have caused their particular kind of montmorillonite. Whether it was a peculiar ash composition, peculiar conditions in the environment in which the ash fell, unusual later conditions of alteration, or something else cannot even be reasonably surmised.

It is interesting that weathering and the change of state of the oxidation of the iron in the Wyoming montmorillonite increases its dispersibility (Foster, 1953). Perhaps this can be used as a clue to ferreting out the uniqueness of this montmorillonite and the factors of origin which caused it.

The lack of significant changes in viscosity characteristics of attapulgite and sepiolite water suspensions with large variations in electrolyte content probably is to be explained in part at least by the presence of hollow channels through the aggregates of these clay minerals into which sodium ions could penetrate. Once within such channels the sodium ions would have little effect on suspension characteristics which would be related to factors operating around the exterior of such aggregates. The gutter-and-channel characteristics of the exterior surfaces of attapulgite and sepiolite particles would be expected to reduce the tendency of such surfaces to develop oriented water, and, further, such particles are not quickly dispersible in water into extremely small units. Along this line Chambers (1959) has developed the following concept:

> The explanation of this extraordinary resistance to salt flocculation undoubtedly lies in the differing physical properties and suspension mechanism of the clay. Unlike the smectites (montmorillonites), sepiolite is not a swelling clay and hence simple dispersion in water leads to coarse dispersion of aggregates rather than a platelet separation. Hence the effect of gravity is stronger than particle charge and the suspension sediments to a comparatively low volume. That this volume is not lower is due to the extreme anisotropy of the crystal habit and the settled floc is open consisting of a bulk of randomly intermeshed acicular aggregated particles. The surface charge is low, and hence, close packing would occur did not the geometrical configuration of the particles prevent it. However, the floc is close packed within the limits of the geometry. The net result of this is that when salt is added there is no accommodation available for the flocs to decrease in volume, so salt flocculation cannot occur to any appreciable extent. On the other hand, the smectites are rapidly broken down into discrete particles of high surface charge leading to complete dispersion. The separated particles are anisometric in one dimension only and so can undergo much closer packing when the surface charge is removed by electrolyte, hence, their sedimentation volumes tend to be seriously decreased by salt additions. The behavior of aqueous suspensions of sepiolite in a rotational viscometer tends to lend substantial substance to this argument. A suspension prepared by high speed stirring and containing 5 percent solid behaves after initial strain as a Newtonian liquid. Such behavior can only be explained by assuming that the suspended solids are without interaction within the liquid phase, *i.e.*, they are not solvated, nor do they set up a rheological structure. If we assume that the particles are randomly oriented during the suspension process,

then it is clear that shearing the suspension does not reorient the particles into any integrated structure.

The elongate particles and bundles of attapulgite and sepiolite would be expected to form an irregular mat on the walls of the bore hole through which water could penetrate easily, thereby explaining the high permeability of this type of clay.

Individual elongate attapulgite and sepiolite units are tied together at their edges through common oxygen atoms. This would be expected to be a fairly strong bond so that individuals would not easily separate, and, therefore, considerable energy would be necessary to break them apart. It would be expected that continuous agitation of a slurry containing such clay minerals would continuously split off units, so that the gradual increase in viscosity on agitation, as in the circulation of mud in the drilling operation, is easily explained.

The bundles of elongate units with their gutter-and-channel structure on the exterior would make it difficult for oriented water molecules to develop to significant thicknesses. This may well be a significant factor in the relatively small thixotropic character of attapulgite and sepiolite clays.

The relatively poor dispersibility of illite, chlorite, and kaolinite clays as compared to montmorillonite and attapulgite clays causes their relatively low yield values and generally lesser value for use in drilling fluids. Poorly organized examples of these clay minerals would be relatively better for drilling-mud use but still not so good as montmorillonite or attapulgite clays. The presence of associated random mixed-layer assemblages would also tend to enhance the drilling-mud properties of such clay minerals.

Clays in Muds Containing Oil

The following statements are taken from Larsen (1955) who has presented a summary discussion of such drilling fluids.

Emulsion Muds

Within recent years the use of emulsions as drilling fluids has become fairly widespread. Both types of emulsion, that is, oil in water and water in oil have been used, but the former is much more common. Such drilling fluids are resistant to variations in the electrolyte content and to the influence of high bottom hole temperatures and pressures. Substantially all of the oil in water type of emulsion drilling fluids presently used contain clay and are most generally made up by the addition of oil to a clay-water mud which has already been in use. The ability of colloidal clay, particularly bentonitic clays, to act as emulsifying agents for oil and water emulsions is so well known that little need be said about it.

In fact, it has been found that some clays are such good emulsifying agents in themselves that no additional chemical emulsifiers need be added, but this property is seldom relied upon in actual practice since the use of the organic emulsifying agents in clay-water muds can easily be made to give great stability to the emulsion. One function of clays in such mud which is generally overlooked, but which nevertheless is the most important, is that of providing a preferentially water-wettable filter cake for the mud to filter against. The fact that the walls of the pores in such a clay filter cake are hydrophilic prevents the passage of the minute droplets of emulsified oil, which presumably are then enabled to block off the pores and to reduce the overall permeability of the cake. The filtrate from such a mud when the emulsion is properly stabilized is substantially 100% water and all of the oil is retained by the cake, which is in accordance with the picture just presented, as is also the very considerable reduction of overall fluid loss resulting from the emulsification of oil into the clay-water base mud.

OIL-BASE MUDS

The attempt to keep intruded water entirely away from oil-bearing formations has led to the development of drilling fluids made up of oil instead of water, the so-called oil-base muds. For the most part such drilling fluids do not have clay added and since they are not ordinarily used for "making hole" as distinguished from drilling into an oil-bearing formation, clays encountered during drilling with such a mud are generally of little consequence aside from the fact that they are generally not dispersible in the fluid in the first place. Clays are of importance, however, in some particular oil base muds which have been used. Rolshausen and Bishkin (1937) proposed the incorporation of bentonite in oil-base mud in order to take up any free water encountered during drilling. Lummus and Dunn (1952) describe a recently developed type of oil-base mud made up of oil and a dry concentrate which is stated to consist of a chemically treated mixture of clay and weighting material.

Another and most interesting type of oil-base mud in which montmorillonite clays play an all important role, is that patented by Hauser (1950), which makes use of the swelling properties in oil of reaction products of long-chain amines and montmorillonite (Jordan, 1949). Such oleophilic bentonites are probably substantially completely coated by the hydrophobic organic cations through a base exchange reaction. They impart gel strength and, because of their platy character, low fluid loss to oil-base muds, and also enable the emulsification of any water encountered during use into the mud as a stable water and oil emulsion. A particular advantage is that the organophilic clay retains its gelling ability even at very high temperatures, thus avoiding a difficulty often encountered with other types of muds in deep holes where the temperature and pressure are relatively high.

It appears that attapulgite clays as well as those composed of montmorillonite can be used successfully in oil emulsion muds and completion muds. The other clay minerals also react with the organic compounds, but their relatively low dispersibility and hence small total surface makes them less satisfactory.

An additional advantage claimed for oil emulsion muds is that they permit the use of a low-solids fluid of adequate viscosity and low water loss which gives fast bit penetration rates.

WELL LOGGING

In exploration in the petroleum industry when a bore hole is completed it is customary to log the hole by electrical or some other means in order to obtain information on the lithology, porosity, permeability, and fluid content of the formations penetrated. Any subsequent development program is frequently based largely on the data derived from the log. The log may depend on the electrical, radioactive, or chemical attributes of the formations, their interstitial fluids, the fluid in the well, and/or a combination of these.

The literature on the interpretation of such well logs on the basis of variations in fluid content, electrolyte content, porosity, and permeability of the formations is abundant. Although it is generally agreed that the amount and nature of the clay in a formation exerts an important influence on the log, very little information concerning this point is to be found in the literature. Only the influence of clay mineral composition will be considered herein.

Electric Logs

The electric log generally comprises two sets of measurements: a measure of self-potential (S-P curve) and a measure of resistivity (R curve). The latter is a plot of the electrical resistivity of the formations as a function of their depth below the surface. The S-P curve is measured as the potential difference between a moving electrode transversing the bore hole and a fixed datum, commonly an electrode in the mud pit at the surface; the varying difference potential is recorded as a continuous curve. The S-P curve is ascribed (Wyllie, 1955) to a combination of electrokinetic effects, that is, a streaming potential occurring as a result of the flow of mud fluid from the bore hole into a permeable formation, and to an electrochemical potential existing at the interface of clay material and formation fluids.

The resistivity curve is presumed to be a measure of the fluid content and porosity of formations. Griffiths (1946) has pointed out that the kind and amount of clay also play a role in the resistivity value. Thus, the high water-adsorbing and ion-carrying capacity of montmorillonites as compared with other clay minerals would probably influence the nature of the associated formation fluids.

Griffiths (1952) has presented data showing that a range of 3 to 30 per cent of clay in a formation is sufficient to account for the minimum to maximum range of self-potentials measured (Fig. 6-3). Bacon (1948) states that "it is evident that when an unconsolidated sand contains more than 10 percent of disseminated clay mineral, the potential from the sand will be almost the same as from the clay mineral itself." The same author notes that as little as 1 per cent clay may have a significant effect on both laboratory and field data. It seems likely that the generality regarding the influence of small amounts of clay can be carried too far, as the type of clay, texture, and perhaps other factors are all involved. Bacon (1948) concludes that in the order of descending magnitude of potential difference the clay minerals are to be listed as follows: montmorillonite, illite, and kaolinite. McCardell et al. (1953) have also indicated that the self-potential derived from the clay minerals should be in the decreasing order: montmorillonite, illite, and kaolinite.

Hill and Milburn (1956) have shown that the effect of clay minerals on the electrical properties of reservoirs is related to the cation-exchange capacity per unit of pore volume. So far as the clay minerals alone are concerned one would expect the self-potential to increase and the resistivity to decrease as the exchange capacity of the clay mineral components increased. Pirson (1950) has stated that illitic sands always exhibit low resistivity regardless of oil and gas saturation. He has also stated that formations with very low permeabilities exhibit high resistivity. Wyllie (1955) has pointed out that marine shales have lower resistivities than those of nonmarine shales. Winsauer and McCardell (1953), Wyllie (1955), and others (see Wyllie, 1955) have emphasized the importance of the adsorptive properties of the clay minerals on their electrical properties and particularly the importance of the density of the charges on the surfaces of the clay mineral particle.

The effect of clay on the resistivity log represents a balance between the conductance resulting from the water in the pores of the rock (modified by textural effect of the rock—the formation factor) and the conductance resulting from the exchangeable ions on clays present in the rock. This conductance depends on a geometrical factor which includes the volume of clay, its arrangement, and the ion-exchange capacity. Thus, if the conductance

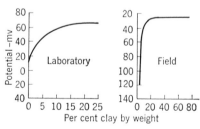

Fig. 6-3. Self-potential in relation to clay content of formations, after Griffiths (1952).

of the water in a rock containing clay is diminished by substituting some oil for the water or decreasing its salinity, the conductance of the clay becomes relatively greater (to a first approximation the two conductances are additive; *i.e.*, the water and clay conductance is parallel, and the clay conductance is independent of the water salinity) (Patnode and Wyllie, 1950). According to Wyllie (personal communication), the effect of clay on the S-P curve stems directly from the same considerations outlined above in their influence on the cation-transference number.

DISCUSSION

The data in the literature indicate that the character of the clay minerals exerts an important influence on electric logs, *i.e.*, clay mineral composition is one of the factors determining the electric-log characteristics of a rock. It is of interest, therefore, to theorize as to how the particular attributes of the various clay minerals might influence electric logs. Clay minerals with high adsorptive capacity for electrolytes, such as montmorillonites, vermiculites, and to a slightly less degree the sepiolite-palygorskites clay minerals, would be expected to produce relatively high self-potential and conductivity because of the relative abundance of cations which could dissociate at the clay mineral–water interface. The clay minerals, such as illite and chlorite, with moderate to low adsorptive capacity but with interlayer cations, might be expected to yield variable S-P and R values, depending on particle size, crystallinity, and composition of the silicate layer itself, which would in turn influence the proportion of the potassium that could ionize from the illite or of the magnesium from the chlorite. In other words, illite and chlorite might yield quite variable S-P and R values, depending on the ionizability of the potassium and magnesium, which in turn would depend on the structure factors noted above. Degraded illites and chlorites would be expected to exert an influence approaching that of the montmorillonites in direct relation to the degree of degrading. Kaolinite and halloysite with very low adsorptive capacity and without interlayer cations of potential ionizability would be expected to yield uniformly low S-P and high R values.

The clay minerals should play a role in electric logging for another reason than that due to their adsorptive capacity and ionizable components, namely, in influencing the permeability of the formations. One would expect that the permeability of a clayey sand, for example, would be less if the clay were composed of montmorillonite instead of kaolinite. A relatively small amount of montmorillonite would have a relatively great effect in reducing permeability. The action of montmorillonite would vary with the nature of its adsorbed cation and the electrolyte content of the fluid coming in contact with the clay minerals. The montmorillonite would have this effect because of its exceedingly high dispersibility into very fine particles effectively able to clog pores.

Radioactive Well Logs

GAMMA-RAY LOGS

Gamma-ray logging is dependent upon the radioactivity or spontaneous disintegration of chemical elements contained in the geologic formation. Potassium is the only radioactive element that is found as as an essential component of any of the clay minerals. Its radioactivity is, of course, extremely slight as compared to that of the uranium, thorium, and actinium series, which would not be expected in argillaceous formations as components of the clay minerals. Table 6-2 illustrates the

TABLE 6-2

RADIOACTIVITY OF SEDIMENTS
(in Radium Equivalents per Gram $\times 10^{-12}$)
(After Russell, 1943)

Black shales	20–26
Shales	15–20
Bentonites and volcanic ash	15–20
Clays	5–15
Sandy and limy shales	5–10
Sand	3–5
Limestone and dolomite	3–5
Coal	3–5
Salines (not containing potassium)	3–5

relatively high activity of shales due, no doubt, to the frequent presence of the potassium-bearing–clay mineral illite. Argillaceous sediments composed of other clay minerals without potassium as an essential component give lower values.

Obviously, sediments may occasionally contain components other than clay minerals with high radioactivity, and thus exceptions to the values given in Table 6-2 would be expected sometimes. Actually, in the case of shales, elements other than potassium may frequently provide a significant portion of the radioactivity.

NEUTRON-GAMMA LOGS

In neutron logging the formations are subjected to neutron bombardment, and the secondary radioactivity developed thereby is measured (Russell, 1952). Hydrogen slows and absorbs the neutrons. Secondary radioactivity is developed by other elements. Hydrogen in water, hydrocarbons, and the hydroxyls of the clay minerals would all absorb the neutrons, and neutron logging is used primarily to determine the presence of hydrogen-bearing substances; thus porosity can be estimated provided the water bound to the clays does not introduce a serious error. In combinations with other types of logs the nature of the fluid may be determined. Since all the clay minerals contain hydroxyls, and in some cases water as well, no great difference in the effect of the various clay minerals would be expected on neutron logs.

Chemical Logs

Bernard (1954) has presented a process for obtaining a continuous log of the variations of cation-exchange capacity with depth. Since cation-exchange capacity is a property of the clay minerals which varies with the identity of the clay mineral, the cation-exchange-capacity log would be essentially a clay mineral log. Cation-exchange-capacity values for the clay minerals are given in Table 2-1.

PRODUCING OPERATIONS

Introduction

The movement of gas, oil, fresh water, and brine in rock formations is a controlling factor in the completion of producing oil wells and in their continuing production. In the literature particular attention has been paid to fluid movements in reservoir rocks in the secondary recovery operation during which fluids are pumped into the reservoir to flush out oil which cannot otherwise be recovered. In secondary recovery operations it is obviously necessary that the reservoir rocks have an adequate permeability and that the permeability be retained as the liquids continue to move through them.

Initially, permeabilities of reservoir rocks were determined in air. Fancher et al. (1933) showed that the permeability of a given rock is generally not the same in air and in water. Johnson and Beeson (1945) and many others (see Dodd et al., 1955) have confirmed this finding and have shown also that permeabilities in fresh water and brines are not the same.

The permeability of rocks is expressed in darcys or millidarcys obtained from an equation relating velocity of flow, pressure drop in the direction of flow, and viscosity of the flowing medium. The D'Arcy (1856) equation asserts that for a given fluid flowing through a given porous medium there is a linear relationship between fluid velocity and pressure drop. Von Engelhardt and Tunn (1954) have shown that such a linear relationship does not exist either for sodium chloride solutions or for pure water in natural sands and that one cannot calculate from the velocity of flow and viscosity a "permeability" that may be regarded as a specific constant. Von Engelhardt and Tunn indicated that the flowing process cannot be described solely by two independent constants—permeability and viscosity. In order to explain the variations with air, water, and brine, these authors conclude that a reaction between the fluid and the solid phase of the rock must be another factor, one which would alter the effective cross section of flow. Adsorption of fixed water layers on the surface of the grains of the rock and the swelling and dispersion of clay mineral particles would certainly tend to alter the effective diameter of the pores.

Effect of Clay Mineral and Water Composition on Permeability of Reservoir Rock

Numerous investigators have shown that permeability in fresh water is much less than in air and that in sodium chloride solutions the permeability tends to increase as the salt concentration increases until, in the concentrated brines, permeabilities equal to air permeabilities may be obtained. The results from Baptiste and Sweeney (1955) illustrate this point (Table 6-3). Sample A, for example, becomes substantially impermeable in distilled water and has 15 per cent of its air permeability in the strongest brine. Sample D, however, has 72 per cent of its air permeability in distilled water and has substantially the same permeability in air and in the concentrated brine.

The data in Table 6-3 show not only the variable permeability of a

TABLE 6-3

PERMEABILITIES AND CLAY MINERAL ANALYSES
OF SAMPLES FROM FRONTIER FORMATION
(After Baptiste and Sweeney, 1955)

Sample	Initial air permeability, millidarcys	Ratio of other permeability to air permeability, %				Amount of minus 2 μ fraction in sample, %	Clay minerals in minus 2 μ fraction, %		
		k_{b1}/k_{ai}	k_{b2}/k_{ai}	k_w/k_{ai}	k_{af}/k_{ai}		Kaolinite	Illite	Mixed-layer
A	27	15	1	0	89	9.6	4	7	26
B	76	22	18	8	68	4.0	16	5	15
C	52	64	64	19	115	4.0	14	14	0
D	46	99	98	72	100	4.7	3	5	0

KEY: k_{ai} = air initial, k_{af} = air final, k_w = distilled water, k_{b1} = water containing 16,500 ppm NaCl and k_{b2} = water containing 8,250 ppm NaCl.

given sand in air, distilled water, and brine, but also that the amount of such variation depends on the nature of the clay mineral. Baptiste and Sweeney (1955) show that the greatest variation in permeability among air, distilled water, and brine occurs in those sands containing mont-morillonite or mixed-layer assemblages containing this mineral. Thus, sample A, with the highest mixed-layer content, becomes substantially impermeable in distilled water and brine of low concentration, whereas sample D, without mixed-layer material, shows little variation in per-meability under the same conditions. It is significant that sample C, without mixed-layers but with considerable illite, shows significant varia-tions in permeability in air, distilled water, and brine. Bates et al. (1946) had earlier pointed out that this relationship appeared to exist in the Bradford sands of Pennsylvania. Dodd et al. (1955) presented data to show that expandable clay minerals when present in the finest fraction (−325 mesh) of a sand to the extent of 5 to 10 per cent are adequate to cause the sand to be water sensitive, that is, to cause its water permeability to be less than 60 per cent of its air permeability.

Von Engelhardt and Tunn (1954) have shown that variations between permeability in air and in brine, with varying sodium chloride concen-tration, are found also in cores which contain only the clay minerals illite and kaolinite without any montmorillonite. The effect, therefore, of the clay minerals on permeability is not restricted to montmorillonites, although they would be expected to have the greatest effect of any of the clay minerals. Von Engelhardt and Tunn (1954) show that the relative effect is likely to be in decreasing order: montmorillonite, illite, and

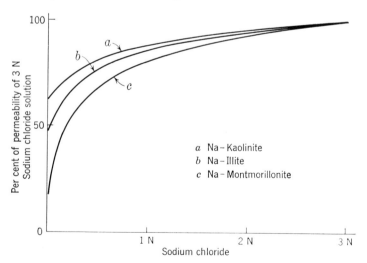

Fig. 6-4. Permeability of mixtures of quartz sand with 4 per cent sodium clay, after Von Engelhardt and Tunn (1954).

kaolinite. Figure 6-4 illustrates this relative effect for various concentrations of sodium chloride brines. The curves indicate that the relative difference in the effect of these clay minerals disappears as the concentration of the sodium chloride increases. The data in Fig. 6-4 were obtained on mixtures of quartz sand and 4 per cent clay. Consolidated natural cores with different amounts of clay could conceivably show somewhat different results.

Dodd et al. (1955) have indicated that the effect of montmorillonite is relatively greater in sands of low permeability. That is, high-permeability sands can tolerate more expandable clay minerals. Numerous authors have pointed out that flooding waters of the same composition as the formation water are least likely to disturb permeability. Novak and Krueger (1951) have indicated that, in general, polyvalent cations in solutions tend to maintain higher permeabilities than monovalent cations because of their tendency to keep the clay flocculated. Hughes (1947) has shown that low-pH waters may be effective in maintaining high permeability and that a change in input waters may quickly affect the permeability (Fig. 6-5).

There is a growing literature on the clay mineral composition of reservoir rocks as it is becoming realized that the clay mineral components of such rocks are vitally important in recovery operations. Thus, Bates et al. (1946) indicated that illite is the chief clay mineral component in the Upper Paleozoic Bradford sands of Pennsylvania, and small amounts of kaolinite and montmorillonite are also present. Hughes (1950) and Nahin et al. (1950) have shown that the Tertiary producing horizons of California contain montmorillonite, kaolinite, and illite, with expandable clay minerals sometimes of major importance.

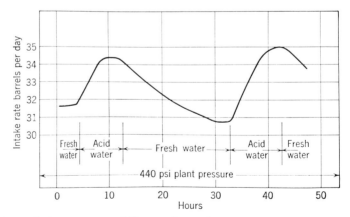

FIG. 6-5. Relation of permeability as shown by intake rate to change in input waters, after Hughes (1947).

Recently, Morris et al. (1959) have indicated that montmorillonite is the dominant clay mineral component in the producing horizons of the California oil fields examined by them.

Dodd et al. (1955) determined the clay mineral composition of about 90 core samples from a wide selection of reservoir sands of different geologic ages and geographic locations. They report varying abundances of illite, chlorite, kaolinite, and expandable minerals and point out that a selection of samples from West Texas sands of Permian age were the only samples older than the Mesozoic found to contain expandable clay minerals. Unpublished data by the author and his previous colleagues in the Illinois State Geological Survey indicate that illite and chlorite with some kaolinite are the clay mineral components of the Paleozoic producing horizons in Illinois—montmorillonite is completely absent or present only in very small amounts.

Analytical results are not sufficiently abundant for many generalities; however, it seems established that in Mesozoic and Tertiary reservoirs montmorillonite is likely to be present and may be the dominant clay mineral, whereas in Paleozoic beds montmorillonite is likely to be absent or present only in minor amounts. This is in accord with the generally lesser abundance of montmorillonite in sediments older than the Mesozoic (Grim, 1953).

A further generality of some consequence is that the three-layer clay minerals rather than kaolinite or halloysite are likely to be found in marine sediments. Since petroleum reservoirs are likely to be in marine sections, kaolinite or halloysite are likely not to be important clay mineral components. Exceptions to this generality would be expected, and some have been reported. Thus, Von Engelhardt and Tunn (1954) studied cores of Cretaceous age that contained kaolinite as the predominant clay mineral, and Witherspoon (personal communication) has recently examined Cambrian oil sands in which kaolinite appears to be the only clay mineral.

Kulbicki (personal communication) has identified detrital illite and kaolinite in some Precambrian reservoir rocks of North Africa. The petroleum is believed to have occupied the reservoir about Jurassic time accompanied by brines which partially altered the kaolinite to secondary illite. The recognition of this clay mineral sequence has greatly aided prospecting operations.

Discussion

The clay mineral components of a reservoir rock can conceivably alter its permeability to the movement of aqueous fluids in several ways. The water molecules may be adsorbed on the clay mineral surfaces and thereby reduce the effective size of the openings and cause a drag on the movement of the fluid by an interaction of the adsorbed water and the liquid. The water adsorbed directly on the clay mineral surfaces is composed of oriented water molecules securely tied by hydrogen bonds to the clay mineral surfaces. This oriented water would act as a part of the rock particle and serve to reduce the size of the pores. Outward from the surface of the clay minerals the orientation of the water molecules decreases and at some distance either abruptly ends or grades gradually to liquid water (Chap. 2). It would be expected that the interaction of the adsorbed water and the moving water would be greater in cases where there was a gradual transition from oriented to liquid water.

All the clay minerals possess the property of orienting adsorbed water but not to the same degree. Montmorillonite appears to have this property to the highest degree, and this mineral also provides the largest amount of surface for adsorption. The cations adsorbed on the mineral surfaces largely determine the thickness of adsorbed water and the nature of its transition to liquid water. Thus, a moderate concentration of sodium favors thick adsorbed water layers gradually changing to liquid water, whereas calcium favors a thinner adsorbed water layer (in the presence of abundant water) and an abrupt transition to liquid water. Sodium in large amounts appears to cause a reduction in adsorbed-water thickness as compared with lower sodium contents.

In the case of calcium montmorillonite, the oriented-water thickness is probably of the order of 5 molecular layers (see Chap. 4), so that a reduction in pore diameter of about 30 A would be expected. When sodium is present in small amounts, the oriented-water layer is several times thicker, and the outermost layers have relatively less orientation, which would physically interfere with water movement.

It is obvious from the foregoing that all the clay minerals would have the described effect in permeability and that montmorillonite would have the greatest effect. Also the presence of sodium in small concentrations would have a large effect, especially when expandable clay minerals are important components.

On theoretical grounds, there is another way in which the clay minerals may affect the permeability of reservoir beds, namely, as a consequence of their dispersibility in water. That is, the clay mineral particles may be dispersed or dislodged from their position in the rock to move with the fluid and be lodged somewhere else. Von Engelhardt and Tunn (1954) have considered the colloid chemistry aspects of the matter, and it is desired here merely to point out the clay mineral implications. Griffiths (1946) has pointed out that in an undisturbed reservoir rock the clay mineral particles are in equilibrium with the formation waters, which are likely to be saline and carry sodium. It is a well-known fact that moderate amounts of sodium tend to disperse clay particles, whereas larger concentrations of sodium and multivalent cations tend to flocculate the clay minerals. Stated in other words, this means that in the dispersion the clay mineral particles are separated from each other and may be dislodged from their original position. If, therefore, fresh water tended to reduce the sodium concentration, it would be likely to favor dispersion. Brines or multivalent cations changing the concentration in the direction of flocculation would reduce the tendency to dislodge the clay mineral particles with possible consequent plugging of pores and the reduction of permeability.

The foregoing statements regarding dispersion effects apply to all the clay minerals. There is an additional factor for the expandable clay minerals, namely, that the dispersion will not only separate the particles from each other but will tend to split up the individual particles along cleavage planes into extremely thin flakes. The particles might not only be dislodged but also split into many extremely thin particles. The ease of the splitting is related to the nature of the adsorbed cation. Thus, splitting is favored when sodium is present in moderate amounts rather than in higher concentrations or when multivalent cations are present.

It is known that expandable clay minerals tend to develop an adsorbed-interlayer-water thickness in equilibrium with the adsorbed-cation composition in the available water. Any change in the cation composition may well disturb this equilibrium and permit the easier splitting of the units composing the particle. There is a reason, therefore, why maintaining the composition of the formation fluids is the safest way to maintain permeability in a water-flooding operation.

Some experiments, notably those of Hughes (1947) shown in Fig. 6-5, indicate that the permeability may be reversible with changes in the character of the water. This apparent reversibility is not in accord with the substantial dislodgment of clay mineral particles due to dispersion. Perhaps it can be concluded that dislodgment, which certainly can take place, is not as likely as would be anticipated on theoretical grounds.

The clay minerals have the property of adsorbing organic compounds, especially those having polar and/or ionic attributes. Hydrocarbons would not be expected to fit into this category, although it has been shown by Jordan (1949) that the adsorption of ionic and/or polar organic molecules may prepare the clay mineral surfaces for reactions with hydrocarbons. Thus, small amounts of such organic compounds might have a large effect on the fixation of hydrocarbons in the reservoir rock. It might be expected that other types of organic molecules would serve to reduce the possible fixation of hydrocarbons by clay mineral surfaces. Thus, small amounts of various types of organic molecules present in formation waters or added to flood waters might well have a large effect in freeing the hydrocarbons in the reservoir rocks. Further, organic compounds could probably be selected which would favor either dispersion or flocculation of the clay mineral particles. Smoot (1959) has shown that some clay minerals, particularly expandable and degraded three-layer types, have a strong affinity for some organic compounds found in the crude oil in the Mississippian sands in Illinois. Such clay mineral–organic complexes tend to be flocculated. Care must be taken that any additives to flood waters do not break up such complexes and disperse the clay particles.

REFERENCES

Anonymous, Standard Field Procedure for Testing Drilling Fluids, 4th ed., *Am. Petrol. Inst. Rept.* 29 (1957).

———, Attapulgus Clay in Oil Well Drilling, *Mineral Chem. Philipps Corp. Tech. Inform.* 552 (1949).

Bacon, L. O., Formation Clay Minerals and Electric Logging, *Penn. State Univ. Mineral Ind. Expt. Sta. Bull.* 52, pp. 53–75 (1948).

Baptiste, O., and S. A. Sweeney, Effect of Clays on the Permeability of Reservoir Sands to Various Saline Waters, *U.S. Bur. Mines Rept. Invest.* 5180 (1955).

Bates, T. F., R. M. Gruver, and S. T. Yuster, Influence of Clay Content on Water Conductivity of Oil Sands, *Oil Weekly*, pp. 48–50, Oct. 21 (1946).

Bernard, G. C., "Logging of Cation Exchange Capacity," U.S. Patent 2,691,109 (1954).

Burst, J. F., "Glauconite" Pellets: Their Mineral Nature and Application to Stratigraphic Interpretations, *Bull. Am. Assoc. Petrol. Geologists,* 42, 310–328 (1958).

Chambers, G. P. C., Some Industrial Applications of the Clay Mineral Sepiolite, *Silicates Inds.,* April, pp. 3–11 (1959).

D'Arcy, H., "Les fontaines publiques de la ville Dijon," Victor Dalmont, Paris (1856).

Degens, E. T., E. G. Williams, and M. L. Keith, Environmental Studies of Carboniferous Sediments: I, Geochemical Criteria for Differentiating Marine from Fresh Water Shales, *Bull. Am. Assoc. Petrol. Geologists* 41, 2427–2483 (1957).

Dodd, C. G., R. F. Conley, and P. M. Barnes, Clay Minerals in Petroleum Reservoir Sands and Water Sensitivity, *Natl. Acad. Sci. Publ.* 395, pp. 221–238 (1955).

Fancher, G. H., J. A. Lewis, and K. B. Barnes, Some Physical Characteristics of Oil Sands, *Penn. State Univ. Mineral Ind. Exp. Sta. Bull.* 12, pp. 65–171 (1933).

Foster, M. O., Geochemical Studies of Clay Minerals: Relation between Ionic Substitution and Swelling in Montmorillonites, *Am. Mineral.,* 38, 994–1006 (1953).

Gray, G. R., M. Neznako, and P. W. Gilkeson, Solidification of Lime-treated Muds at High Temperatures, *World Oil,* 134(4), 101–104, 106 (1952).

Griffiths, J. C., Clay Research and Oil Development Problems, *J. Inst. Petrol.*, **32**, 18–31 (1946).

———, Grain-size Distribution and Reservoir-rock Characteristics, *Bull. Am. Assoc. Petrol. Geologists*, **36**, 205–229 (1952).

Grim, R. E., Relation of Clay Mineralogy to Origin and Recovery of Petroleum, *Bull. Am. Assoc. Petrol. Geologists*, **31**, 1491–1499 (1947).

———, "Clay Mineralogy," McGraw-Hill Book Company, Inc., New York (1953).

———, Concept of Diagenesis in Argillaceous Sediments, *Bull. Am. Assoc. Petrol. Geologists*, **42**, 246–253 (1958).

——— and G. Kulbicki, "Montmorillonite: High Temperature Reactions and Classification," manuscript (1959).

Hauser, E. A., "Application of Drilling Fluids," U.S. Patent 2,531,812 (1950).

Hendricks, S. B., R. A. Nelson, and L. T. Alexander, Hydration Mechanism of the Clay Mineral Montmorillonite Saturated with Various Cations, *J. Am. Chem. Soc.*, **62**, 1457–1464 (1940).

Hill, H. J., and J. D. Milburn, Effect of Clay and Water Salinity on Electrochemical Behavior of Rocks, *AIME, J. Petroleum Technol.*, **8**, 65–72 (1956).

Hughes, R. V., Importances of Clay Studies in Water Flood Operations, *Producers Monthly*, **11**(4), 13–16, (5), 12–14, (6), 10–17 (1947).

——— and R. J. Pfister, Advantages of Brines in Secondary Recovery of Petroleum by Water Flooding, *Trans. AIME*, **170**, 187–201 (1947).

Hurdle, J. M., Gyp Muds Now Practical for Louisiana Coastal Drilling, *Oil and Gas J.* Oct. 28 (1957).

Johnson, N., and C. M. Beeson, Water Permeability of Reservoir Sands, *Trans. AIME*, **160**, 43–55 (1945).

Jordan, J. W., Organophilic Bentonites I: Swelling in Organic Liquids, *J. Phys. & Colloid Chem.*, **53**, 294–306 (1949).

Knechtel, M. W., and S. H. Patterson, Bentonite Deposits in Marine Cretaceous Formations of the Hardin District, Montana and Wyoming, *U.S. Geol. Survey Bull.* 1023 (1956).

Larsen, D. H., Colloid Features of Drilling Fluids, *Colloid Chem.*, **6**, 509–530 (1946).

———, Use of Clays in Drilling Fluids, *Calif. Div. Mines, Bull.* **169**, pp. 269–281 (1955).

Lummus, J. L., and T. H. Dunn, "A New Type of Oil Base Drilling Fluid," paper presented at American Petroleum Institute meeting, Casper, Wyo. (1952).

McAtee, J. L., Heterogeneity in Montmorillonite, *Natl. Acad. Sci. Publ.* 566, pp. 279–288 (1958).

McCardell, W. M., W. O. Winsauer, and M. Williams, Origin of Electric Potential Observed in Wells, *Trans. AIME* (Petrol. Branch), **198**, 41–50 (1953).

Millot, G., Relations entre la constitution et la genèse des roches sédimentaires argileuses, "Géol. applique et pros. min.," 2, Nancy (1949).

Milne, I. H., and J. W. Early, Effect of Source and Environment on Clay Minerals, *Bull. Am. Assoc. Petrol. Geologists*, **42**, 328–338 (1958).

Morris, F. C., Q. A. Aune, and G. L. Gates, Clays in Petroleum Reservoir Rocks, *U.S. Bur. Mines, Rept. Invest.* 5425 (1959).

Nahin, P. G., W. C. Merrill, A. Grenall, and R. S. Crog, Mineralogical Study of California Oil-Bearing Formations, *AIME, J. Petroleum Technol.*, **192**, pp. 151–158 (1951).

Novak, T. J., and R. F. Krueger, The Effect of Mud Filtrates and Mud Particles on the Permeabilities of Cores, "Drilling and Production Practice," pp. 164–181, American Petroleum Institute (1951).

Patnode, H. W., and M. R. J. Wyllie, The Presence of Conductive Solids in Reservoir Rocks as a Factor in Electric Log Interpretation, *Trans. AIME*, 189, *Tech. Publ.* 2797 (1950).

Pirson, S. J., "Elements of Oil Reservoir Engineering," McGraw-Hill Book Company, Inc., New York (1950).

Powers, M. C., Clay Diagenesis in the Chesapeake Bay Area, *Natl. Acad. Sci. Publ.* 327, pp. 68–80 (1954).

Ratcliffe, G. L., "Treatment of Bentonite Clays," U.S. Patent 2,724,696 (1955).

Riviere, A., Sur l'origine des argiles sédimentaires, *Congr. geol. intern.*, 18, 177–180 (1953).

Rolshausen, F. W., and S. L. Biskin, "Oil Base Hydratable Drilling Fluid," U.S. Patent 2,099,825 (1937).

Russell, W. L., The Radioactivity of Sedimentary Rocks, *Geophysics*, 8, 180–190 (1943).

————, Interpretation of Neutron Well Logs, *Bull. Am. Assoc. Petrol. Geologists*, 36, pp. 312–341 (1952).

Sedletsky, I. D., and S. M. Yussupova, Variations in Parameters of Montmorillonite as Affected by Petroleum, *Compt. rend. acad. sci. URSS*, 46, pp. 27–30 (1943).

Smith, P. V., Studies on Origin of Petroleum: Occurrence of Hydrocarbons in Recent Sediments, *Bull. Am. Assoc. Petrol. Geologists*, 38, 377–404 (1954).

Smith, R. J., New Developments in Gyp Muds, *World Oil*, pp. 138–140, November (1958).

Smoot, T. W., "Clay Mineralogy of Pre-Pennsylvanian Sandstones and Shales of the Illinois Basin," Ph.D. thesis, University of Illinois (1959).

Van Olphen, H., Pumpability, Rheological Properties, and Viscometry of Drilling Fluids, *J. Inst. Petrol.*, 36, 223–234 (1950).

Von Engelhardt, W., and W. L. M. Tunn, The Flow of Fluids through Sandstones, *Heidelberger Beitr. Mineral. u. Petrog.*, 2, Parts 1 and 2, 12–25 (1954). Trans. P. A. Witherspoon, *Illinois Geol. Survey Circ.* 194, (1955).

Weaver, C. E., A Discussion on the Origin of Clay Minerals in Sedimentary Rocks, *Natl. Acad. Sci. Publ.* 566, pp. 159–173 (1958).

————, Geological Interpretation of Argillaceous Sediments, *Bull. Am. Assoc. Petrol. Geologists*, 42, 254–309 (1958).

Williams, F. J., B. C. Elsley, and D. J. Weintritt, The Variations of Wyoming Bentonite as a Function of the Overburden, *Natl. Acad. Sci. Publ.* 327, pp. 141–151 (1954).

————, M. Neznayko, and D. J. Weintritt, The Effect of Exchangeable Bases on the Colloidal Properties of Bentonite, *J. Phys. Chem.*, 57, 6–10 (1953).

Winsauer, W. O., and W. M. McCardell, Ionic Double-layer Conductivity in Reservoir Rocks, *Trans. AIME* (Petrol. Branch), 198, 129–134 (1953).

Wyllie, M. R. J., Role of Clay in Well-log Interpretation, *Calif. Div. Mines Bull.* 169, pp. 282–305 (1955).

CHAPTER 7

Clays in Refining and Preparation of Organic Materials

CATALYSIS

It has been known for a long time that clay materials generally possess catalytic properties towards various organic liquids and that this property is not present to the same degree in all kinds of clay materials. The catalytic property plays a role along with other properties in many industrial uses of clays. Sometimes, as in the manufacture of gasoline and the decolorizing of some oils, the catalytic property is an asset. At other times, as in some insecticide preparations, it is detrimental (see Chap. 8).

Within the last 20 years, clay catalysts have been developed which have found wide industrial use. In such cases, the catalytic property is a major determining factor rather than a supplementary one. The successful production of the clay catalysts for the cracking of petroleum and the manufacture of gasoline has been of particular importance.

PETROLEUM CRACKING CATALYSTS FOR THE MANUFACTURE OF GASOLINE

General Statement

Catalytic cracking of heavy petroleum fractions was first introduced in 1936 (Houdry et al., 1938) and has developed tremendously so that currently more than 500 tons of fresh catalysts are required daily for this purpose. In the cracking process, heavy oil in the vapor state is contacted with the catalyst at 425 to 500°C under atmospheric pressure and for contact times of 6 to 20 sec. Under the influence of the catalyst a series of complicated reactions takes place leading to the formation of about 5 per cent methane and propane, 10 per cent butane, 45 per cent gasoline, and 40 per cent recycle oil (i.e., unchanged feed stock). In addition, about 1 to 3 per cent of the charge stock is reduced to carbon, called *coke,* which is deposited on the catalyst. In general, such product distri-

307

bution is more desirable than that obtained from thermal cracking, and, further, the gasoline produced is of superior quality in that it has a higher octane number and is more susceptible to improvement by lead additions (Milliken, Oblad, and Mills, 1955).

There are two somewhat different catalytic processes in current use. One process uses a pelleted or spherical catalyst carried as a bed in the reactor; the bed is either fixed or, more likely at the present time, moves and transfers the catalyst from the cracking zone to the regeneration zone. The catalyst particles are of the order of $\frac{1}{8}$ to $\frac{1}{4}$ in. in diam. A second process uses a fine granular particle, which is fluidized in the vapors and continuously flows from the reactor to the regenerator. The particle size of the fluid catalyst is closely controlled with a major amount having diameters between about 20 and 80 μ. About 0.5 to 1.5 tons of catalyst per bbl of feed stock are used in the cracking operation. In the cracking installations several hundred tons are continuously circulated, and, in a given operation, 1 to 5 tons of fresh catalyst may be required daily to regain that lost by friction and to maintain the catalytic activity. The catalytic operation consists essentially of two parts, a reaction zone and a regeneration zone where the catalyst is revived by burning off the coke. The coke is removed by controlled combustion at about 600°C, usually in the presence of steam.

Types of Catalysts Used

In catalytic cracking two types of catalysts, both essentially composed of aluminum and silicon, are used. One type is synthesized from silicon and aluminum compounds; the product containing aluminum in the range of 15 to 30 per cent Al_2O_3. Roquemore and Strickland (1957) have shown that the product distribution produced may vary with the Al_2O_3 content of the catalyst. The other catalyst is produced from clays of certain types, and in such a catalyst the Al_2O_3 content may also vary. Fluid and pellets or spherical catalysts (beads) are produced both synthetically and from clays. According to Milliken et al. (1955), clay catalysts accounted for about 40 per cent of the total catalysts manufactured in 1952.

Catalysts' specifications can be stated only in general terms, since there are particular specifications for each operation depending on the nature of the feed stock, the product distribution desired, and the operating characteristics of the refinery unit. The catalyst must give the desired level of conversion and a satisfactory product distribution. That is, it must produce an adequate percentage of gasoline of high quality, a small amount of gas, further gases of a type most suitable for reforming processes and/or petrochemical use, and only a small amount of coke. In general, gasoline of the highest octane number is desired, but conversion to gasoline beyond a given level may not be desired, because in some cases it might make difficult the operation of a particular refinery unit. Likewise, the economics of demand and markets may determine the desired gas composition and yield.

In addition to the above specifications, the catalyst must be very hard in order to resist abrasion in the operation of the unit, and it must have stability under the operating conditions of temperature and the presence of steam so that the catalytic activity will be maintained for a long time, measured in days or months. Also it must be resistant to poisoning; i.e., it must retain its catalytic activity in the presence of such elements as sulfur in the feed stock which have a tendency to react with the catalyst to reduce activity and change product distribution.

It follows from the above statements that it is extremely difficult to make any simple evaluation of a catalyst's properties. Numerous relatively simple evaluation procedures (for example, cat. A tests) are available; however, each laboratory interested in such catalysts usually has its own evaluation procedure. Simple evaluations show whether or not a catalyst is sufficiently promising for a large pilot plant or full-scale test, which is the only method of determining finally whether or not a catalyst is satisfactory for commercial operation. Obviously, the evaluation of a given clay as a source for catalyst manufacture is a difficult thing.

Recently, Stone and Rase (1957) have shown that the differential thermal analytical procedure may provide a simple method of evaluating some catalysts by measuring the intensity of the thermal reactions at various temperatures when the catalyst adsorbs such gases as water, nitrogen, and organonitrogen compounds.

Types of Clay Used in Catalyst Manufacture

Clay catalysts are produced from bentonites composed of montmorillonite, from halloysite, and from kaolinite clays. In the United States montmorillonite clays from Arizona and Mississippi are used in catalyst manufacture. Bentonites from elsewhere in the United States are not used, and it is certain that only some of them are suitable for catalyst manufacture. The montmorillonite must have a very low iron content, but beyond that the requirements of montmorillonites for catalyst manufacture have not been revealed. Relatively pure montmorillonites are known in many countries, and the literature, for example, Ruiz and Gonzales (1955), suggests, from the basis of simple tests, that many of them are suitable for catalyst manufacture. However, information on their actual commercial use at the present time is not available.

Grim and Kulbicki (1959) have recently shown that aluminous montmorillonites can be classified into two categories primarily based on the population of the octahedral positions in the montmorillonite structure. Their Cheto-type (Cheto, Arizona) montmorillonite, which has a relatively high replacement of magnesium for aluminum in octahedral position, appears to be the most likely to be found satisfactory for catalyst manufacture. It cannot, however, be concluded on the basis of present available data that some other montmorillonites might not be found usable for this purpose.

Halloysite from the Eureka district in Utah is used in the making of cracking catalysts. Deposits of pure halloysites are not abundant and information as to whether or not other deposits of halloysite have been tested and have yielded satisfactory results is not available.

Kaolinite clays from sedimentary formations of Georgia are used for catalyst manufacture. Again, information is not available indicating that pure kaolinite clays can or cannot generally be used for catalyst manufacture. The Georgia kaolin is composed of well-crystallized kaolinite particles, but information regarding the possible use of poorly ordered kaolinite has not been published.

Kaolinite and halloysite clays as well as the montmorillonite clays must be low in iron and be substantially free from various elements, such as the heavy metals, which would favor either the poisoning of the catalyst or the production of an unfavorable product distribution. For example, traces of certain metals, such as iron and vanadium, would greatly increase the amount of coke-make of the catalyst; an advantage of halloysite and kaolinite is that they are substantially pure aluminum silicates. They are likely, therefore, to be available either without considerable contents of iron and other detrimental compounds or with such elements in a form that permits easy removal in the catalyst manufacturing operation.

Manufacture of Catalysts from Clays

The precise procedures for the production of cracking catalysts from clays have not been published by the manufacturers. However, an examination of the patent and trade literature reveals the general process that is followed.

In the case of montmorillonite clays, the crude clay is treated with sulfuric, or possibly hydrochloric, acid at a moderately elevated temperature. The treatment is sufficient for substantially complete removal of adsorbed alkalies and alkaline earths. The exchangeable cations are replaced by hydrogen. The proton penetrates the octahedral part of the montmorillonite lattice displacing octahedral magnesium, iron, and aluminum, in about that order. The protons from the acid probably join with oxygens in the octahedral unit to form hydroxyls thereby freeing the octahedral cations. Magnesium, aluminum, and iron proceed from octahedral positions to exchange sites and then into solution at a rate and to a degree depending on treatment procedure, for example, acid dosage, acid concentration, temperature, and time.

Following the acid treatment, the clay is washed to eliminate the alkalies and calcium, to reduce the iron content, and to develop the desired magnesium and aluminum composition. As shown in Fig. 7-1, the activity of the catalyst is a function of the severity of the acid treatment. In general, the activity increases with treatment up to a certain optimum; further treatment causes decreased activity. Bond (1951) states that catalytic advantages are gained by treating, leaching, and then treating again with an aluminous solution to replace some of the previously leached aluminum. It is likely that the optimum aluminum content is not the same for all feed stocks or for the same clay for different feed stocks. The optimum must be determined empirically. Also the same dosage, acid concentration, heating conditions, etc. will not necessarily give the optimum aluminum content or activity for different montmorillonite clays.

Following the washing process the clay is dried, prepared into the proper particle-size distribution, and calcined at 500 to 600°C. The calcining is necessary to develop hardness and thermal stability.

It appears from the patent literature that there are several possible ways of preparing satisfactory catalysts from kaolinite and halloysite clays. It is claimed that certain calcining procedures to increase the surface area are sufficient to develop catalytic activity without acid treatment. This suggests that the surface of kaolinite provides adequate catalytic activity, and it is only necessary to increase the surface area to produce a commercial product. Most statements indicate that acid treatment of the clay is required, and sulfuric acid (Mills, 1947 and 1948; Shabaker, 1947) is usually specified. In some instances the clay treated is crude; in others it has been calcined above the dehydration temperature (500 to 600°C) and below the temperature required for the nucleation of mullite (950 to 1000°C). Following acid treatment the material may be washed to reduce the alumina con-

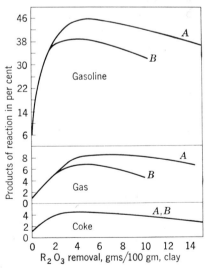

Fig. 7-1. Catalytic cracking activity as function of severity of acid treatment, after Mills et al. (1950).

tent and to remove the sulfate, or the sulfate may be removed thermally. There appears to be no correlation between the alumina content of the prepared kaolin catalyst and its activity as there is in the case of the montmorillonite catalysts.   Unlike montmorillonites, the kaolinites and halloysites contain substantially no alkalies and no alkaline earths, so a washing process is not required to remove reaction products of these elements.   Clays with very low iron contents are used, but some treatment may be necessary to reduce further the iron content of the catalyst. Numerous procedures have been suggested to reduce the Fe_2O_3 content to the desired order of 0.01 to 0.03 per cent (Shabaker et al., 1947; Thomas, 1951).

Following the acid-treatment process the clay is prepared into the desired shape and particle distribution and then calcined to develop the required hardness and heat stability.   Calcining temperatures of about 500 to 700°C are required, but the precise conditions of time, temperature, etc., are the undisclosed technical knowledge of the producers.

Characteristic Properties of Clay Catalysts

Acid activation of montmorillonite followed by leaching serves to increase the surface area and porosity and to decrease the particle density. Figure 7-2 shows that the above changes are directly related to the amount of R_2O_3 removed.   The surface area is increased from about 20 to more than 300 sq m per g in the finished catalyst.   Generally, a substantial increase in surface is necessary to develop adequate commercial catalytic properties, but there is no direct correlation between the amount of surface and catalytic activity; i.e., a material with a high surface area is not necessarily a satisfactory catalyst. Acid treatment serves to change the pore-size distribution; Fig. 7-3 shows the pore-size distribution in relation to the surface area for a montmorillonite catalyst.   The figure shows a concentration of pores with a radius of 26 to 27 A.   It may be concluded that the pore radius must not be too small to prevent entrance of the hydrocarbon molecules to the surfaces and yet small enough to produce a large surface area.

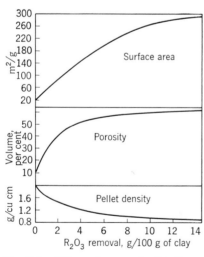

Fig. 7-2.   Effect of removal of R_2O_3 on properties of montmorillonite catalyst, after Mills et al. (1950).

X-ray diffraction analyses of montmorillonite catalysts reported by Davidson (1947), Grenall (1948),

and Holmes and Mills (1951) show that the montmorillonite crystallization is retained following catalyst preparation. The X-ray diffraction
patterns are more diffuse than those of untreated montmorillonite, which
indicates that the montmorillonite has somewhat less order, is of smaller
particle size, and/or also contains some material with very little order.
It is significant that some montmorillonite crystallization is retained, and
if the activation is carried to the extent that no montmorillonite organization remains, the catalytic activity decreases. Davidson (1947) has presented differential thermal curves of fresh catalysts prior to calcination
and after use which suggest that the montmorillonite structure is gradually lost as the catalytic activity declines during use.

It is essential that the catalyst have a low iron content in order to get a
satisfactory product distribution; Fig. 7-4 shows the decrease in volume of
gasoline, the decrease in gas gravity, the increase in amount of gas, and
the increase in amount of coke that follow increasing amounts of Fe_2O_3.
These changes are obviously detrimental.

No data are available on the density and porosity of halloysite and
kaolinite catalysts, but they are probably of the same order of magnitude
as those for montmorillonite catalysts. Surface areas of 150 to 200 sq m
per g are reported by Milliken et al. (1955) for halloysite and kaolinite
catalysts.

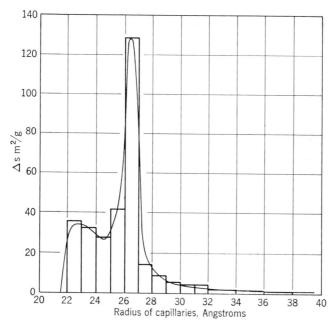

FIG. 7-3. Distribution of pore size versus surface area for an acid-activated montmorillonite clay, after Oulton (1948).

Unlike montmorillonite, at least some halloysite and kaolinite catalysts no longer possess sufficient order for X-ray diffraction to reveal crystallinity after calcining to the temperature (600°C±) required in the catalyst preparation. Although halloysite and kaolinite catalysts may not provide X-ray diffraction characteristics, it must not be concluded that they have no organization, i.e., that the material is amorphous. The literature (Grim, 1953) provides abundant evidence that firing kaolinite clays to temperatures slightly above that necessary for loss of hydroxyls does not cause complete loss of structure. Further, aluminum can be removed from the kaolinite lattice in substantial quantities without the complete loss of order.

No satisfactory comparative values of the catalytic activity and product distribution are available for various types of clay catalysts and synthetic catalysts. Actually such data would be of little significance, as the activity and product distribution are determined to some extent by the

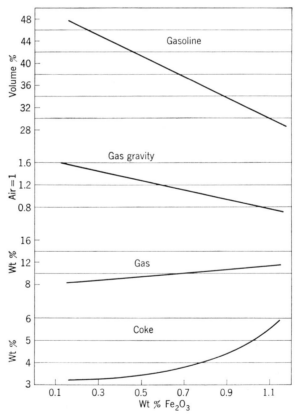

FIG. 7-4. Effect of iron on catalyst selectivity, after Milliken et al. (1955).

feed stock and conditions of operation of the cracking unit. Further, the particular product distribution desired as well as the activity may determine which catalyst is most satisfactory. According to Milliken et al. (1955) the catalytic activity, as determined by cat. An evaluation for kaolinite and halloysite catalysts compares favorably with that of montmorillonite catalysts.

A significant property of catalysts is the period of time during which they preserve their catalytic activity and the rate of loss of activity during their life. Thus, a catalyst with lower initial activity but with a very slow rate of decline may be much more satisfactory commercially than one with a high initial activity but with a rapid loss of activity. That is, catalytic activity is determined by the activity and product distribution after some use, i.e., equilibrium activity, rather than by initial activity. One would expect that clay catalysts, because they possess a structural organization that is relatively stable in the temperature range of the cracking operations, would have a relatively long life as compared to synthetic catalysts, which have relatively little, if any, structural organization.

Catalysts must have adequate hardness to resist abrasion and must themselves not unduly abrade the catalytic unit. Arbitrary test procedures have been set up within the industry to measure hardness. It is sufficient to state that all types of clay catalysts develop ample hardness on calcining to about 600°C. The cause of the hardness is not clear. The development of an amorphous cement does not seem a likely explanation, as it would almost certainly serve to seal off pores and reduce available surface. It seems more likely that the intergrowth of the ordered units in the catalyst is responsible for the hardness.

Concept of Catalytic Activity in Clays

A vast literature exists concerning the catalytic phenomenon and the possible explanation of the action of petroleum-cracking clay catalysts (see Mathieu, 1948; Ries, 1952; and Milliken, Oblad, and Mills, 1955, for selected bibliographies). It is beyond the scope of this volume to analyze this literature in detail. It is desired only to consider what the available evidence indicates as the role of the structural attributes of the clay minerals in the action of clay catalysts. It is desired also to present a concept of the catalytic action of clay catalysts based largely on structural attributes. It is not intended to convey the idea that structural attributes are the sole determining factor of catalytic action. It is believed, however, that a satisfactory concept of catalytic activity cannot be evolved without considering the atomic structure of the catalysts.

It has been shown that some aspects of the organization of the clay minerals remain in the catalysts after manufacture and that the structural remnant is essential to the properties of the clay catalysts. This means that some aspect of the structure of the clay minerals plays an essential role in the properties of the clay catalysts. It seems likely that the silica tetrahedral part of the clay mineral structure is the most important part and that the hexagonal-network organization of oxygens in the flat plane surface of this sheet is the important surface structure. This conclusion seems warranted because it is the only extended surface of the montmorillonites and also it is the part of the structure which would be retained on acid treatment of halloysites and kaolinites. Other reasons for this conclusion will be indicated presently. It is not thought that all the silica of the clay mineral remains in sheets following acid treatment because some of it undoubtedly loses its structure, as is indicated by the fact that following acid treatment some of the silica becomes readily soluble in a dilute alkaline solution (Perrin-Bonnet and Mering, 1953). The silica around the edge of the flake units would undoubtedly be the first to lose its structure.

The surface of the oxygen network must be clean of cations. Any broken or unsatisfied negative charges would be satisfied with hydrogens. There is good evidence that the surface must be able to donate protons in the catalysis.

The silica sheets are probably tied together by aluminums in octahedral coordinations in a poorly ordered fashion. It seems likely that such alumina rather than amorphous silica is the glue of the catalysts. The silica surface alone is not sufficient for catalytic activity—there must be something to activate the surface. This something is probably aluminum, and it is suggested that the organization of the aluminum behind the surface is vital; that is, some particular distribution of aluminums is necessary for substantial catalytic activity. The aluminums should not be on the surface. Davidson (1947) has shown that exposed aluminum is too active in that it produces too much coke and gas. For proper commercial activity in cracking, the aluminum should be locked up, and almost certainly the locking up would be in octahedral coordination. The pattern of the octahedral alumina is probably critical.

It is well known that only some montmorillonites can be activated. There seem to be two possible explanations for this fact. First, the silica should have little replacement of aluminum, as otherwise the silica-tetrahedral sheet would not be preserved following acid treatment. Substantial acid treatment would dissolve the alumina from the tetrahedral portion of the structure and destroy the tetrahedral-sheet configuration (Brindley, 1952). Secondly, there may well be some preferred pattern of population of octahedral positions in the crude clay which favors the development of the proper octahedral alumina pattern in the acid-activated catalyst. It seems that the structure must be essentially diocta-hedral. Davidson, Ewing, and Shute (1943) indicated that only mont-morillonites which have extensive substitution of magnesiums for alumi-nums can be activated. This is in accord with the recent finding of Grim and Kulbicki (1959) that the Cheto type of aluminous montmorillonite is most likely able to be activated.

Mathieu (1947) and Davidson, Ewing, and Shute (1943) have indicated the close approximate fit of the hydrocarbon structure and the oxygen net of the silica-tetrahedral plane, the concept being that the close fit causes the hydrocarbon chain to seek the oxygen surface. The lack of a perfect fit causes strains in the hydrocarbon chains; consequently the chains are broken. Protons donated by the surface would in effect cause a healing of the broken ends of the chain. The role of the aluminums is not clear, but in some way they must favor the bringing of the organic materials to the surface and/or the setting up of strains within the mole-cules.

Acid treatment produces clean surfaces which have the property of donating protons and increases the amount of surface area. It also produces some poorly organized silica which possibly acts as wedges (Lopez-Gonzalez and Dietz, 1952, and Perrin-Bonnet and Mering, 1953) to separate the sheets with montmorillonite organization and to keep them apart to maintain a high surface area. Bradley (personal com-munication) has suggested that small masses of such unorganized silica on the oxygen surfaces might cause a bending of the hydrocarbon chains causing strains and thereby contributing to their breaking.

A further point seems worthy of mention. In the reaction of clay minerals and sulfuric acid, aluminum sulfate hydrates are formed. There are many such compounds. It seems likely that the structure of the particular aluminum sulfate hydrate would be important perhaps be-cause of its relation to the clay mineral structure or because of the struc-ture developed on its dehydration and desulfation. It may well be that the reason treatment with certain acid concentrations, temperatures, etc., yields more satisfactory catalysts is really because of the particular sulfate hydrate reaction product even though such a product is transient in the process of catalyst manufacture.

On continued use, according to Milliken et al. (1955), iron tends to leave lattice positions and become free with the consequent increase in coke-make and the other changes in catalytic properties indicated in Fig. 7-4. Davidson (1947) has shown that treatment with steam before en-tering the cracking zone prevents to a large extent the harmful action of the iron. It would be expected that such treatment would serve to re-constitute the iron in a bonded condition. In any event the occurrence of the iron whether free or coordinated with oxygens or hydroxyls and the pattern of distribution are essential factors in the action of clay catalysts.

CATALYSTS IN MISCELLANEOUS ORGANIC REACTIONS

A considerable literature claims that clays act as catalysts in a large number of organic reactions. Robertson (1948) has summarized this catalytic activity as follows:

Essential Oils

As long ago as 1915 Gurwitsch showed that pinene polymerises with marked rise in temperature to sesqui- and poly-terpenes in the presence of attapulgite clay but not with alumina. Some montmorillonites and activated earths also catalyse this reaction. Since then many workers have studied the catalytic action of different 7, 10, and 14 Å clay minerals on many essential oil chemicals including geraniol, *laevo*-linalool, citronellal, camphene, *para*-cymene, etc. Every type of catalytically induced reaction seems to have been recorded, dehydrations, esterifications, polymerisations, depolymerisations, isomerisations, including cyclisations, and others, if there are such. The products are of interest to the fine chemical industry dealing with flavors and perfumes, especially, though camphor can be prepared from turpentine by clay catalysis and other products, including plasticizers for plastics. Some of this work purports to throw light on the catalytic action of the clays. Oxygenated diluents such as acetone, alcohol, ether, and especially water exert a strong inhibiting influence on the heat producing reaction while benzene and carbon tetrachloride merely act as diluents. Besides alumina, iron, silica gels, and activated charcoal fail to promote the reaction with α-pinene. The attapulgite clay must have a total moisture content of 8 percent corresponding with the drying temperature of 400°C. Sulphuric acid, zinc, and aluminum chloride, however, also promote the reaction. Some Japanese acid clays (montmorillonite) were enormously more heat producing than attapulgite but the products were different. Later such work as Howard and Sons found some terpene reactions were possible at high temperatures with silica, bauxite, and kaolin; and the Japanese workers found that activated carbon gave an interesting collection of products when camphor vapor was passed over it at 480°–500°C. Vermiculite has also been used in the preparation of camphenes.

Glyceride Oils

Clay catalysts have been used, experimentally at any rate, for dehydrating castor and fish oils to produce drying oils, to eke out limited supplies of linseed and tung oils; and contrariwise in China where petroleum products were unobtainable, tung oil and other glyceride oils were cracked with a clay catalyst to yield hydrocarbon products.

General Organic Synthesis

DEHYDRATIONS

Resin alcohols produced from colophony or abietic acid by hydrogenation can be dehydrated by some acid activated montmorillonites to produce unsaturated hydrocarbons utilizable in the textile industry. Simple reactions have been studied with the production of unsaturated hydrocarbons and ethers from primarily aliphatic alcohols over Japanese acid clays (montmorillonite), *cyclo*hexanol can be converted to *cyclo*hexene. Under severer conditions, that is to say at higher temperatures, the reactions are called pyrolytic and are akin to the cracking of petroleum crudes in heterogeneous catalysis. Many single chemicals have been pyrolysed over clays.

CONDENSATIONS

An enormous number of condensation reactions have been catalysed by clays. Aldehydes and ketones passed over kaolin with ammonia yield pyridine bases. Nitriles are formed over clays with ammonia acting on acetic acid, adipic acid, fatty acids, etc. Alcohols and amines are formed from *para*-toluidine and other compounds. Members of the anthraquinone series condense with phthalic anhydride over clay catalysts.

DECHLORINATIONS

A chloride atom is removed in other condensations as when benzylchloride and benzene form diphenylmethane over clay. Chlorbenzol, chlortoluol, and chlorinated paraffins have been dechlorinated with clays.

ISOMERIZATION AND CYCLIZATION

Aldehydes may be converted to ketones over clay catalysts and cyclisation is by no means confined to the hydrocarbons already mentioned. Thus unsaturated aliphatic acids yield *cyclo*pentenones. Some elegant examples have been given of such reactions among the essential oils.

OXIDATIONS AND REDUCTIONS

Natural gas has been oxidized to alcohols mainly over silicates. Silica gel helps to form phenols from benzol in water, but I have no record of clays being used in this reaction. Among examples of reductions there is a conversion of *cyclo*hexanol to *cyclo*hexene, diphenyloxide to benzene (not very cleanly, however) and several others.

HYDROGENATION

Clays may play a part in the hydrogenation of unsaturated compounds either as a simple mixture with a nickel or other metallic catalyst, or as a prepared catalyst on which nickel is deposited and reduced on the clay surface. As unsaturated compounds tend to be preferentially adsorbed on the surface of the "active" clays one might suppose that the nickel-catalysis would take place more effectively in the adsorbed layer. The use of clays with nickel has been advocated for both glyceride and hydrocarbon oil hydrogenation.

MISCELLANEOUS

Coleman and McAuliffe (1955) indicate that hydrogen montmorillonite is a catalyst for ester hydrolysis and sucrose inversion. Kayser and Bloch (1952) have shown that montmorillonite catalyzes the inversion of sucrose and the formation of sulfanilic acid. Murray (1947) stated that kaolin catalysts are used in dehydrating amyl alcohol. Alberada et al. (1953) pointed out that kaolins and montmorillonite clays catalyse the oxidation of ethyl alcohol.

The foregoing statements probably do not provide a complete catalogue of the catalytic action of clays towards organic reactions. They do not include the use of clays in purifying organic compounds, which will be considered elsewhere.

Robertson (1948) has pointed out that "no general rules can be given to explain the catalytic behavior of clays. Each reaction must be considered separately." It is known that in some reactions definite hydration states are required, and one would expect some relationship between the amount of surface and the catalytic activity. Unfortunately, the character of the reactions is so diverse and specific data on particular reactions are so scant that no general theory of the catalytic action can be formulated.

DECOLORIZATION

Clay materials are widely used to decolorize oils. In the decolorization there is often some purification, i.e., the elimination of some parts of the oil not wanted in the final product. Decolorization is applied to mineral, vegetable, and animal oils. An example of decolorization of a mineral oil is the preparation of a water-white, extremely pure, hydrocarbon liquid for medicinal uses. Also, for certain lubricating purposes, the elimination of wax may be required, and a certain color may be desirable. Earths are used extensively to refine such oils as cottonseed, soy, palm, and lard prior to their manufacture into soaps, paints, and various edible products. The earths serve to deodorize, dehydrate, neutralize, and/or decolorize the oils, but decolorization is generally a major objective of such processes.

Clays may be used in the decolorizing and purifying process in two ways. The oil may be filtered through a granular product of 10- to 60-mesh particles, or the oil may be put in contact with a finely ground clay of approximately minus 200 mesh and then the oil separated from the clay by some sort of filter pressing operation. The percolation process is essentially a low-temperature process with the temperatures ranging from 100 to 250°F and the average about 180°F. Flow rates are in the range of 0.5 to 3 bbl per ton per hr. In the contact process, the temperatures used are in the range of 300 to 600°F for as long as 30 min, and earth dosages are in the range of 0.5 to 30 per cent of the oil by weight. In the filtering process, the oil retained in the clay when the clay is no longer sufficiently active for commercial use may be reclaimed by the use of solvents. If the reclaimed oil has no value, if it cannot be reclaimed in a usable form, and/or if it cannot be removed completely by solvents, the clay may be regenerated by heating to drive off the retained oil. In the contacting process the clay is used once and is not regenerated. It appears that filtration is the better process for some oils and contacting for others. The decision as to which process is most desirable is also a matter of economics, involving the cost of the clay, oil retention, etc.

Types of Clay Material Used

A wide variety of clay materials have been used for decolorization. The materials range from fine-grained silts to clays composed of almost pure clay minerals. The materials may be substantially crude clay or clay which has been prepared by chemical and physical treatment. In earlier times crude clays called *fuller's earths* were used. The name comes from the use of these clays in cleaning, or fulling, wool with a water slurry of an earth thereby removing oil and dirt particles from the wool. This very ancient process is referred to in the Bible.[1] The persons carrying it out were called *fullers,* and the earth they used was called *fuller's earth.* At the present time the term is applied to any clay which has an adequate decolorizing and purifying capacity to be used commercially in oil refining without chemical treatment; it implies nothing so far as the composition and origin of the earth is concerned. In England, the term "fuller's earth" has certain stratigraphic implications referring to Cretaceous beds in southeastern England which have produced decolorizing earths for centuries. For a presentation of the early history of the use of fuller's earths, the work of Porter (1907), Wesson (1912), Parsons (1913), and Robertson (1949) should be consulted.

Various silty materials have moderate decolorizing and adsorptive capacities, which permitted their early use. It was soon found that many clays composed of attapulgite and some montmorillonites possessed superior decolorizing power, and such clays supplanted the silts (Grim, 1933; Nutting, 1943). In the preparation of these clays they are dried at 400 to 600°C and ground to various sizes. The activity of the attapulgite clay can be substantially enhanced by extrusion under high pressure at

[1] "And his raiment became shining, exceeding white as snow: so as no fuller on earth can whiten them." *Mark, 9:3.*

low moisture contents (Amero and Cappell, 1943). Increases in decolorizing ability of from 25 to 40 per cent following extrusion are reported by these authors. So far as is known montmorillonite clays are not improved by such extrusion.

Nutting (1943) has shown that only some montmorillonite clays possess substantial decolorizing power, and that this is not solely a matter of the purity of the montmorillonites. Various investigators (deLapparent, 1955; Charrin, 1946; Zvanute, 1937) have stated that halloysite may have decolorizing power. Piersol et al. (1933) have shown that a kaolinite clay from southern Illinois has high decolorizing power. Grim and Bradley (1939) have shown that an unusual illitic clay from northern Illinois has high decolorizing power. Chambers (1959) has shown that sepiolite clays from Spain are excellent decolorizing materials. This same author has also indicated that the addition of small amounts (about 10 to 20 per cent) of sepiolite to conventional bleaching and activated earths serves to improve filtration rates in many instances. So far as is known, clays other than those composed of montmorillonite, attapulgite, and sepiolite find little commercial use at the present time. As will be shown presently, decolorizing power is not the sole factor determining commercial use.

Acid activation frequently enhances the decolorizing power of montmorillonite clays several-fold. Nutting (1943) has shown that only some montmorillonite clays can be improved by acid treatment, and, in fact, such treatment is detrimental for some other clays of this composition. In the United States, bentonites from Arizona and Mississippi are acid activated. Outside the United States acid activation is practiced on bentonites from Algeria, Morocco, and Germany and perhaps also on bentonites from Russia and Japan. The substantially higher power developed in acid-activated clays for decolorizing some oils has given these clays considerable economic advantage in some instances over fuller's earths.

So far as is known acid activation is not practiced on any clays other than those composed of montmorillonites. Certainly some research must have been done on this matter, but it is not known how far the possibilities of acid activation have been explored for clays of other clay mineral compositions.

In the acid-activation process, the montmorillonite is slurried with sulfuric or hydrochloric acid for some time at a moderately elevated temperature. The precise conditions of acid dosage, acid concentration, treating time, and temperature cause variations in the properties of the final product and are closely controlled. Following the acid treatment the slurry is washed, dried, calcined, and prepared in the desired particle-size distribution. The properties of the finished product can also be varied by changes in the washing procedure. It is possible, by varying the treatment procedure, to produce a variety of activated products which have specific advantages for particular processes and oils. The precise treatment conditions necessary to produce decolorizing clays with specific properties is the undisclosed know-how of the industry.

As the intensity of the acid treatment is increased, the decolorizing property increases up to an optimum value. Further treatment causes a decline in activity. The acid-treatment process is much the same as that used in the manufacture of catalysts from montmorillonites. It probably should not be concluded that the optimum treating conditions for catalyst manufacture are the same as those for the preparation of a decolorizing clay. The acid activation serves to remove the alkalies and calcium and to reduce the contents of magnesium, iron, and aluminum, in that order. Acid activation also serves to increase the surface area and change the pore-size distribution just as it does in the preparation of catalysts by acid treatment of montmorillonites.

No simple preliminary tests have been described whereby the potential use of a montmorillonite for acid activation can be predicted; indeed, from Nutting's work (1943), it seems that such a test is unlikely. To determine potential value, the montmorillonite clays must be treated with acid under a variety of conditions and their decolorizing properties measured. Since the decolorizing power varies with the treatment process, no single treatment of a given sample can be considered a trustworthy evaluation of the possibilities for preparing a satisfactory acid-activated material. It is interesting to point out that the widely known bentonite from Wyoming is not usable for acid activation and has a very low natural decolorizing power. The work of Grim and Kulbicki (1959) suggest that their so-called Cheto type of montmorillonite, which contains a substantial replacement of magnesium for aluminum in the octahedral position, is likely to be satisfactory for acid activation. This is only a probability, and further work is necessary to determine how broadly the conclusion can be applied.

There are some "acid clays," for example, Japanese acid earths (Yamamoto, 1940) and clays from the Pembina area, Manitoba, Canada, which apparently have been subject to natural leaching with low-pH water so that they have been changed naturally in the direction of acid activation.

Properties Required of Decolorizing Clays

For satisfactory use the ability of the materials to decolorize must be high; that is, a relatively small amount of earth must cause a large amount of color reduction. It is not possible to state any general decolorizing specifications. The valuation of a given earth is determined by a comparative test of its decolorizing power against that of other earths. Properties other than decolorizing power and the cost of the earth may dictate that one is more economical than another even though its decolorizing power is somewhat less. Obviously the decolorizing power of an earth must be determined for the particular oil that is to be refined; an earth satisfactory for one type of oil may not be at all satisfactory for another type.

In addition to the decolorizing power the clay must have low oil retention; that is, only a small amount of oil is retained by the earth in the course of the decolorizing process. This property is particularly critical if the oil is of the sort which cannot be reclaimed by the use of a solvent or by distillation. The clay must also have good filtration characteristics —in the percolation process there must be fairly rapid movement of oil through the earth, and in the contact process the earth must not unduly bind the filters. The earth, particularly for filtration, must provide fairly hard particles that do not disperse in use or during regeneration. For filtration use, the earth must be capable of regeneration; that is, it must not lose its characteristics on calcining at temperatures of about 500 to 600°C, which are required to drive off the retained oil; also, its particle-size distribution on such calcining must not change substantially.

Any change in the composition or character of the oil during the process of decolorizing is very important. The change in the character of the oil may be desired; for another material, depending on the oil and the product desired, it may be detrimental, making an earth completely unsuitable. There is no general specification of porosity, surface area, or pH, although porosities on the order of 60 to 70 per cent, surface areas of 120 to 140 sq m per g, and slightly alkaline to slightly acid pH values are frequent. In the case of acid-activated earths, the degree of acidity depends on the amount of washing, and for some purposes fairly low pH values may be desired.

There are no general specifications of chemical composition, although acid-activated earths may be produced within narrow limits of chemical composition. Particle-size distribution is closely specified for percolation grades of earth and for contact grades; in general, the percentage finer than a certain size is the specification given.

In general, in the case of edible oils, any catalytic activity is very undesirable, and the earth must not impart an obnoxious odor or taste to the oil. There are instances of earths with high decolorizing power which cannot be used commercially because of the odor and taste they impart to the oils. For edible oils the retained oil cannot generally be salvaged from the earths, so that the contact process is used with earths of very high decolorizing power. Natural earths composed of attapulgite and acid-activated montmorillonites are the types most frequently used in the contact process.

Theory of Decolorizing Action

The cause of the decolorizing reaction is undoubtedly the result of a number of factors which may be listed as follows:

1. Simple filtration, which is the physical entanglement of colored bodies by the earth. This is perhaps the major factor in the decolorizing action of silts.

2. Selective adsorption is probably a major factor. For attapulgite it has been indicated (Johnston, 1959) that selective adsorption takes place in the following order: paraffins, cycloparaffins, aromatics, neutral esters, olefins, ketones, aldehydes, and in each series, the higher the molecular weight, the more readily the molecules are adsorbed.

3. Catalytic activity plays a role in two ways: first in causing reactions which give compounds of different colors and second, probably of greater importance, by causing reactions yielding products which in turn are more readily adsorbed.

In selective adsorption, the amount and kind of surface must be significant factors. Acid activation serves to increase the surface area per unit weight of the montmorillonite and to develop a surface of oxygen atoms free of adsorbed cations except hydrogen and possibly some aluminum. Thus the flat surface of the sheets of silica tetrahedrons appears to favor the decolorizing process. That the character and amount of this surface is not the sole factor is shown by the fact that all montmorillonites are not activable. The fact that very extensive acid treatment which removes more than a certain amount of octahedral cations from the montmorillonite decreases decolorizing ability indicates also that the amount of this surface is not the sole factor. That is, an earth activated to the point at which only silica surfaces remain has little decolorizing power. It is important to point out in this connection that substantially all the octahedral cations can be removed from some montmorillonites without destroying the silica-sheet portion of the montmorillonite structure. There must be something within the structure remaining after acid activation, such as the population of octahedral positions by aluminum, that is important in decolorizing, just as it is in catalysis. The number and distribution of the hydrogens on the surfaces must also be important as is testified to by the fact that the varying degrees of acidity of the earth is related to decolorizing.

Montmorillonites having only relatively small amounts of aluminum replacing silicon would theoretically be most likely able to be activated. This is probably because acid treatment of a montmorillonite with much aluminum-replacing silicon tends to cause a loss of aluminum from tetrahedral, as well as from octahedral, positions thereby tending to destroy the whole structural network. The suggestion that the Cheto type of montmorillonites, as indicated previously, are very likely to be activated seems to indicate that some population of octahedral positions or some population which is susceptible to change by acid leaching favors the development of the selective adsorption powers. The excellent decolorizing ability of attapulgite and sepiolite clays shows that the gutter-and-channel surface of the constituent particles of these clays favors the decolorizing process. It is not difficult to visualize how such a surface would favor selective adsorption of certain molecules, and Barrer and MacKenzie (1954) have shown by experimentation that attapulgite does in fact have selective adsorption capacity. Attapulgite clays have their decolorizing capacity enhanced approximately 35 per cent by extrusion through a die at low moisture contents and under high pressures (Amero and Cappell, 1943). Unpublished microscopic studies in the author's laboratory have shown that the extrusion serves to break and tear apart the bundles of attapulgite needles thereby developing more of the gutter-and-channel surface. It is probable that extrusion enhances decolorizing power also by serving to develop broken bonds on some of the particle surfaces. Similar researches in the author's laboratory on montmorillonite clays have indicated that at least in many instances decolorizing power is not enhanced by extrusion. Apparently, the shearing stress developed on extrusion is released in montmorillonite particles by slippage along basal cleavage planes without substantially tearing the particles and developing new surfaces.

It is interesting to observe that a decolorizing clay from the Macon, Georgia, area in the United States is composed, according to Brindley (1957), of lath-shaped units of montmorillonite and cristobalite. It is conceivable that the shape of montmorillonite particles may be significant in determining whether or not they possess any decolorizing power. It seems unlikely that the cristobalite adds substantially to the decolorizing power of this Georgia clay.

MISCELLANEOUS APPLICATIONS

Clay is used for removing sulfur compounds from natural, virgin, and straight-run gasolines; such removal is important to eliminate the deleterious effects on the leaded octane number of the gasoline. Amero and Wood (1947) claim that attapulgite is satisfactory for this purpose and point out that the efficiency of this clay is not the same for all gasoline stocks. Attapulgite is more effective in removing some types of sulfur compounds than others. According to Johnston (1959), attapulgite clay will convert the sulfur of alkyl sulfur compounds (mercaptans and alkyl sulfides) to hydrogen sulfide and by such catalysis effect the removal of the sulfur from saturated hydrocarbons. Attapulgite clays are not used when unsaturated hydrocarbons are present in the feed because of the complications produced by its polymerization tendencies. The conversion is carried out at temperatures in the range of 700 to 800°F.

Clays may be used to remove undesirable asphaltic and resinous products from petroleum products. In Gray tower operations vapors from the cracking plant are passed through earths causing unsaturated hydrocarbons to polymerize into higher-boiling compounds, and the compounds are then separated from the gasoline. Clays may be used to polymerize olefins, diolefins, and cracked distillates into heavier products and thus enhance their removal.

Some of the catalysts used in reforming operations carry active metals like platinum and nickel, and their catalytic activity is very sensitive to traces of arsenic, sulfur, etc., in the feed stock. Clay may be used to remove these deleterious compounds from the feed stock and hence preserve the desired functioning of the expensive catalysts.

Clays may be used in a variety of ways to neutralize residual acid in acid-treated oil stocks and as dehydrating agents in refining operations. An example is the purification of electrical insulating oils. The electrical industry has a large demand for fluid having high electrical resistivity. While many transformer and switch oils are still hydrocarbons of petroleum origin, there has been a continually increasing demand for highly fluid oils that are noninflammable and resistant to oxidation. This has been met by a variety of chlorinated hydrocarbons. When received by the users, these synthetic oils may contain traces of water and acidic-reaction products which reduce their resistivity. These contaminants can be removed commercially by clays, either by a slurring method or by percolation. Attapulgite clay is frequently used for this purpose. It is removed from the shipping bags and heated to 400°F for 4 to 8 hr to drive out free moisture, after which it is stored at 250°F until used. It is brought into contact with the oil at 250 to 300°F. The oil is then filtered and blotter pressed. The scouring with the blotter press is necessary to remove any trace of fines which might affect resistivity; initial resistivities of 3,000 to 5,000 megohms are brought to 6,000 to 8,000 megohms by such treatment. In the percolation process a temperature of the order of 160°F is used, and somewhat higher resistivities are reported.

There is an increasing use of acrylic polymers for which monomeric, glacial, acrylic acid is the starting material. In order that the monomer be shipped, methylene blue is added to inhibit any random polymerization. The methylene blue must be removed before use. This can be done by percolating the inhibited monomer through a column of attapulgus clay. Before use, this clay should be exposed to the atmosphere, so that it is in equilibrium with atmospheric moisture. The presence of this free moisture is required to suppress the polymerizing action of the clay and does not interfere with the adsorption of methylene blue. The percolation is conducted at atmospheric temperatures.

For the production of organic chemicals by catalytic conversion, the largest volume of raw materials is hydrocarbons of petroleum or coal-tar origin. Although feed stocks have usually been concentrated and purified by such processes as fractional distillation, they still contain traces of material which may poison the catalysts, reduce the amount of conversion, or promote undesirable side reactions. This is even more true of unreacted portions of hydrocarbons recycled to the feed. Attapulgite clay, because of its generally basic reaction, low affinity for aromatics, and ability to polymerize unsaturates, is versatile and provides a means of purifying most hydrocarbon stocks. Adsorptive purification by attapulgite is best applied to feed stocks whose principle constituents are from the paraffin, cycloparaffin, or aromatic series of hydrocarbons or to non-polar liquids, such as the chlorinated hydrocarbons, derived from these series. Contaminating trace materials that are removable from such feed stocks include arsenic compounds, nitrogen compounds, esters of strong acids, acidic compounds, basic compounds, resins, selective solvents, and polymers. As yet such purification has not been applied to feeds much above C_8, and as yet no great amount of investigation has been made on complete adsorptive purification of higher-boiling and lower-viscosity feeds. Also no information is available regarding the use of other types of clay in such purification processes.

Many of the hydrocarbon feed stocks go into processes which use acidic catalysts, such as sulfuric acid, boron trifluoride, and aluminum chlorides. Usually traces of these catalysts appear in the product either as a carry-over or in the form of complexes generated during the reaction. Their removal is essential since they affect the basic properties of the product as well as produce undesirable colors and odors. Clay is now being used to purify resins, polymers, alkylates, and esters derived from a wide variety of petroleum and coal-tar hydrocarbons. Both percolation and slurring methods are used with operating temperatures from 80 to 106°F.

Monomeric isobutylene of high purity has many uses as a starting material for chemical reactions in the formation of plastomers. It is often found as a by-product of petroleum refining, but its normally gaseous state makes it difficult to supply it to users in locations not adjacent to refineries. Such users have resorted to producing high-purity isobutylene by dehydration of tertiary butyl alcohol. However, some refiners are prepared to furnish a liquid, cold acid polymer which consists of the dimers and trimers of isobutylene. Ciapatta, Macuga, and Leum (1948) discovered that the dimer and trimer could be decomposed to high-purity mono-isobutylene by passing the liquid polymer over attapulgite clay at about 600°F. The conversion is about 60 per cent per pass, and, based on fresh feed, a space velocity of 1.1 vol per vol per hr is used. The reaction is strongly endothermic, so that the success of the operation depends on furnishing the additional heat required.

Clays are used to reclaim a wide variety of oils and solvents.

1. Engine oils. Automotive engines are designed to be lubricated and, to a considerable extent, cooled by hydrocarbon oils. Through the catalytic action of engine metals and high temperatures in the presence of air and dirt, these oils tend to break down through oxidation, cracking, and condensation to nonlubricants. To slow this action modern automotive engine oils contain up to 10 or 12 per cent of additives, which include oxidation inhibitors, metal deactivators, oiliness agents, and detergents. In the used oil the additives have been depleted, and the unchanged hydrocarbon portion of the oil is contaminated with acids, other oxidation products, water, carbon, silica, dirt, lead compounds, and heavy ends from fuels. With the exception of the fuel dilution, all of these contaminants may be removed by adsorption, and clays are widely used for this purpose. In reclaiming oil, bus and truck companies try to put the oil in shape so that refortification will enable its safe reuse for a normal drain period. In other cases, reclaimers may be more interested in the color and appearance of the oil which is to be offered for resale.

In some cases with stationary engines where straight mineral oils are frequently used and where the actual operation is more uniform and under less severe conditions than with automotive engines, the reclaiming operation is an integral part of the lubrication system through which the oil circulates before returning to the engine.

2. Electrical insulating oils. These oils are principally switch and transformer oils which act as dielectrics in areas of high current stress. Their principle mechanism of deterioration is oxidation from air, catalysed by metallic copper. Contamination through the solution of resins and lacquers from insulation and through water from air breathing are also factors. Adsorbing clays are used to remove these contaminants.

3. Cleaner solvent. Although the proportions will vary widely, used cleaner solvents nearly always contain contaminants. A list of these contaminants would include water, dry cleaners, soap, soot, silica dust, fatty acids, fatty oils, greases, and proteins. Sugars and other hydrocarbons might be present also. Reclaiming processes frequently include the use of clay adsorbents to remove some of these contaminants and distillation to separate others.

The foregoing list of miscellaneous uses should not be considered complete, and there may well be other uses of major significance which have not come to the author's attention. Also it is frequently impossible to determine from the literature whether a described application is merely a suggested possibility or has been tried and is in use. Also the literature frequently states that a given type of clay is usable for a particular purpose without giving any indication as to whether or not other types of clay have been tried and found either satisfactory or unsatisfactory. In general, however, for the miscellaneous uses discussed above, clays with high adsorbing properties, such as attapulgite and acid-activated montmorillonite, find the widest use.

REFERENCES

Albareda, J., M. Alexandre, and T. Fernandez, Influencia de la Composicion Mineralogica de las Arcillas de los Cationes de Cambio en la Oxidacion Catalitica del Alcohol Etilico en Fase Vapor, *Anales edafol. y. Fisiol. vegetal (Madrid)*, 12, 89–140, 281–308 (1953).

Amero, R. C., and R. G. Cappell, Effect of High Pressure Extrusion on the Adsorption Capacity of Floridin, *Petrol. Refiner*, January (1943).

Amero, R. C., and W. H. Wood, Catalytic Desulfurization, *Oil Gas J.*, 45, May (1947).

Barrer, R. M., and N. MacKenzie, Sorption by Attapulgite: I, Availability of Intracrystalline Channels, *J. Phys. Chem.*, 58, 560–568 (1954).

Bond, G. R., "Acid-treated Clay Catalyst for Cracking Hydrocarbons," U.S. Patent 2,551,580 (1951).

Brindley, G. W., Structural Aspects of Some Thermal and Chemical Transformations of Layer Silicate Minerals, *Proc. Intern. Symposium on Reactivity of Solids*, pp. 349–361, Gothenberg, Sweden (1952).

———, Fuller's Earth from Dry Branch, Georgia, a Montmorillonite Cristobalite Clay, *Clay Minerals Bull.* 3, pp. 167–169 (1957).

Chambers, G. P. C., Some Industrial Applications of the Clay Mineral Sepiolite, *Silicates inds.*, pp. 3–11, April (1959).

Charrin, V., Les gisement de terres Décolorantes du Perigord, *Génie civil*, 123, 146 (1946).

Cipiatta, F. G., S. J. Macuga, and L. N. Leum, Depolymerization of Butylene Polymers, *Anal. Chem.*, 20, 699–704 (1948).

———, ———, and ———, Depolymerization of Butylene Polymers, *Ind. Eng. Chem.*, 40, 2091–2099 (1948).

Coleman, N. T., and C. McAuliffe, H-ion Catalysis by Clays, *Natl. Acad. Sci. Publ.* 395, pp. 282–290 (1955).

Davidson, R. C., Cracking Sulfur Stocks with Natural Catalyst, *Petrol. Refiner*, 26, 3–12, September (1947).

———, F. J. Ewing, and R. S. Shute, Catalysts of the Activated Montmorillonite Type, *Natl. Petrol. News*, July 7 (1943).

deLapparent, J., Les argiles des terres à foulon, *Cong. intern. mines mét. et géol. Appl.*, 1, 281–287 (1935).

Grenall, A., Montmorillonite Cracking Catalyst, X-ray Diffraction, *Ind. Eng. Chem.*, 40, 2148–2151 (1948).

Grim, R. E., Petrography of the Fuller's Earth Deposits, Olmsted, Illinois, with a Brief Study of Some Non-Illinois Earths, *Econ. Geol.*, 28, 344–363 (1933).

———, "Clay Mineralogy," McGraw-Hill Book Company, Inc., New York (1953).

——— and W. F. Bradley, A Unique Clay from the Goose Lake, Illinois, Area, *J. Am. Ceram. Soc.*, **22**, 157–164 (1939).

——— and G. Kulbicki, "Montmorillonite: High Temperature Reactions and Classification," manuscript (1959).

Gurwitsch, L. G., Action of Florida Earth on Unsaturated Compounds in Petroleum, *J. Russ. Phys. Chem. Soc.*, **47**, 827–830 (1915).

Holmes, J., and G. H. Mills, Aging of Bentonite Cracking Catalyst in Air or Steam, *J. Phys. & Colloid Chem.*, **55**, 1302–1320 (1951).

Houdry, E., W. F. Burt, A. E. Pew, Jr., and E. W. A. Peters, Jr., Catalytic Processing by the Houdry Process, *Natl. Petrol. News*, **30**, R570–R580 (1938).

———, ———, ———, and ———, Catalytic Processing of Petroleum Hydrocarbons by the Houdry Process, *Refiner Nat. Gasoline Mfr.*, **17**, 574–582, 619 (1938).

Johnston, W. A., "Adsorption and Catalysis," manuscript, Minerals and Chemicals Philipps Corp., Menlo Park, N.J. (1959).

Kayser, F., and J. M. Bloch, Some Catalytic Properties of Montmorillonite, *Compt. rend.*, **234**, 1885–1887 (1952).

Lopez-Gonzalez, J., and V. R. Dietz, Surface Changes in an Original and Activated Bentonite, *Natl. Bur. Standards J. Research*, **48**, 325–333 (1952).

Mathieu, M., Structure et activité catalytique, *Bull. soc. chim. France*, **14**(5), 14–27 (1947).

Milliken, T. H., A. G. Oblad, and G. A. Mills, Use of Clays as Petroleum Cracking Catalysts, "Clays and Clay Technology," *Calif. Div. Mines, Bull.* 169, pp. 314–326 (1955).

Mills, G. A., "Process of Activating Kaolin Clay," U.S. Patent 2,477,639 (1947).

———, "Catalytic Conversion of Hydrocarbons," U.S. Patent 2,485,626 (1948).

———, J. Holmes, and E. G. Cornelius, Acid Activation of Some Bentonite Clays, *J. Phys. & Colloid Chem.*, **54**, 1170–1185 (1950).

Murray, K. E., The Catalytic Dehydration of the Amyl Alcohols of Fusel Oil with a Kaolin Catalyst of High Activity, *J. Council Sci. Ind. Research*, **19**, 438–441 (1946).

Nutting, P. G., Adsorbent Clays, Their Distribution, Properties, Production and Uses, *U.S. Geol. Survey Bull.* 928-E, pp. 127–221 (1943).

Oulton, T. D., The Pore Size-Surface Area Distribution of a Cracking Catalyst, *J. Phys. & Colloid Chem.*, **52**, 1296–1314 (1948).

Parsons, C. L., Fuller's Earth, *U.S. Bur. Mines Bull.* 71, pp. 1–36 (1913).

Perrin-Bonnet, J., and J. Mering, Sur la constitution des argiles activées, *Chim. ind.* **69**, 459–460 (1953).

Piersol, R. J., J. E. Lamar, and W. H. Voskuil, Anna "Kaolin" as a New Decolorizing Agent for Edible Oils, *Illinois Geol. Survey Rept. Invest.* 27, (1933).

Porter, J. T., Properties and Tests of Fuller's Earth, *U.S. Geol. Survey Bull.* 315, pp. 268–290 (1907).

Ries, H. E., Structure and Sintering Properties of Cracking Catalysts and Related Materials, in "Advances in Catalysis and Related Subjects," vol. 4, pp. 87–149, Academic Press, Inc., New York (1952).

Robertson, R. H. S., Clay Minerals as Catalysts, *Clay Minerals Bull.*, **1**(2), 38–42 (1948).

———, The Fuller's Earth of the Elder Pliny, *Classical Revue*, **63**, 51–52 (1949).

Roquemore, R. W., and C. D. Strickland, Cracking with High Alumina Catalyst, *Petrol. Refiner*, **36**, 231–233 (1957).

Ruiz, J. C., and J. D. L. Gonzalez, External and Total Surface of a Natural and of an Acid-activated Montmorillonite, *Anales edafol. y fisiol. vegetal (Madrid)*, **14**, 125–135 (1955).

Shabaker, H. A., "Process of Acid-activating Kaolin Clay," U.S. Patent 2,477,664 (1947).

———, G. A. Mills, and R. C. Denison, "Preparation of Clay Catalyst," U.S. Patents 2,466,046; 047; 048; 049; 052 (1947).

Stone, R. L., and H. F. Rase, Differential Thermal Analysis—New Techniques for Testing Silica-Alumina Catalysts, *Anal. Chem.*, **29**, 1273–1277 (1957).

Thomas, C. L., "Removal of Iron from a Cracking Catalyst," U.S. Patent 2,576,653 (1951).

Wesson, D., The Bleaching of Oils with Fuller's Earth, *Mining Eng. World*, **37**, 667–668 (1912).

Yamamoto, K., Acid Clay and Activated Clay in Japan, *J. Soc. Chem. Ind., Japan*, **43**, 303–304B (1940).

Zvanut, F. J., X-ray Investigation of the Pyrochemical Changes in Missouri Halloysite, *J. Am. Ceram. Soc.*, **20**, 251–256 (1937).

CHAPTER 8

Clays in Miscellaneous Uses

INTRODUCTION

Clays are used as ingredients in a vast number of products, for example, paints, paper, and rubber. They are also used as agents in many processes, for example, water purification, and as a source of a desired material, for example, aluminum.

In this chapter an attempt is made to list the important miscellaneous uses and, further, to consider the types of clays used for particular purposes and the reasons for their selection. No claim is made that the list is complete, but it is hoped that no important uses have been overlooked.

For many uses, there is substantially no technical literature describing the specifications of the clay required. Also the advantages to be gained or the specific purpose for which a clay is to be used are often not disclosed by the user. In some cases the patent literature provides clues in these matters, but in general pertinent information is very scant for many of the uses considered in this chapter.

ADHESIVES

Clays are used in a wide variety of adhesives, such as those prepared with lignins, silicate of soda, starch, latex, and asphalt. They are used extensively in adhesives for paper products and in the cements for floor coverings, such as linoleum, rubber, and asphalt tile.

Clays in adhesives are not always merely inert diluents but may provide improved properties. They tend to reduce the amount of penetration of the adhesive into the members to be joined; because adhesion occurs only at the interface or at the surface of the joined members, much of any adhesive that penetrates far below the surface of the member is wasted. They increase the solids content of the adhesive and cause a faster setting rate and superior bond strengths. The clays increase the amount of bonded surface; for example, in the paper industry, they increase the so-called mileage obtained with a given amount of adhesive. They also permit the control of the suspension and viscosity characteristics for more satisfactory application. In the paper industry, the addition of clay to the adhesive permits greater machine speeds and, hence, greater production rates.

Each adhesive in general has its own particular requirements from a clay standpoint, and actual plant formulations and runs are normally made to select the most desirable clay. Kaolinite-type clays are used commonly in adhesives. For applications other than in paper where color is not essential, grit-free illites might also be satisfactory.

The flat flake-shaped particles of kaolinite act as extenders. Their flat surfaces tend to spread out the adhesive, and at the same time their low adsorptive capacity tends to deactivate a minimum amount of it. For example, the flakes would be plastered on the surface of sheets of paper and act as a barrier to prevent the adhesive from seeping into the paper fibers.

The kaolin producers market a variety of clays for the adhesive trade with different particle-size distributions. Claxton (1957) has shown that reduced penetration is attained with moderately coarse kaolins rather than with extremely fine ones.

Because of their high adsorptive capacity, attapulgite and montmorillonite clays would not be satisfactory in many adhesives. However, the high dispersion and suspension characteristics of montmorillonite and attapulgite would make them particularly useful in some other adhesives, such as those made with latex and asphaltic materials. A considerable number of United States patents disclose starch, casein, and sodium silicate adhesives containing bentonite as well as those compounded with latex and asphalt.

Organic-clad montmorillonites are said to be used in some types of adhesive because of their gelling properties for certain organic liquids.

ALSIFILM

If a gel of montmorillonite, free from grit, is spread onto a smooth surface and subjected to careful drying, a film will form which, being coherent and self-supporting, can be removed from its support. Such clay films exhibit the properties of the original clay, and in contact with water they will revert to a sol. Hauser (1941) showed that it is possible to transform the swellable and redispersible film into a nonswellable condition by binding the clay particles to each other by means of certain cation-exchange reactions. The replacement of the cation carried by the montmorillonite in the gel (usually sodium) by another cation; e.g., potassium, causes the loss of the swelling property. Hauser also showed that the same result could be obtained with some organic ionic compounds. According to Hauser (1955) such clay films, called *alsifilm*, are excellent electric insulators and, because they are oil resistant and are not affected by organic solvents, fats, and waxes, should find interesting applications in the field of packaging. It is believed that the tendency of such clay films to be brittle has retarded their commercial use.

ALUMINUM ORE

Introduction

Many clays contain as much as 30 to 40 per cent of alumina and, consequently, are potential ores of aluminum. Much research has been done on a variety of processes for extracting alumina from clays (Woody, 1943). At the present time, the world's metallic aluminum comes almost wholly from bauxite ores, which are composed essentially of aluminum hydrates, either gibbsite or boehmite. The alumina is recovered by the Bayer process or a modification of it. The ore is leached with caustic soda, and alumina is precipitated from the leach liquor by treatment with carbon dioxide. The aluminum is recovered from the alumina electrolytically (Edwards et al., 1930).

During World War II, the sources of bauxite in the Guianas of South America and in the West Indies for the aluminum industry in the United States were threatened by the activity of enemy submarines, and a large research effort was made to perfect processes for extracting alumina from clays. Several processes were investigated, and the researches were carried to the point of placing several large pilot plants in operation. With the end of the war and the availability once again of foreign bauxite ores to the United States, it seemed to be more economical to import bauxite than to obtain alumina from clays. This does not necessarily apply to all countries; thus alumina is said to be obtained from clays in some Scandinavian countries.

Bauxites occur widely in many countries, particularly those in warm or tropical regions. Huge deposits are still being found, for example, the recent discovery in the York peninsula of Queensland in Australia. However, in the United States, prospecting for bauxite has been very intensive, and clays may be a needed and economical source for alumina in the not too distant future.

There are five major processes that have been investigated extensively for extracting aluminum from clays. Each process has advantages and disadvantages, both economical and operational. A large literature exists for each process, and in the following discussion an attempt will be made to briefly outline the processes and to indicate their advantages and the problems involved in their use, particularly in relation to clay mineral composition.

Acid Process

In this process the aluminum is dissolved from the clay by attack with an acid. In the United States, procedures using sulfuric acid have been studied most and seem most favored (Walthall et al., 1945). Nitric acid has also been tried, but the operational difficulties are substantial. Hydrochloric acid has been tried elsewhere, and where economics favor its use, it appears to have promise (Woody, 1943).

The solubility of the clay minerals in acids varies with the nature of the acid, the acid concentration, the acid-to-clay ratio, the temperature, and the duration of treatment (Grim, 1953). Also the solubility of the various clay mineral groups is quite different, and there is great variation in the solubility characteristics of members of some individual groups. Thus, in general, a magnesium-rich montmorillonite is much more soluble than one rich in aluminum, with an iron-rich member somewhere in between. In the case of clay minerals showing variations in degree of crystallinity, such as kaolinite, the solubility increases as the crystallinity decreases. The solubility would, of course, increase as the particle-size decreased. Calcining the clay minerals changes their solubility characteristics and their relative solubility with respect to each other. Depending on the temperature and the clay mineral, calcining may enhance or reduce solubility.

Pask and Davies (1945) have shown (Table 8-1), using 0.5 g of clay dried at 130°C in 30 cc of a 20 per cent solution of sulfuric acid and boiling for 1 hr, that only 3 per cent of the total alumina is dissolved from kaolinite and only 9 per cent from a so-called anauxite. Halloysite is moderately soluble, showing the solution of from 50 to 90 per cent of the total alumina under similar conditions. Illite is slightly soluble, with 11 per cent of total alumina going into solution in one sample. The solubility of montmorillonite ranges from low to high, showing 33 to 87 per cent of total alumina soluble. The attapulgite-sepiolite clay minerals would probably have characteristics similar to those of the montmorillonite minerals.

With acid of the same concentration and with a similar acid-to-clay ratio, but with digestion under pressure at 155°C, the solubility of all the clay minerals increased (Table 8-1). All the alumina of halloysite became soluble, and almost all of it was dissolved from the montmorillonites (85 to 93 per cent). Even the ordinarily relatively insoluble kaolinite and illite lost a major part of their aluminum, 70 and 87 per cent, respectively, going into solution.

TABLE 8-1

EXTRACTION OF ALUMINA FROM VARIOUS CLAY MINERALS WITH SULFURIC ACID
(After Pask and Davies, 1945)

Clay mineral	Alumina extracted, % total alumina present		
	Clay dried at 130°C[a]	Clay calcined at 800°C[a]	Pressure digestion at 155°C[b]
Kaolinite....................	3	100	70
Anauxite....................	9	95	
Halloysite...................	63	100	98
	50	96	
	90	...	
	78	100	100
Illite.......................	11	52	87
Montmorillonite..............	87	28	85
	33	19	93
Muscovite...................	17	29	

[a] Determinations made after boiling 0.5 g of sample in 35 cc of 20 per cent solution of sulfuric acid for 1 hr.

[b] Clay dried at 130°C then digestion of 0.5 g sample in 35 cc of 20 per cent solution acid for 1 hr.

Under similar conditions of extraction, but after calcining the clay minerals to 800°C, all, or substantially all, the alumina of the kaolinite, anauxite, and halloysite was soluble, whereas the solubility of the alumina in the illite was increased only moderately, and for the montmorillonites it was actually decreased (Table 8-1). The explanation resides in the fact that the kaolinite and halloysite structures are considerably disrupted at this temperature, and no new high temperature phases have yet been formed (Chap. 3, pages 94–95). In the case of illite and montmorillonites, the structure has been changed slightly but not disrupted substantially; hence the solubility of the alumina has been changed but not so that it can be completely removed. When kaolinite is heated to still higher temperatures (975°C), new crystalline phases develop, and the solubility of the alumina decreases. Similarly, when the other clay minerals are heated to about this same temperature, new high temperature phases form, which would affect their solubility in acid. In the case of some clay minerals, such as the montmorillonites and illites, the high temperature phases forming vary with substitutions within the structure and with the exchange-ion composition, and correlative variations of solubility in acid would be expected.

A comparison of data obtained by Thiebaut (1925) with those of Pask and Davies (1945) shows the great variation in results obtained under different treatment conditions. Using a 50 per cent hydrochloric acid, a treatment temperature of 80 to 85°C, a treating time of 2 hr, and a clay dried at 105 to 108°C, Thiebaut found that, based on cation solubility, biotite was 100 per cent soluble; muscovite, 5 to 32 per cent; kaolinite, 10 per cent; halloysite, 6 to 15 per cent; and montmorillonite, 62 per cent. Using sulfuric acid of a similar concentration and the same minerals but evaporating to dryness, Thiebaut found that the solubility of all the above minerals was complete, again based on their cation solubility. This work indicates that the uncalcined clay minerals are more soluble in sulfuric than in hydrochloric acid and also that both kaolinite and halloysite are less soluble in hydrochloric acid than the three-layer clay minerals are.

The solubility of the clay minerals in other acids is not well known. However, investigations of anion-exchange reactions indicate that the solubility is likely to be considerable, especially for the acids with an anion having a size and geometry approximating that of the component parts of the clay mineral structures. As a consequence some relatively weak acids may strongly attack certain clay minerals. Murray (1951) has shown, for example, that phosphoric acid attacks kaolinite under some conditions with greater vigor than sulfuric acid does.

Wolf (1933) has presented interesting data showing the effect of acid concentration on solubility. Using 10 g of well-crystallized kaolinite cooked for 2 hr and 100 cc of hydrochloric acid, he found that a 0.02 N solution dissolved 3.1 mg of alumina, that a 0.5 N solution dissolved 53.5 mg of alumina, and that a 5 N solution dissolved 124 mg of alumina.

Kaolinite clays are favored as sources of alumina because they possess the highest amounts of alumina, because moderate calcining renders the alumina soluble, and because they do not contain any iron, alkalies, or alkaline earths as essential components which would go into solution in acids along with the aluminum. Unfortunately it is impossible to find deposits of substantially pure kaolinite of the size necessary to support commercial alumina-extraction plants. Deposits of adequate size are certain to contain at least small amounts of other clay minerals and possibly iron compounds, so that some iron, alkalies, and/or alkaline earths are bound to be found in the leach liquors along with the alumina. This causes significant operational difficulties, as these components are likely to pass along into the alumina and into the electrolytic reduction cells. They may shorten the life of the electrolytic cell or carry on into the metallic aluminum and reduce its purity. A vast amount of work has been done on the problem of reducing the concentration of iron and these other components in the leach liquor (Walthall et al., 1945). Iron can be taken care of with considerable success by preliminary calcination of the clay in a reducing atmosphere to produce spinel-type oxides carrying the iron in a relatively insoluble form, or by chemical treatment of the leach liquor by a variety of processes, e.g., using manganic acid (Walthall et al., 1945). The problem of the presence of potassium is likely to be most severe because it is difficult to remove from leach liquors. Further, it is likely to be present since the kaolin ore is almost certain to contain potassium-bearing minerals, such as mica and possibly feldspar.

After the acid attack, the leach liquors are concentrated and then heated above their decomposition temperature to recover the acid for recycling and to precipitate the alumina. In the case of sulfates, the calcination is above about 550°C and a reducing atmosphere is favorable (Walthall et al., 1945). The acid process is favored by its simplicity and the easy recovery of the alumina and the acid for recycling. Also it requires only a moderate calcining temperature for the clay. The problem of the solubility of the iron, alkalies, and alkaline earths is a disadvantage. As a by-product of the process, large tonnages of silica residue are produced. Finding some economic use for this residue would go a long way toward making the process competitive with the extraction of alumina from bauxite.

Manufacture of Alum

In earlier years bauxites were used as a source of aluminum in the manufacture of alum and other aluminum chemicals. This is still true when chemicals of high purity are required, but in the case of alum which can tolerate some latitude in composition, kaolinite-type clays are now used as a source of alumina. The process is one of attacking the clay with sulfuric acid, the clay having been previously calcined to increase the solubility of the aluminum.

In the acid activation of montmorillonite clay for the preparation of decolorizing agents for oils, leach liquors are produced containing substantial amounts of aluminum sulfate along with the sulfates of calcium and magnesium (Chap. 7). The montmorillonites used for this purpose have little or no potassium in their composition. These leach liquors now supply part of the alumina going into the production of aluminum chemicals.

Ammonium Sulfate Process

In very general terms, this process involves the following steps: sulfating the alumina in the clay by baking with ammonium sulfate at approximately 400°C, leaching with water to extract the aluminum sulfate and ammonium sulfate, crystallizing the ammonium sulfate and separating it from the aluminum sulfate, converting the aluminum alum to aluminum hydroxide using the ammonia gas given off during the baking, and calcining the aluminum hydroxide to alumina (St. Clair et al., 1944; White, 1945).

The clay is prepared by crushing it to less than about $\frac{1}{4}$ in., and in some cases it may be roasted to about 1500°F, which is adequate to dehydrate kaolinite and increase its reactivity. In the crystallization step any titanium, calcium, magnesium, silicon, phosphorus, and ferrous iron show little or no tendency to go into the alum crystals, but appreciable amounts of any sodium, potassium, and ferric iron are crystallized with the alum. According to St. Clair et al. (1944), the potassium and sodium are present in the ammonium alum crystals, but they are eliminated from the alumina in the precipitation of aluminum hydroxide. The iron presents a more difficult problem, and suggested detailed processes contain some definite step to remove or at least reduce the iron content (Sweet and Gardini, 1948). Another difficulty is that the precipitation of aluminum hydroxide by adding ammonia to alum solutions forms a gelatinous precipitate which is difficult to filter and wash. The addition of alum crystals with the ammonia and careful control of the pH are claimed to produce satisfactory filtration characteristics.

This process appears to have been tried only on kaolinite clays, and it would certainly seem that such clays would cause the least difficulty with the process. It might be, however, that this process would experience less difficulty than the acid process when applied to clays of other clay mineral composition or to kaolins containing other clay minerals as significant components. The alkalies and alkaline earths would probably cause less difficulty in the ammonium sulfate process than in the acid process.

Lime-Sinter Process

This process (Archibald and Jackson, 1944; Archibald and Nicholson, 1948) in brief consists of mixing ground siliceous alumina-bearing ore, for example, clay, with ground calcium carbonate in proportions giving a mixture corresponding approximately in percentage composition (ignoring volatile constituents present) to a mixture of dicalcium silicate and pentacalcium trialuminate. This material is then heated at a suitable temperature (of the order of 1375°C) and for such a time as may be necessary to develop dicalcium silicate and some calcium aluminate compound or compounds which can be acted upon by a dilute alkali carbonate solution in such manner as to dissolve alumina and leave undissolved all, or nearly all, the silica, lime, and any other material present in the sintered material. The dicalcium silicate plays an extremely important dual role. First its development is complete enough to tie up nearly all the silica present in a form not soluble in the leach liquor. Second it undergoes a crystallographic transformation on cooling below about 675°C with an increase in volume which results in reduction of the sintered mass to a powder, making the soluble alumina compounds easily accessible to the action of the leach liquors without grinding. This phenomenon is commonly called *dusting*.

Grim, Machin, and Bradley (1945) have investigated the effect of the clay mineral composition of clay used in the lime-sinter process, and the following conclusions are taken from their work:

Kaolinite clays and gibbsite kaolinite (bauxitic) clays gave higher percentage yields of alumina than clays composed of the other clay minerals. In such clays, yields well over 90 percent were obtained. When such clays were composed of poorly crystallized kaolinite, the yield of alumina was reduced slightly. Halloysite clays gave yields comparable to those for kaolinite clays only if they were heated to unusually high temperatures. Diaspore-clay sinters fused and did not dust so that they were less satisfactory for this process as commonly practiced.

It is probably significant that the more desirable sinters all resulted from those two clay minerals, kaolinite and halloysite, which yield relatively poorly organized material on dehydration.

Within the range of variations in the CaO/Al_2O_3 ratio from 1.5 to 1.8, only the illite clays, perhaps because of their high iron content, showed considerable variation in the yield of alumina. Illite clays frequently gave considerably higher yields with increasing amounts of CaO. In the case of pure kaolinite clays, however, the lime in the mixture can be reduced considerably below the quantity required to give the pentacalcium trialuminate composition without seriously affecting extractability. All of the conclusions regarding montmorillonite refer to the aluminous variety. Kaolinite, illite, and montmorillonite clays all showed optimum yields when sintering temperatures were around 1360° to 1380°C. Sinters made with illite and montmorillonite clays were more sensitive to overburning than those made with other clays. At 1360°C. sinters made with diaspore and gibbsite-kaolinite clays fused, whereas those made with halloysite clays required sintering temperatures of 1400°C. and higher for moderately good yields.

The yield of alumina from kaolinite and montmorillonite clays was not influenced by furnace atmosphere. The effect of variation in the furnace atmosphere on illite clays was erratic except that high-iron illite clays gave improved yields when sintered under reducing conditions.

Sinters prepared with illite and montmorillonite clays tended to dust less completely and less rapidly than sinters made with other types of clay.

The amount of silica in the leach tended to be somewhat larger for illite and montmorillonite clays than for those of other clay mineral compositions. Only in the case of kaolinite clays was the silica content decreased by increasing the sintering temperature. Varying the CaO/Al_2O_3 ratio caused small variations in the silica in the extracts from kaolinite, illite, and montmorillonite clay sinters.

Phosphate, even in small quantities, inhibited dusting and sharply reduced the yield of alumina. Iron in the form of Fe_2O_3 did not reduce yields of alumina much, unless it exceeded one or two percent. In larger amounts, iron caused considerable reduction in alumina yield.

The dicalcium silicate was usually in the gamma form and attained a maximum size of about 10 microns in kaolinite-clay sinters and 60 microns in illite- or montmorillonite-clay sinters.

Kaolinite-clay sinters fired at 1320°C. contained a considerable amount (40% ±) of material that suggested poor development of new phases. At 1360°C., the new phases were completely developed, but on increasing the sintering temperature to 1400°C., the units of dicalcium silicate became larger and more completely inverted to the gamma form. New phases were completely developed in illite- and montmorillonite-clay sinters fired at 1320°C. Higher sintering temperatures served only to increase the size of the dicalcium silicate units. New phases were completely developed also in diaspore-clay sinters fired at 1320°C. Gibbsite-kaolinite-clay sinters showed about the same relation to sintering temperature as kaolinite clays except that there was slightly better phase development at the lower temperature. In the case of halloysite-clay sinters, extensive new phase development was not attained until about 1450°C. The amount of material with poor phase development in sinters made with kaolinite and halloysite-clays was reduced by increasing the time the sinter was held at the top temperature.

Xray diffraction analyses indicate that the material suggesting poor development of new phases was largely beta dicalcium silicate in extremely fine units in which minor variations in cell dimensions have been observed that could retard inversion to the gamma form.

Xray and differential thermal analyses suggested that in the diaspore-clay sinters, the reaction of components to form new phases began as soon as the CO_2 was driven off and continued slowly without pronounced thermal effects. In the case of kaolinite clays, the loss of CO_2 was followed immediately by the formation of gehlenite which was accompanied by a sharp endothermic reaction at about 950°C. In such mixtures (kaolinite clay) fired at 1000°C., gehlenite and free lime were prominent phases. As the temperature was carried from 1000°C. to 1300°C., free lime and gehlenite disappeared gradually and beta dicalcium silicate, tricalcium aluminate, and pentacalcium trialuminate developed in the order named, the latter at the expense of the tricalcium aluminate.

Xray and differential thermal analyses for mixtures containing illite and montmorillonite clays did not indicate the formation of gehlenite. Apparently there was little reaction of components until about 1200°C., when the beta dicalcium silicate and possibly the aluminates developed sharply with a pronounced thermal effect. The higher temperature required for the reaction of illite and montmorillonite with lime as compared to kaolinite and lime was probably the result of the higher temperature required for the destruction of the lattice structure of the former clay minerals.

Attempts to prepare sinters from attapulgite clays resulted in cinder-like masses which disintegrated slowly into coarse sand-like particles. The low content of alumina in the attapulgite-sepiolite minerals also would render them unsuitable as sources of metallic aluminum.

The lime-sinter process yields large tonnages of dicalcium silicate in very small particles. The economic use of this process would be greatly aided if some use could be found for this silicate so that it would reduce costs instead of adding charges necessary for its disposal. A major problem in the lime-sinter process is to carry out the leaching step so as to dissolve the smallest amount of silica with the alumina and/or to devise a satisfactory means of desilicating the leach liquors (Archibald and Nicholson, 1948).

Lime-Soda-Sinter Process

From the chemical point of view, the lime-soda-sinter process (Copson et al., 1944; Grim et al., 1945) is not fundamentally different from the lime-sinter process. The ground, siliceous, alumina-bearing ore (clay) is mixed with calcium carbonate and sodium carbonate in proportions giving a mixture corresponding approximately in percentage composition (ignoring volatile constituents) to a mixture of dicalcium silicate and sodium aluminate, $NaAlO_2$. The mixture is then heated to such temperature and for such a period of time as may be necessary to render a maximum proportion of alumina and soda and a minimum proportion of other materials present soluble in a dilute alkali-carbonate solution. The temperature necessary is not so high or so critical as for the lime-sinter process. As in the lime-sinter process, the primary function of the lime is to tie up the silica in a form not soluble in the leach liquor. The transformation of the dicalcium silicate, when or if it occurs, does not result in dusting of the sinter. The sintered mass is usually considerably less dense than that produced when the lime-sinter method is used. It is rather friable, porous, and easily ground when not overburned.

Grim, Machin, and Bradley (1945) have also investigated the influence of clay mineral composition on the lime-soda-sinter process, and the following conclusions are taken from their work:

> The introduction of soda into the alkali extraction process as practiced in the lime-soda method results in reactions with the clay at temperatures much lower than when lime is used alone. With clays of the high alumina variety (diaspores and bauxites) fairly good extractions were obtained with sintering temperatures of 1000°C. Kaolinite-clay sinters required slightly higher temperatures, whereas sinters prepared from illite and montmorillonite clays had to be heated to temperatures as high as 1200° to 1300°C. to give satisfactory yields of alumina. This is in accord with the fact that

kaolinite passes into a poorly organized state on dehydroxylation whereas illite and montmorillonite retain fairly good organization on dehydration and preserve it until fairly high temperatures. Unless raw materials containing sufficient soda are available there is little advantage in using the lime-soda as compared to the lime process with the three-layer clay minerals insofar as sintering temperature is concerned. All of the conclusions regarding montmorillonite refer to the aluminous variety.

Kaolinite clays and gibbsite-kaolinite clays may yield about 90 per cent of their alumina by the lime-soda process when they are relatively free from iron and other clay minerals. Halloysite and montmorillonite clays may also yield over 90 per cent of their alumina, but it is more difficult to get top yields. The highest yields for illite clays were 10 to 12 per cent below those for the other clay minerals. Yields for clays composed of mixtures of clay minerals were in agreement with results predicted from pure types.

Diaspore clays and gibbsite-kaolinite clays yielded nearly as much alumina on sintering to 1000°C. as to 1300°C. Pure kaolinite clays showed no increase in yield when sintered above 1100°C., other factors being the same, and yielded about 75 per cent of their alumina when sintered to 1000°C. Montmorillonite clays yielded none of their alumina on sintering to 1100°C., 50 per cent on sintering to 1200°C., and 90 per cent on sintering to 1300°C. Like montmorillonite clay, illite clay required sintering above 1200°C. for good alumina yields.

In sinters fired to 1100°C., increasing the time held at top temperature caused only a slight increase in yield of alumina from diaspore clays, only moderate increases from clays composed of gibbsite, kaolinite, and halloysite, and a very great improvement in the yield from illite clays. Regardless of sintering time, montmorillonite clay yielded no alumina on firing to 1100°C.

Sinters of the various clay minerals fired under strong reducing conditions gave the same yield as similar sinters fired under oxidizing conditions.

Although some of the results are erratic, the data show definite improvement in the yield of alumina from all types of clay, except those containing diaspore, as the Na_2O/Al_2O_3 ratio is increased from 0.8 to 1.2.

Sinters of kaolinite and illite clays give sharply reduced yield when the CaO/SiO_2 ratio was less than 2, but the yields were not improved when the ratio was above 2. Montmorillonite clay showed greatly increased alumina yields with CaO/SiO_2 ratios somewhat greater than 2.

Extracts from illite clays and montmorillonite clays contained a slightly larger percentage of silica than extracts from the other clay mineral. Kaolinite clays which contained appreciable amounts of illite and montmorillonite gave extracts with higher silica contents than pure kaolinite clays, but the difference was small.

Xray and optical data concur in the conclusion that in sinters with a lime to silica ratio of 2 and a soda to lime ratio of one, the compound $NaAlO_2$

as described by Brownmiller and Bogue (1932), is well developed only in sinters prepared with high alumina clays (gibbsite, diaspore). In kaolinite clays the aluminate appears to be pentacalcium trialuminate with soda and perhaps silica in solid solution. In illite and montmorillonite clays, the development of aluminate was very poor, but the compound seemed to be more nearly like pentacalcium trialuminate.

The aluminate was found in irregular aggregates and interstitial masses composed of indistinct individual units less than one micron in diameter.

Soda in excess of that required for a ratio of soda to alumina of one caused an enhanced development of aluminate with characteristics more like $NaAlO_2$.

The dicalcium silicate occurred in distinct units only a few microns in diameter in sinters made with kaolinite clays. In sinters made with illite or montmorillonite clays this silicate attained a maximum diameter of over 20 microns. The dicalcium silicate was in the beta form with little inversion to the gamma form.

In sinters prepared with gibbsite and diaspore clays, new phases began to develop as soon as loss of CO_2 released CaO and Na_2O or perhaps sooner, under the attack of the fluid double carbonate, hence the large amount of alumina extractable from sinters made at relatively low temperatures. Again in sinters made with kaolinite clays, new phases began to form before the carbonates were completely broken down. In the kaolinite and gibbsite clays, the phases appeared to develop continually throughout a temperature interval of several hundred degrees without a sharp thermal effect.

In sinters prepared with illite and montmorillonite clays, new phases did not develop extensively until about 1200°C., and consequently little alumina was extractable unless the firing was carried to this temperature. Further there was a sharp thermal reaction which began at about 1175°C. corresponding to the formation of the new phases in illite and montmorillonite. The foregoing difference in the reaction of kaolinite as compared to illite and montmorillonite can be explained by the difference in the organization of the dehydrated minerals and the temperature required for the complete destruction of their structures.

A major problem in the commercial utilization of both the lime-sinter and the lime-soda-sinter processes is that the leachate is likely to contain a higher amount of silica than is desired for the reduction of the alumina to metallic aluminum. This difficulty can be alleviated somewhat by only a very moderate leaching of the sinter. This permits much alumina to remain in the sinter which is uneconomical unless the sinter can be used for some other purpose. The sinters have cementitious properties and the partially leached sinter can go into the manufacture of portland cement. The combination of portland cement production and alumina extraction from clays is said to be feasible economically in some Scandinavian countries.

A vast amount of work (Archibald and Nicholson, 1948) is recorded in the literature in an attempt to find a commercial process to reduce the silica content of the leachates. So far these attempts appear to have been only moderately successful.

Electrothermal Processes

In addition to the extraction processes noted, many additional processes have been suggested in which there is a direct reduction of the aluminum in the clay to alumina or to aluminum nitride, carbide, chloride, sulfide, etc. The reduction is carried out at a very high temperature, generally in an electric furnace. Edwards, Frary, and Jeffries (1930) describe a variety of such processes. Machalske (1913) proposes to fuse clay with carbon in an electric furnace and then to subject the molten alumina to centrifugal action to remove the impurities. Richmond (1917) mixes kaolin with pyrites and carbon and then fuses the material in an electric furnace. The silicon sulfide formed by the reaction is volatile and passes off along with the carbon monoxide. Weber (1903) proposes to smelt kaolin in an electric furnace with coke to produce a mixture of aluminum carbide and silicon carbide. The mixture is then decomposed with water to form methane, aluminum hydrate, and unchanged silicon carbide. The aluminum hydrate is washed out from the heavier silicon carbide and calcined. The patent literature contains many additional processes and variations of the above. Generally no specific clay is mentioned, but the context of the patent often suggests kaolin. There is no information available indicating whether or not clay minerals other than kaolinite would be better, or in some cases worse, for the suggested processes. It appears that, for economic reasons, the interest in such processes has been so slight that the influence of variations in the type of clay mineral has not been assessed.

ANIMAL BEDDING

Granular grades of clay of about 10 to 30 mesh are used for animal bedding, particularly for household pets. The clay serves as an absorbent and deodorizing agent. Clay for this purpose must have a high absorbent capacity, and must not break down to fine particles on use either when dry or wet. It must not form a sticky or plastic mass nor must it become dusty. Also it must not be toxic to animals.

Attapulgite and some montmorillonite clays are found satisfactory for this use. The clays are calcined to a temperature slightly above that at which all the absorbed water is lost and below that at which the clay mineral structure is completely destroyed (above 400°F and below about 1000°F). Detailed specifications for the crude clay have not been published.

Some animal bedding compounds have been prepared in which a chemical has been added to the dried granular clay to further control odor and to provide disinfectant and pesticide properties. Obviously such additives must not be toxic to the animals, and their character must not be changed by any catalytic action of the clay.

ATOMIC (RADIOACTIVE) WASTE DISPOSAL

The disposal of waste waters and solutions carrying radioactive materials of high biological toxicity is a vital problem in the development of atomic energy. The problem is difficult because these wastes may be concentrated and contain isotopes with a relatively long half life, for example, 90Sr and 137Cs. Much research has been done on this problem.

The use of clay has been suggested for the disposal of highly active wastes by adsorbing the ions and then fixing them against leaching by calcining to temperatures in excess of $1000°C$ which would be adequate to vitrify the clay and thereby to tie up the radioactive material in insoluble compounds. The liquid waste is thus converted into a solid form which can be buried without fear that the radioactive materials will be dissolved and carried into the ground water. The process has the advantage that it can be carried out by remote control, an essential requisite for processing highly active materials. The solution may be filtered through a solid mass of clay which is then calcined, or there may be gelation of the clay and liquid followed by calcination.

The ease of fixation is not the same for all ions. Amphlett (1958) has given the order $Pu^{4+} < La^{3+}$, Ce^{3+}, etc., $< Sr^{2+} < Cs^+$ for the rates of travel for a mixed waste introduced into a soil material which indicates that the cesium and strontium would be relatively difficult to fix. It is well known that this matter of fixation would vary with the clay mineral composition of the soil, the proportionate concentrations of the ions in the solution, and the character and concentrations of the ions in the soil. Ruthenium appears to be particularly difficult to fix (Table 8-2) because, although Ru^{3+} ions behave similarly to other trivalent ions, much of the ruthenium in waste solutions is present in complex uncharged or anionic species which are not fixed.

Early work suggested that clays with high cation-exchange capacity were required for such waste disposal, and vermiculite and montmorillonite clays with cation-exchange capacities in the range of 130 to 150 meq per 100 g were investigated. These clays also fuse at relatively low temperatures. More recently it has appeared that exchange capacity is not necessarily the controlling property, and other types of clay minerals have been studied. Thus, attapulgite and a shaly material

TABLE 8-2

REMOVAL OF ACTIVITY BY SLURRYING WITH CLAY

(Local shale from Oak Ridge with cation-exchange capacity of 29 meq/100 g)

(After Lacy, 1954)

Activity	Ionic form	pH	Per cent removal			
			Parts per million			
			1,000	2,000	3,000	4,000
$^{90}Sr–^{90}Y$	Cationic	7.7	83.4	89.1	92.9	95.0
$^{140}Ba–^{140}La$	Cationic	7.8	88.8	92.0	94.3	97.1
$^{141,144}Ce–^{144}Pr$	Cationic	8	99.7	99.8	99.9	99.9
$^{95}Zr–^{95}Nb$	Cationic and colloidal	7.5	98.0	99.1	99.4	99.6
$^{106}Ru–^{106}Rh$	Mixed	5.2	50.5	59.3	61.5	
Aged fission product	Mixed	8.8	82.0	82.9	86.3	90.3
^{131}I	Anionic	7.5	4.9	50	. . .	3.4

composed of a degraded illite (Kerr, 1959) appear to have been used with considerable success because of the ease with which the isotopes mix with a nitrate solution, the behavior of the clay mix on drying and firing, the relative amount of clay required, and the retentivity upon leaching of the clay sinter. Nishita et al. (1956) have reported also a kaolinite retaining large amounts of certain fission products.

Cronan (1959) has suggested the use of ceramic sponges for waste disposal; the sponges to be highly porous ceramic bodies prepared by firing a frothed body or one that contained combustible material.

CEMENT, MORTAR, AND AGGREGATES

Portland Cement

The burning of limestones to produce hydraulic limes early led to the discovery that a cement, remarkably superior to the hydraulic limes, could be made by causing a mixture of lime and clay (or a rock containing both lime and clay) to be heated to such a temperature that practically the entire product was sintered, and then finely grinding the sinter (see Bogue, 1955, for the history and the development of the industry). The term *portland cement* is used to designate such sintered material as distinguished from various limes and natural cements.

Table 8-3 lists the chemical requirements of the five major types of portland cement currently in use, and Table 8-4 gives typical chemical compositions of the various types of cement.

TABLE 8-3

CHEMICAL REQUIREMENTS FOR PORTLAND CEMENT
(According to ASTM Specifications C–150–53 from Bogue, 1955)

Requirement	Type				
	I	II	III	IV	V
SiO_2, min. %	. . .	21.0			
Al_2O_3, max. %	. . .	6.0			
Fe_2O_3, max. %	. . .	6.0	. . .	6.5	
MgO, max. %	5.0	5.0	5.0	5.0	5.0
$CaSO_4$ in hydrated portland-cement mortar, at 24 hr expressed as SO_3, max. g/l	0.50	0.50	0.50	0.50	0.50
Loss in ignition, max. %	3.0	3.0	3.0	2.3	3.0
Insoluble residue, max. %	0.75	0.75	0.75	0.75	0.75
$3CaO \cdot SiO_2$, max. %	. . .	50	. . .	35	50
$2CaO \cdot SiO_2$, min. %	. . .	. . .	. . .	40	
$3CaO \cdot Al_2O_3$, max. %	. . .	8	15	7	5

Clay minerals either in the natural lime rock or in the clay or shale mixed with the limestone would contribute silica, alumina, and possibly iron, alkalies, and alkaline earths depending on the identity of the clay minerals. It would seem that the magnesia content is the only specification that would generally determine the suitability of particular clay minerals for portland cement manufacture. According to Bogue (1955), MgO in excess of 5 per cent in the cement may be dangerous to the soundness of concrete especially at later stages. It may be concluded that the magnesium-rich clay minerals, attapulgite-sepiolite and chlorite, would be relatively undesirable constituents for portland cement manufacture. The presence of these minerals in moderate amounts would not, however, cause the amount of MgO to exceed the 5 per cent specification.

Kaolinite would perhaps be the optimum clay mineral constituent since it would contribute only alumina and silica. It would be especially desirable in the manufacture of white portland cements and other special types requiring careful control of chemical composition.

The illite and montmorillonite clay minerals would in many cases be equally satisfactory. The content of iron, alkalies, and alkaline earths of these clay minerals would in general not be high enough to be detrimental in the cement composition. Actually since these clay minerals have a higher silica content than kaolinite, they may in some cases be more desirable. Schwiete (1956) has suggested that kaolinite is more

TABLE 8-4

TYPICAL COMPOSITIONS OF VARIOUS CEMENTS
(in Per Cent)
(From Bogue, 1955)

Cement	SiO₂	Al₂O₃	Fe₂O₃[a]	CaO	MgO	SO₃	Ignition loss	Insoluble
Portland								
Type I	21.3	6.0	2.7	63.2	2.9	1.8	1.3	0.2
Type II	22.7	4.7	4.3	63.1	2.5	1.7	0.8	0.1
Type III	20.4	5.9	3.1	64.3	2.0	2.3	1.2	0.2
Type IV	24.3	4.3	4.1	62.3	1.8	1.9	0.9	0.2
Type V	25.0	3.4	2.8	64.1	1.9	1.6	0.9	0.2
White	25.5	5.9	0.6	65.0	1.1	0.1	n.d.	n.d.
Natural	27.3	5.5	4.3	35.6	21.2	0.5	4.1	n.d.
Aluminous	5.3	39.8	14.6	33.5	1.3	0.1	0	4.8
Pozzolana	26.0	6.9	3.6	52.3	4.2	1.8	4.8	9.4

[a] Includes any FeO.

KEY: I, General-use cement; II, Moderate heat-of-hardness cement; III, High early-strength cement; IV, Low-heat cement; and V, Sulfate-resisting cement.

satisfactory than illite in the wet manufacturing process because of its better burning characteristics and because there is less dusting during grinding.

Mortar Mix

Finely ground clay material is sometimes added to cement masonry mortars as a replacement for some of the cement. It is claimed that the clay improves the plasticity and general workability of the mortar. It increases the water retention, which is considered to be an index of workability, and also it is desirable because it increases the resistance of the mortar to drying out when in contact with absorbent masonry units, which consequently would weaken the bond.

Hursh, Lamar, and Grim (1944) investigated the effect of the clays of varying clay mineral composition on the water retention and compressive strength of cement mortars. In these tests the proportion of clay to cement was varied from 1:4 to 1:1. These authors found little difference when clays of various clay mineral compositions were added, except that those composed of montmorillonites were relatively less desirable because they required large amounts of water to give a suitable working consistency which in turn tended to result in mortars of inferior strength.

With the exception noted above, a considerable amount of shale and clay may be incorporated in mortar without reducing the strength below the minimum specification requirements in common use. In general clay materials may replace 30 to 35 per cent by weight of the cement in 1:3 mortars intended for severe conditions of exposure. Mortars containing equal parts of clay and cement show sufficient strength to meet the specifications for other types of use. These investigators also concluded that the mortars containing the clay are equal or superior to lime-cement mortars from the standpoint of water retention. It was observed that the workability of the clay-cement mortars was generally much better than that of lime mortars.

Hursh et al. (1944) showed that, so far as strength is concerned, the clay additive need not be ground finer than about 8 mesh. There apparently is sufficient slaking, even of harder shales, in the mixing of the mortar to obviate the need of finer grinding. Finer grinding causes a higher water requirement for the development of the desired consistency, but, except for the montmorillonite clays, this difference is not large enough to be significant.

Cement and Concrete Additive

From time to time it has been suggested that clay added to concrete mixtures causes the development of certain specific, desirable properties. Thus, in cases where high impermeability is desired, this property might be obtained by the addition of small amounts of certain clays. Little specific data on this matter are available, but the situation seems to be that in general the strength of the concrete decreases as the amount of added clay increases. However, desirable properties might, in some cases, be obtained without significant reduction of strength.

Judging from the results of the experiments of Hursh, Lamar, and Grim (1944) on adding clays to cement mortars, it would seem that the clay mineral composition of any added clay would make little difference except for the montmorillonite clays. This clay mineral would be expected to give maximum impermeability but at the same time increase the required amount of water for working consistency to an extent that the reduction in strength might be relatively greater than that developed when clays of other compositions were used. Bechtner (personal communication) states that additions of Wyoming bentonite (sodium montmorillonite) to concrete in amounts less than 2 lb per bag of cement does not damage strength, but it does significantly improve workability, lessen aggregate segregation and form leakage, and enhance impermeability.

Uren (1942) states that the addition of ½ to 2 lb of Wyoming bentonite with each sack of cement enhances the properties of cement slurries used to cement oil and gas wells. The presence of the bentonite confers thixotropic properties on the cement slurry, helping to hold the cement particles in suspension in high-water-ratio slurries, increasing their plasticity, and reducing water loss to the formations. It has been claimed that similar bentonite additions would improve cement grouting mixtures.

Lightweight Aggregate

Some clays and shales may be processed by calcining at elevated temperatures into satisfactory lightweight aggregate for concrete, mortar, and plaster. Several types are produced which are marketed commercially under the trade names "Haydite," "Rocklite," "Gravelite," "Cel-Seal," etc. (Mielenz and King, 1955; Cordon and Hickey, 1948; Price and Cordon, 1949; Tuthill, 1945; Kruge et al., 1949; Petersen, 1950). Firing is accomplished in rotary kilns or sintering machines. In either case the raw material is heated rapidly to the range between incipient and complete fusion. Bloating or vesiculation is accomplished by the entrapment of released gases by the viscous, partially fused clay or shale. Clay and shales are fired alone or after admixture with iron oxides, carbonaceous material, and/or sulfur compounds. The raw clay or shale is sometimes fired without preliminary crushing. Often it is crushed to $1\frac{1}{2}$ to 1 in. before firing. The clinker is crushed to desired sizes after firing. In some cases, particularly where an additive is used, the clay or shale is crushed, plasticized with water, extruded through a multiple die to form cylinders which are cut to desired lengths, and then fired. In some processes the extruded and cut cylinders are passed through a revolving drum to make them round. The rounded nodules may be coated with fine silica or another type clay to develop a smooth surface and to prevent their sticking together in the firing operation.

Firing is carried out at temperatures in the range of 2000 to 2200°F. Bulk dry weight of the coarse aggregate is generally in the range of 35 to 50 lb per cu ft, although in some cases material as light as 15 lb per cu ft has been produced. Very good structural concrete can be produced from lightweight aggregates with unit weights ranging from 50 to 100 lb per cu ft and with crushing strengths ranging from 1,000 to 5,000 psi. The concrete is resistant to freezing and thawing and wetting and drying. Expansion in the concrete as the result of alkali-aggregate reaction is negligible (Mielenz and King, 1955).

Despite extensive investigations of manufacturing processes and means of controlling the expansion of clays and shales in the production of lightweight aggregate, little information on the fundamental phenomena involved has been published. Most comprehensive are the investigations of Conley, Wilson, and Klinefelter (1948), Riley (1951), and White (1959). Expansion and vesiculation require the presence of one or more substances which release gas after fusion has developed sufficient molten material to prevent its ready escape, and they also require that the molten material be of sufficient viscosity to retain the expanding gas. Riley (1951) correlated the viscosity of the melt produced by firing with the bulk chemical composition of the raw material. Using data published by Conley et al. (1948) as well as original data, he found that all the bloating clays and shales among some 80 investigated contained at least 5 per cent of compounds of iron, alkalies, and alkaline earths. Increasing alumina content increased refractoriness and decreased vesiculation. The clays and shales classified as "bloaters" contained less than 25 per cent of Al_2O_3, but three-fourths of the nonbloaters likewise contained less than this amount of alumina. The work demonstrated that the determination of pH usually permits the identification of a bloating material. The nonbloaters produced a water slurry with a pH of less than 5; for the bloaters the value was greater than 5. Murray and Smith (1958) showed that there are clay materials with Riley's preferred composition which do not bloat, and that chemical composition alone does not identify a bloating clay on shale.

In the firing of natural clays and shales, Austin, Numes, and Sullivan (1942) identified H_2O, CO_2, and SO_3 as gases evolved. In addition (Mielenz and King, 1955), it is likely that CO, O_2, and possibly H_2 are evolved in the vesiculation of many clays and shales. Riley (1951) concluded that the most significant reaction involved in gas generation is the partial reduction of ferric oxide according to the equation

$$6Fe_2O_3 = 4FeFe_2O_3 + O_2$$

The ferric oxide is furnished by original limonite or hematite in the raw shale or clay or by the decomposition, with or without oxidation, of original ferric or ferrous compounds, such as biotite, amphiboles, montmorillonite- and illite-type clay minerals. Calculation indicates that at least 7.6 per cent by weight of Fe_2O_3 must be available from these sources for adequate vesiculation if this source alone furnishes the gas (Riley, 1951). White (1959) has shown, however, that 3 to 4 per cent of Fe_2O_3 was adequate for bloating in the clays and shales studied by him. Complex silicates such as micas, amphiboles, and the clay minerals probably also release O_2, H_2, and H_2O, as the result of other reactions. Experiments by Conley et al. (1948) and by Riley (1951) demonstrate that the gases evolved by reactions of dolomite, pyrite, sulfates, carbonates of the alkalies and alkaline earths, and possibly of calcite may be significant in vesiculation. Less than 1 per cent by weight of these minerals is required for adequate vesiculation. On rapid firing it would be expected that some of the hydroxyl water of the clay minerals would be retained until high temperatures are reached. Further sulfur released by compounds breaking down at lower temperatures (e.g., iron sulfides) is likely to react with other constituents in the clay and then be retained to a high temperature.

In the rapid firing of lightweight aggregate some organic material, if present, would probably be retained into the vitrification range to produce gas. White (1959) states that probably an organic content of 0.3 to 1 per cent is most desirable and that organic matter in excess of 2 per cent causes firing problems. The best bloating occurs when the organic matter is adsorbed on the clay mineral surface.

According to Mielenz and King (1955), the fabric of the original clay or shale is significant in the expansion process. Most beneficial is a dense, relatively impervious fabric which resists shrinkage during heating and retards release of vapors and gases before fusion effects a sealing of the particles. The fabric is especially significant in firing carbonaceous clays and shales; a porous, open fabric permits ready burning out of the carbon, and a dense fabric retards oxidation by the kiln atmosphere and retains CO and CO_2 produced by the reaction with interstitial water or with water or oxygen released by dehydration or decomposition of hydrated compounds or hydroxylated silicates. Murray and Smith (1958) state that particle size of the mineral is important. Large particles of pyrite, dolomite, and calcite, for example, result in nonuniform bloating.

White (1959) showed that laminated shales bloat better than non-laminated clays and that the bloating is greatest perpendicular to the lamination. In general the lamination is perpendicular to the basal-plane surfaces of the clay minerals, which have a gross parallel orientation in many shales. This oriented bloating is attributed to the lesser permeability of the laminated materials, which prevents both easy entrance of oxygen and escape of reaction gases. White (1959) also shows that weathering decreases bloating ability, probably because it tends to reduce the content of organic material.

Clay and shales containing illite, montmorillonite, chlorite, vermiculite, and/or attapulgite-sepiolite would be expected to be good bloaters because of their content of alkalies, alkaline earths, and/or iron. The absence of these components in kaolinite and halloysite would indicate that they would be unsatisfactory bloaters. Shales composed largely of illite and chlorite are extensively used for the preparation of lightweight aggregates. The presence of small amounts of nonclay minerals containing fluxes and gas-forming constituents may in some cases cause satisfactory bloating where the clay mineral composition is not itself very favorable. In general raw materials with a high clay mineral content are wanted—thus a very siliceous clay or shale with a large amount of quartz would not be very satisfactory because the quartz would act as a diluent. Also a very high content of calcium is not desirable as it would shorten too much the vitrification range. The quantity of iron and alkalies and alkaline earths is too high if it causes fusion that is too rapid to an extremely fluid mass. The presence of a moderate amount of potassium is particularly favorable, as this element reduces the tendency of the three-layer clay minerals to form high-temperature crystalline phases and also gives a broad vitrification range. For this reason, materials containing illite are especially favored for making lightweight aggregates. The composition of illite with about 5 per cent K_2O and a total content of oxides of iron, alkalies and alkaline earths of about 10 per cent is in the desired range. Obviously, from the previous discussion, clays and shales which do not have a satisfactory composition can usually be made to bloat by the use of additives.

Pozzolanas

Pozzolanas are siliceous or siliceous-and-aluminous materials, natural or artificial, processed or unprocessed, which, though not cementitious in themselves, contain constituents that will combine with lime in the presence of water at ordinary temperatures to form compounds which have low solubility and possess cementing properties (Lea, 1938). The use of pozzolanas as a replacement for part of the portland cement in concrete has come into prominence in recent years and is increasing. Certain pozzolanas have been found to participate in chemical and physical-chemical reactions with alkalies released during the hydration of portland cement (Hanna, 1947; Mielenz et al., 1950). As a consequence, deleterious reactions involving the alkalies, such as the alkali-aggregate reaction, are inhibited or prevented (Fig. 8-1).

Mielenz, White, and Glantz (1950) and Mielenz, Greene, and Schieltz (1951) have classified pozzolanas into five "activity types," depending upon the substances responsible for the pozzolanic action as follows:

1. Volcanic glass
2. Opal
3. Clay minerals
   a. Kaolinite group
   b. Montmorillonite group
   c. Illite group
   d. Mixed clays with vermiculite-chlorite
   e. Palygorskite
4. Zeolite
5. Hydrated aluminum oxides

In the natural condition, the clay minerals are nonpozzolanic or only weakly so. However with calcination, particularly in the range of 1200 to 1800°F, partial dehydration and structural changes result in significant

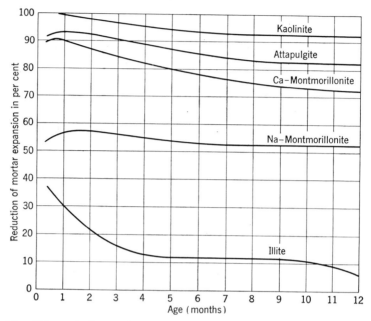

Fɪɢ. 8-1. Effect of clay and shale pozzolanas after calcination at 1400°F on expansion of mortar as result of alkali aggregate reaction, after Mielenz and King (1955).

reactivity with lime and alkalies for most types of clay. Although certain calcined clays control or markedly reduce expansion of mortar as the result of alkali-aggregate reaction, the water requirement may be excessive and strength development may be low, especially for pozzolanas of type 3*b* (Fig. 8-2).

The pozzolanic properties of kaolinite clays undergo remarkable changes, both physical and chemical, with calcination (Mielenz et al., 1951). Water requirements decrease from 72.8 to 46.0 per cent for tested materials calcined at 2000°F. Neither initial nor final set of the lime-kaolinite paste occurs before 14 days unless the kaolinite is calcined at or above 800°F. The beginning of new high-temperature crystalline phases above about 1800°F increases again the time necessary for the set of the lime-kaolinite paste and in general reduces pozzolanic properties.

Test data indicate that uncalcined kaolinite is comparatively ineffective in controlling alkali-aggregate reaction but that the material calcined between 1000 and 1600°F is highly effective with the optimum calcination temperature being 1400 to 1600°F. With the formation of new crystalline phases at higher temperatures, the effectiveness of kaolinite in controlling mortar expansion and in reducing alkali-aggregate reaction decreases.

It is clear that the pozzolanic properties of kaolinite are developed when the mineral is heated just above the dehydroxylation temperature. With the loss of hydroxyls, the kaolinite structure is altered and perhaps partially disrupted, and it is not difficult to visualize that in this condition the maximum reactivity for lime would prevail. At higher temperatures with the nucleation of a definite crystalline phase (mullite) beginning at 1600 to 1800°F the reactivity would be expected to decrease, and this is the case.

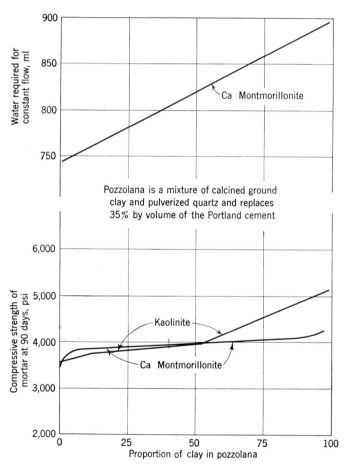

Fig. 8-2. Effect of calcined clay pozzolanas on water requirement and compressive strength of portland cement mortar. Clay calcined at 1400°F, after Mielenz and King (1955).

The pozzolanic properties of montmorillonite clays change greatly on calcination in the range 800 to 2000°F (Mielenz et al., 1951). The water requirement is markedly decreased by calcination. For material of this type the water required to produce a lime-pozzolana paste of normal consistency ranges from 32 to 165 per cent. The setting time also decreases markedly with calcination, usually to a minimum after calcination at 1000 to 1400°F. With calcination at higher temperatures, the time of set is increased. Compressive strength of portland-cement–pozzolana mortar increases with calcination of the pozzolana; the maximum strength being obtained after calcination between 1000 to 1800°F, depending upon the composition of the pozzolana.

The effect of calcination upon the alkali reactivity of montmorillonite pozzolanas depends upon the chemical composition of the clay mineral and the exchangeable cations. Thus sodium montmorillonite has been found to be comparatively ineffective (Fig. 8-1), because the presence of the exchangeable sodium prevents the clay from reducing the concentration of alkalies in the solutions permeating the portland-cement mortar. If the sodium is exchanged for calcium, the clay is likely to become effective after calcination.

Like kaolinite, the pozzolanic properties of montmorillonite clays are developed in the interval following dehydroxylation and before new high-temperature crystalline phases form. In the case of dioctahedral montmorillonites, the loss of hydroxyls is accompanied by relatively little structural change, and, therefore, the pozzolanic properties would be expected to be lesser than those for kaolinite. Trioctahedral montmorillonites appear to undergo greater structural change and disruption on dehydroxylation, and they, therefore, would be expected to yield better pozzolanas. The trioctahedral montmorillonites would be expected to require slightly higher calcination temperatures than kaolinites before pozzolanic properties were developed.

Pozzolanic properties of illite clays are affected significantly by calcination in the range from 800 to 1800°F. Water requirement is decreased moderately especially after calcination to 1800°F. The time of set is reduced to a minimum by calcination at 1400°F. Compressive strength of lime-pozzolana mortar is improved slightly or moderately by calcination, with the maximum occurring after heating to about 1800°F. There is little change in alkali reactivity with calcination in the range 800 to 1800°F—in every case the clay is relatively ineffective.

Illite clays react on heating about like the montmorillonite clays with the exception that the potassium acts as a potent flux tending to cause the rapid formation of a glass phase following the destruction of the illite structure. This would probably not favor the development of pozzolanic properties. Also the presence of potassium in the illite would prevent the reduction of the alkali content so that the clay would not be effective in controlling the alkali-aggregate reaction.

Vermiculite and chlorite clays would be expected to yield pozzolanas with properties like those of montmorillonite. Mielenz and King (1955) have stated that such clays are distinctly inferior as pozzolanas. Of several samples tested by these authors, none developed set with lime in the uncalcined state, and many showed no final set with lime after calcination at 1000°F. Compressive strength of mortars ranged from inferior to good, the maximum strengths being developed after calcination of the clays at 1800°F.

Sparse data are available for the pozzolanic properties of attapulgite-sepiolite clay minerals. Attapulgite clay calcined at 1400°F yielded good results in tests of the mortar expansion resulting from control of the alkali-aggregate reaction (Fig. 8-1). In this respect the clay was superior to montmorillonite and only slightly less effective than kaolinite.

Siliceous shales of the Monterey formation of California, which owe their pozzolanic properties to opaline material and montmorillonite-type clay minerals, have been used in the production of commercial pozzolanas. An oil-impregnated shale containing montmorillonite, also from the Monterey formation in California, has also been used as a source material for pozzolanas. Mielenz and King (1955) record other instances in which montmorillonitic shales and altered pumices have been used with satisfactory results in the preparation of pozzolanas in the United States. The latter type of materials has been used fairly widely in other countries, notably in Italy, for the manufacture of pozzolanas.

CLARIFICATION OF WINES, CIDER, BEER, ETC.

Saywell (1935) pointed out that the colloidal impurities in wine carried positive charges and that they could be coagulated and removed by stirring a small amount of a negatively charged material into the wine. Saywell also pointed out that Wyoming-type bentonite was a very effective agent for this purpose. The montmorillonite particles attracted the wine impurities and they settled out together. In addition, it has been indicated that the montmorillonite adsorbs and removes about 50 per cent of the iron in the original wine. Granular bentonite has been found to give the best results. With some wines as little as $2\frac{1}{4}$ lb per 1,000 gal gives satisfactory results; with others up to 10 or 12 lb per 1,000 gal may be required. Granular Wyoming bentonite can be dispersed in wine so that the clay can be added directly to the wine. Halperin (1945) has suggested that this type of clay can be used to recover tartrates from winery wastes.

Saywell (1934) has also pointed out that Wyoming-type bentonite can be used to clarify cider and vinegar. The amount of clay required for clarifying vinegar is generally larger than for wines—for vinegar 1 lb of bentonite to 180 gal may be necessary. The vinegar is preferably heated at 70°C for 10 min before the bentonite is added. With some vinegars, pretreatment with casein produces better results than either casein or bentonite alone.

Wyoming bentonite may also be used to clarify cider. With some ciders, particularly those that ferment slowly, the results are attained by adding granular bentonite directly to the cider. With ciders that ferment quickly it has been found better to disperse the bentonite first in water. A 5 per cent bentonite suspension is prepared which is then stirred into the cider.

According to Silva (1948), the use of clay for clarifying sugar-cane juice is very old, but it appears not to have attained wide commercial application. This author claims that Wyoming-type bentonite when used in conjunction with lime is superior to lime alone for the clarification, purification, and decolorization of cane juice. The clarification is said to depend on the formation of insoluble compounds of lime, mainly tricalcium phosphate, and organic compounds which are adsorbed by the clay and which in turn flocculate the montmorillonite of the bentonite. The bentonite is used in the proportion of 0.3 to 1.5 lb per ton of cane.

Déribéré and Esme (1951) have recently summarized the considerable quantity of literature on the use of montmorillonite clay for the clarification of wines, liqueurs, cider, beer, vinegar, etc., and the following statements are obtained largely from their publication.

A sodium montmorillonite, such as the Wyoming bentonite, has been largely used for this purpose. It is added to the wine, etc., in the form of a dilute suspension in an amount equal to about 1 to 2 parts per 1,000. The clay becomes flocculated, settling to the bottom, and thereby producing great clarity and sometimes a certain "brilliant appearance."

The clay treatment removes colloidal ferric-iron particles (hemoglobin) and reduces the protein content and the acidity. The action of the bentonite is speeded up by heating the wine to about 80°C. It is claimed that clay is particularly used for wines which are difficult to clarify, such as port and muscatel.

Bardollet and Paine (1927) describe a use for Wyoming bentonite in the clarification of starch-conversion liquors. Fiero (1929) reports that the same type clay is satisfactory to entirely renovate rancid cocoanut oil but that it would not entirely renovate lard, although the rancid odor was diminished. Lothrop and Paine (1931) describe the removal of colloids from honey with bentonite, and Hall and Lothrop (1934) used the same type of clay to clarify honey for culture media.

COATING SEEDS

There are some seeds, for example, those for sugar beets, which are too small to be planted by mechanical means. They require hand planting or the later thinning of the growing plants. Coating the seeds with clay increases their size to permit mechanical planting. It also permits fertilizers to be placed directly on the seed. Also, in the case of seeds packaged for garden use, various dyes may be incorporated in the coating to distinguish seeds of particular varieties.

Coated seeds have been prepared in rolling drums by adding powdered clay to moistened seeds. Some difficulty was encountered in preventing the development of pellets of the clay itself. Various montmorillonite clays have been used, but clays of other compositions might well be satisfactory.

DE-INKING NEWSPRINT PAPER

From time to time processes have been suggested in the literature for de-inking old newsprint paper as a step in using it again (Wells, 1922; Esme, 1928; Anon., 1927; Matagrin, 1943). These processes in general involve heating the paper in a caustic soda solution to break the shellac and other vehicles of the ink and thereby free the ink pigments. This is followed by the addition of a detergent to separate the pigment from the paper fiber and to prevent its agglomeration. This in turn is followed by the addition of a clay of the montmorillonite type which serves to disperse the pigment particles and also to adsorb them on the surface of the clay mineral particle. Final washing serves to remove the clay carrying the pigment.

It is not known if other types of clay with high adsorptive properties have been tried.

DESICCANTS, ABSORBENTS, AND MOLECULAR SIEVES

McCarter et al. (1950) have shown that one of the interesting properties of attapulgite clay is its ability to absorb 40 per cent or more of its weight of liquid active ingredients without losing its flowability, i.e., without becoming soft and plastic. The property of retaining particle size and shape in the course of absorption and regeneration is essential

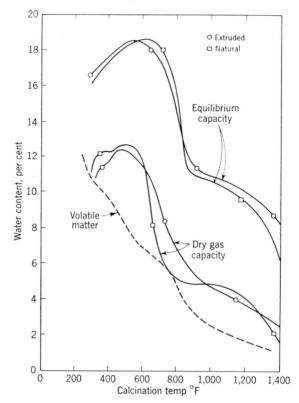

Fig. 8-3.   Effect of calcining temperature on residual water content and drying capacity of attapulgite, after McCarter et al. (1950).

for the use of a material as a desiccant or absorbent. The desirable properties of attapulgite are developed on heating to 450 to 650°F which reduces the volatile matter content to about 6 per cent (Fig. 8-3). At this temperature, the structure of the attapulgite is retained (Fig. 8-4), including the hydroxyls within the silicate lattice, but all the water is removed from the gutter-and-channel units. The heat activation is accompanied by an increase in surface area, which is relatively larger if the clay has previously been extruded through a die under high pressure. However, the extrusion does not serve to increase significantly the absorptive power. Calcining above the dehydroxylation temperature in the region in which the attapulgite structure is lost causes a sharp drop in absorption capacity even though the surface area is not reduced. This is explained by a change in the nature of the surface (see Chap. 4) before the amount of surface is reduced.

Montmorillonite clays that have been dried to temperatures (200 to

300°F) adequate to remove substantially all the interlayer water between the silicate sheets avidly absorb water and other polar molecules. The drying must not be carried to the complete loss of adsorbed water because total collapse of the silicate layers inhibits the later absorption and expansion of the lattice. At moderate to high relative humidities such clays with calcium as the adsorbed cation tend to adsorb two molecular layers of water between each silicate sheet and, hence, have higher capacities than those with sodium which adsorb only one molecular layer between the silicate units under the same relative humidities. Calcium montmorillonites have, therefore, been used as desiccants. However, the tendency of such clays to slake as liquids are adsorbed restricts their use as desiccants.

Considerable attention has been paid to the selective adsorptive properties of the attapulgite and montmorillonite clay minerals, particularly by Barrer and his colleagues (1954). It was thought that such selective adsorptive properties might permit the use of these clay minerals as molecular sieves. Currently molecular sieves appear to be prepared synthetically (Milton, 1959), and it is not known if the properties of the clay minerals will fit them for commercial use.

Chambers (1959) has stated recently that sepiolites also have significant adsorptive properties and has pointed out their possible use as molecular sieves.

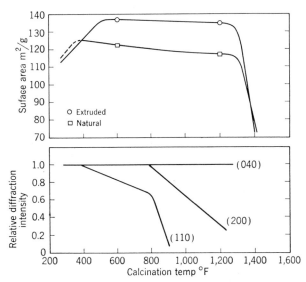

FIG. 8-4. Effect of calcining temperature on surface area and X-ray diffraction intensity of attapulgite, after McCarter et al. (1950).

EMULSIFYING, SUSPENDING, AND STABILIZING AGENTS

Clays, particularly the highly colloidal Wyoming-type bentonites composed of sodium montmorillonite, are used as emulsifying and stabilizing agents in oil-water systems and as suspending agents for solid particles in many liquid vehicles. Attapulgite clays also have properties claiming attention for such uses. There are no definite specifications for these uses except that the clay must perform satisfactorily in actual use, and it must be economical. Such clays are used both in "oil-in-water" emulsions and in "water-in-oil" emulsions. An example of this use of clay is in the preparation of bituminous-emulsion coatings for the surface protection of concrete.

An example of such use of clay in a water system is in a water-abrasive preparation for the grinding of optical lenses with automatic equipment. The clay serves to keep the abrasive uniformly in suspension in the water.

FABRICS

Clays, generally mixed with some sort of adhesive, are reportedly used for filling, sizing, and backing textiles of various kinds. Thus they are said to be used in backing compounds for tufted upholstery fabrics, for corduroy, and for burlap. Clays are said to be used in pigmented, latex, textile backings, and also in sizing compounds for some cotton goods.

Very fine-size grades of kaolinite type clays with particles ranging in size from 2 to 5 μ are commonly used. The whiteness of such clays and their freedom from grit make them satisfactory. Other specifications are not known except that the clays must be easily dispersible in the other ingredients of the compound. In general the only specification is that the clay must "work" in the desired formulation and under the conditions of use.

Cotton and linen may be dressed or finished with a variety of substances including clay frequently in mixtures containing starch. According to Woolman and McGowan (1926), a certain amount of dressing or sizing is legitimate and necessary in order to make the filaments in a spinning yarn more homogeneous and better able to stand the strain and friction of weaving, especially in the case of warp threads. White, fine-grained, kaolinite clays that are free from grit are used.

Printing-paste formulations for fabrics are reported containing either kaolinite or montmorillonite clays (Miller, 1942). Coatings of montmorillonite clays on synthetic yarns to reduce shrinkage (Field, 1950) and to prevent undue filament adherence (Conoway, 1947) are reported.

Alton and Jones (1936) disclose the use of montmorillonite clays in the delustering of textiles. Montmorillonite and attapulgite clays have possible use as filling agents and as suspending agents for other fillers for various fabrics.

FERTILIZERS

Certain types of clays have been added to soils from time to time because they contained substantial quantities of chemical elements needed as plant foods. Thus, illitic and glauconitic materials with relatively large amounts of potassium have been used. Generally such usage of clays has not been widespread for the reason that it is often desirable to add a blend of chemical elements, and the amount of the desired element in the clay is not high enough to be competitive with chemical fertilizers. Also the element in the clay may not be available rapidly enough for the desired plant growth.

Clays may be used as additives to chemical fertilizers as diluents to provide the optimum relative concentration of the elements. In such additions, the clay may be selected so that its composition will contribute to the chemical formulation of the fertilizer. The clay could also be selected so that it would add to the tilth of the soil; thus clays with high adsorptive capacity and water-holding power could be used in areas where the soils are naturally deficient in these characteristics.

Clays are used as prilling materials to coat particles of ammonium nitrate, which are components of many fertilizers. Ammonium nitrate particles are sticky, but a thin coating of some clays makes them free flowing. Attapulgite, and perhaps clays of other compositions, have been found useful for this purpose. Such material conditioned with 0.5 to 1 per cent of attapulgite clay is reported to be free flowing after months of storage. It is highly desirable that the separate chemical compounds of a blended chemical fertilizer be free flowing to permit satisfactory mixing without elaborate equipment and to permit easy and uniform application of the fertilizer by the farmer.

In recent years, there has been a rapidly expanding use of liquid fertilizers. Sawyer et al. (1959) state that in the 1957–1958 season, about 10 per cent of the fertilizer used was in liquid form. It is claimed that liquid fertilizers have cost advantages and that it is very easy to apply them uniformly. A primary requirement of liquid fertilizers is that they maintain uniformity throughout all the necessary handling steps from preparation to application by the farmer. It has been difficult to maintain such uniformity because of reactions between components and because some of the components, which must of necessity be in solid form, are difficult to keep in suspension. Solid particles are necessary because the limited solubility of some components prevents their presence in the required concentration in soluble form. Also highly soluble compounds may in some cases be too expensive. Clays are used in such fertilizers as suspending and stabilizing agents. Sawyer et al. (1959) point out that attapulgite clay is particularly useful because it provides water suspensions that are thixotropic. Also such suspensions have properties relatively resistant to change with substantial variations in electrolyte content. A 2 per cent content of this clay is reported to be adequate. It is not known if other types of clay have been found useful in liquid fertilizers.

Of particular interest is the recent discovery that certain clay minerals when added to the soil along with chemical fertilizers in the seed row appear to enhance the production of certain crops a great deal. Thus, attapulgite clay planted with okra has been shown in some cases to increase several-fold the amount of okra produced and to improve its quality. Results are not yet at hand to indicate whether this clay mineral works similarly for other crops and whether its activity is restricted to certain types of soil. Also the possible specific effect of other clay minerals on particular crops is not known.

Since attapulgite contains no chemical elements, except possibly magnesium, which can be considered plant food, its fertilizer value raises interesting questions to why it is effective. Okra apparently likes magnesium-rich soils, and the fact that attapulgite is a magnesium clay mineral may be an important part of the explanation. Perhaps the attapulgite contributes the magnesium in a manner very acceptable to the okra; also the magnesium would be relatively concentrated at the plant rootlets. Other possible explanations are that the attapulgite has a high water-holding capacity, which would increase the water retention in the soil around the rootlets, that the cation-exchange capacity of the clay mineral may cause the chemical fertilizer to be retained where it is most effective, and that the clay mineral may have certain catalytic properties. This is an extremely important field for future researches.

The clay mineral composition of soils is related to fertilizers indirectly in the attempted uses of organic chemical additives to improve the tilth, water-holding capacity, and other properties of soils. Such chemicals react with the clay minerals, and their effect on soil properties is by way of their reaction with these components of the soils. Since the reaction of organics is not the same for all clay minerals and since the clay mineral composition is not the same in all soils, the reactions and possible benefits would not be the same for all soils. It is important that this vital and fundamental fact be appreciated in the promotion of soil-treating agents.

MISCELLANEOUS FILLERS

Clays are used as fillers in a large number of products. Some particular filler uses of clay, e.g., in paper, will be considered separately, as large tonnages of clay are involved and considerable pertinent technical literature is available. There are many other filler uses for which no specifications can be stated except the production of a satisfactory product at low cost. Examples are asphalt products, such as roofing materials and road oil, and linoleum. In asphalt roofing, and in many other instances, a large variety of clays appear to be satisfactory. In some cases specific product requirements must be met; thus, the filler in road oil must aid in controlling the proper penetration of oil into the earth or pavement.

FLOOR ABSORBENT

Certain types of clay in granular form are used as absorbents in floor cleaning. Their major function is to absorb oily substances which would otherwise be difficult to remove and would cause slipperiness. Clays for this use must have a high oil-absorbing capacity, must not disperse in the oil, and must not make the surface slippery.

Attapulgite and certain types of montmorillonite calcined to a temperature which causes complete loss of adsorbed water and which does not destroy the clay mineral structure are used for this purpose. Calcining in the range 400 to about 1000°F does not reduce substantially the surface area or the oil-absorbing qualities, but it does destroy the ability of the granular particles to break up into small units.

The calcined clay is reduced to 10- to 60-mesh grades. In the case of attapulgite clay, bulk densities of the order of 30 to 35 lb per cu ft are developed by the calcining. A surface area of about 125 sq m per g is retained at the calcining temperature (McCarter et al., 1950). Chambers (1959) states that sepiolite clays are satisfactory for this use. Specifications for montmorillonite clays do not appear to have been published.

FOOD

In the United States, Wyoming-type bentonites (sodium montmorillonite clays) reportedly find use in wet-mash-type feeds. For example, in poultry feed for the final fattening of the fowl, a mixture of 5 lb of clay and 95 lb of dry mash may be added to 300 lb of water. In such proportions, a jellylike mass is formed holding the feed in a coherent shape and increasing its bulk. Without the clay, the coarser grains will settle and leave a top layer of water containing only the finely ground food stuff and fiber. It is said that a fowl will not dip its bill through water to get food and therefore will not benefit by the food that has settled. Hog slops also are frequently prepared with up to 5 per cent of such bentonite primarily because of its bulking and suspending properties.

Sodium montmorillonite clays have recently become widely used in pelleted animal foods of all kinds. In many cases, the natural feed ingredients themselves will impart enough adhesive qualities to make any special bonding material unnecessary. However, there are many cases in which the feed particles will not stick together, and in these cases the bentonite may be added. Also the clay tends to act as a lubricant for the pelleting dies thereby making their production easier. The amount of clay used averages about 2 per cent by weight with the quantity ranging from 1 to 5 per cent. The higher percentages are likely to be found in cattle feeds.

Clay has no food values, and it is essential that it have no toxic components. Thus there must be no traces of such metals as selenium and molybdenum, as measured in parts per million. However, experiments have suggested that small amounts of Wyoming bentonite may actually benefit the growth and health of the animals. Jordan (1953) reports that in a controlled feeding experiment lambs receiving bentonite in their ration consumed slightly more feed per day and were considerably easier to keep on full feed than the controls. Also the lambs receiving the bentonite gained slightly more weight in an 81-day period. Jordan explains the effect of the clay as follows: "In the digestive tract, it would adsorb water and digestive juices. It is theorized that the surface on which the digestive juices and bacteria acted would be increased and thus increase the feed utilization. Another theory is that bentonite may adsorb toxic substances produced in the digestive system." It seems safe to assert that the selective-adsorption properties of such clays for chemicals would play a significant role in the action of bentonite in the digestive tract (see Chap. 8, Medicines, Pharmaceuticals, and Cosmetics). Blakely et al. (1955) have published the results of controlled feeding tests on turkeys indicating a slight gain in weight with feed containing bentonite.

Briggs and Spivey-Fox (1956) investigated the possible vitamin A deficiency in chicks produced by adding bentonite to synthetic diets. No signs of vitamin A deficiency were produced by feeding up to 20 per cent of bentonite in practical chick diets containing vitamin A from natural sources. Twenty per cent of bentonite caused a significant depression in growth and feed efficiency which may have been due to a "dilution effect" or to adsorption of other nutrients by bentonite. It was found that the particle size of the bentonite was a factor in the development of vitamin A deficiency; when the bentonite was 90 mesh or coarser, no untoward symptoms were noted unless very large quantities were used in the feed (20 per cent). These authors point out the necessity of using stabilized vitamin A, because bentonite will destroy the potency of nonstabilized vitamin A products.

Venezia (1948) reports that grapes can be kept in perfect condition for at least five months if properly packed in montmorillonite clay. The author claims that the clay completely envelops the grapes covering them with an impalpable film and affording perfect control of humidity so that sufficient life is left in the grapes to maintain freshness and flavor without permitting the development of mold or other organisms.

Holden (1948) claims that the addition of 0.25 to 1.25 per cent of Wyoming bentonite by weight of the total cereal or flour content reduces staling in bread or other baked cereals. It is claimed that the bentonite addition reduces the amount of yeast required. Esselbaugh (1948) states that additions of 0.8 to 1 per cent of the same type of clay substantially increases the loaf volume of soft and hard wheat bread.

Rosner (1958) claims that the presence of 0.3 to 1.5 per cent of kaolin in a dusting-sugar mixture improves the adherence of the sugar on doughnuts.

It is reported that some people in remote areas of the world include clay or earth in their diets. The reasons for this are not clear, but it appears likely that the custom developed because of a real or fancied health benefit.

GREASES

It has been customary to stabilize the gel properties of lubricating greases with various soaps. Recently, it has been claimed that clays, particularly those composed of organic-clad clay mineral particles, can be used to gel organic liquids and thereby produce greases with superior properties, because the grease consumption is reduced, the adherence to metal is improved, the grease is more water repellent, and the grease works better at extremely high and low temperatures (Hauser, 1950; Jordan, 1950).

Organic-clad montmorillonites sold under the trade name "Bentone" (National Lead Company) are prepared by a cation-exchange reaction whereby the inorganic cation of the natural montmorillonite is exchanged for an alkyl amine organic cation. The clay is first washed to remove all the grit. The reaction produces a hydrophobic clay, because the inorganic cations that can be hydrated have been removed and a large part of the clay mineral surface which formerly adsorbed water has been coated by hydrocarbon chains. Bentones are prepared with organic molecules of various kinds and sizes. The value of particular ones depends on the oil to be gelled. Also the size of the organic molecule can determine the amount of the clay mineral surface coated and, hence, the degree of hydrophobicity.

When such organic-clad montmorillonites are mixed with organic liquids, the alkyl chains become solvated. In effect, each tiny flake of montmorillonite becomes surrounded by a large shell of liquid which is immobilized, and thus the gel structure develops. Such clays are in general adequate to gel pure, moderately or highly polar organic liquids. In the case of nonpolar liquids and those of low polarity an addition of a highly polar liquid, such as methanol, must be made to develop highly the gel structure. Organic-clad montmorillonites of the order of 4 to 7 per cent are required to develop gel structures of sufficient rigidity for use as lubricants. Additions of approximately 0.5 to 3 per cent of a polar liquid may be required in cases where the primary liquid to be gelled is nonpolar.

Jordan (1949) has pointed out that the maximum gelling efficiency is attained when the ratio of the ammonium salt to the clay is equal to approximately 100 per cent of the cation-exchange capacity. Substantial retention of amine can be obtained at higher ratios of amine to mineral, but in general the gelling capacity decreases. Such excess amine would tend to coat the alkyl layer of the organic-clad surface and thereby interfere with the solvation of the alkyl chains.

Information is not at hand as to whether or not other types of clay minerals, clad or unclad, have been used in grease manufacture. However, it seems likely that some other types, for example, attapulgite clays, would have potential value for this purpose.

INK

Printing inks in their simplest form are fine dispersions of pigments and/or solutions of dyes in vehicles capable of imparting the peculiar properties required by the various printing processes (Mattiello, 1943). A wide variety of vehicles, including resins, oils, varnish, and drying components, is used. In black inks, the pigment is usually carbon black. The consistency of the ink varies from quite fluid to fairly viscous depending on the printing process for which the ink is to be used.

Kaolinite-type clays are used largely in printing inks. The whiteness of kaolins is an important advantage. Satisfactory clays must be free from grit and very fine grained—these demands are such that water-washed and chemically bleached products are required. Clays not so extensively processed may be used to a limited extent in nonexpensive inks, such as those for bags and burlap. Fine-particle-size kaolins with substantially all particles smaller than 2 μ are being used in letterpress carbon inks and some halftone inks. A fairly large volume is also being used in certain types of gravure inks (Bernstein, 1956).

A major deterrent to the use of clays in inks has been their essential hydrophilic character. High water wettability tends to produce a poor ink, since the pigment is not tightly bound to the vehicle, assuming that the vehicle is of the drying-oil, hydrophobic type. Stated another way, the resultant cohesiveness of the ink is low, and the ink under certain conditions may show a tendency to pile, even in conventional letterpress inks. In lithographic offset inks, the use of such a hydrophilic pigment, except in very small amounts, obviously would be ruled out. There are, however, certain other types of printing ink in which the clays' affinity for water is of value.

The deficiency in clays caused by their hydrophilic nature has been remedied by coating the fine kaolinite particles with a hydrophobic material thereby changing the character of the kaolins in ink formulations. Hydrophobic kaolins composed of organic-clad kaolinite particles are particularly adapted for use in polar and nonpolar viscous ink systems. The development of such kaolins has extended the variety of vehicles that can be used in such inks. It should be emphasized that in some such systems, noncoated hydrophilic kaolins are still superior (Bernstein, 1956). In fluid-ink systems, such as the gravure inks, where suspension properties are very important, the organic-clad kaolins are said to be definitely superior to the unclad varieties. It is claimed that organic-clad montmorillonites are valuable in some inks to control consistency, tack, and penetration and also that additions of 3 to 4 per cent of such clay to newsprint ink will eliminate most of the normal misting during the printing operation (Curado and Praeg, 1956; Voet and Yelmgren, 1956).

LEATHER

According to Wilson (1935) and Albert (1940) clays are used in the manufacture of leather to lighten the color and to give the leather a softer and smoother feel. In some cases, clay is used to overcome piping and looseness, to improve color, and to develop a better surface. Wilson (1935) states that clays are used in the oil wheel in the manufacture of sole leather and in the fat-liquor drum in the manufacture of white leather. According to this author, fine-grained kaolinite clays have advantageous properties as they readily penetrate the leather. Such clays would also have the advantage of being white.

MEDICINES, PHARMACEUTICALS, AND COSMETICS

Clays have been used for centuries in therapeutic, intestinal, adsorbent preparations. The purpose of intestinal adsorbents is to combat intestinal irritation. The clays are believed to function by adsorbing toxins and bacteria, which are thought to be responsible for the onset of diarrhea, vomiting, nausea, and cramps in various types of intestinal infections; and by coating the inflamed mucous membrane of the digestive tract (Goodman and Gilman, 1955).

Kaolinite clays have been employed almost exclusively as the major adsorbent in intestinal adsorbent preparations for many centuries. According to Barr (1958), attapulgite clays, which have been activated by moderate heating processes, are five to eight times superior as adsorbents for alkaloids, bacteria, and toxins compared with kaolins and kaolinite clays. By its highly effective adsorption of the aqueous part of inflammatory secretions, attapulgite aids in stool formation.

Clays used internally must be substantially free from heavy metals and any other substance that the body will not tolerate. Clays generally contain little or no lead, arsenic, etc.; however, the occurrence of such elements is likely to be sporadic and unpredictable, so that clays for such use must be continuously analyzed to be certain that the specifications are met. Such clays must also be free from grit and not provide an obnoxious taste and odor to the preparations. According to Barr (1958), the toxicity of attapulgite as well as of kaolinite clay is significantly low. Clinical studies have shown that the clays are tolerated excellently, and side effects have not been observed.

Clays are reported to have other medicinal properties, but little can be gained from the literature concerning the extent of such use. The following can be considered only as examples of the reported potential uses of clays for some medicinal purposes. Fantus (1915) states that fuller's earth (probably attapulgite) has an antidotal value in morphine, cocaine, nicotine, and ipecac poisoning. It is said to have less value in strychnine and aconitine poisoning, although, even in such cases, it is capable of saving life when combined with NaH_2PO_4. According to Hanut (1938), kaolin adsorbs the coagulant principles of certain snake venoms. Lemetayer and Uhry (1938) state that kaolin suspensions injected with antiserum reinforces the protection of the latter toward tetanus toxin. Masucci (1943) claims an antigenic composition suitable for injection into living beings consisting of a dilute bentonite suspension of an antigen, such as a diphtheria toxoid.

As a preparation for animals, Whiting (1947) incorporated bentonite in an antihelminthic composition for expelling or destroying intestinal worms.

Clays of various kinds, but particularly those composed of montmorillonite, kaolinite, or attapulgite, have been used for a long time in the preparation of pastes, ointments, and lotions for external use; perhaps the best known of these uses is in the preparation of antiphlogistine for checking inflammation. The suspending, gelling, and adsorptive properties of the clay minerals are valued for such uses. According to Lesser (1941) bentonite is used to suspend barium sulfate in the "barium meal" required for the X-ray study of the internal organs.

Clays are reportedly used by the medical profession in analyses where their selective adsorptive properties make them of value. Thus Fischer and Iwanoff (1943) indicate the use of clays (kaolin and attapulgite are mentioned) in the purification of such substances as caffeine, cantharidin, and santonin in toxicological analyses. Somewhat similar is the determination of tocopherols in muscle tissue using attapulgite (Deolin and Mattill, 1942).

Several authors (Seidell, 1922; Salmon, Guerrant, and Hays, 1928) record the use of fuller's earth (probably attapulgite) and montmorillonite in processes for concentrating and purifying vitamins.

The literature, particularly the patent literature, contains many suggested cosmetic formulations containing montmorillonite, attapulgite, or kaolinite clays that take advantage of their softness, dispersion, gelling, emulsifying, adsorption, or other properties. How widely such clays are actually used in such preparations is not known.

PAINT

Introduction

Paint is essentially a fluid system in which solid bodies, usually identified as pigments, are suspended. The functional purpose of the pigments is to provide color, hiding power, film strength, and resistance to weathering of the protective film developed from the vehicle. Other agents may be a part of the system to influence other properties, such as brushability, body, or film surface (glossy or flat).

Until relatively recently most paints contained an oil as a vehicle. Now the vehicle may be oil, latex, water, and/or a large number of organic chemicals. The vehicle is often a mixture of these substances; for example, emulsion types are very common.

Various types of clays have been used for a long time as paint ingredients. They were first used simply as inert fillers, largely to reduce cost, and because of the lack of refinement, they were held in ill repute. However, with the advance in the knowledge of clays and their refining, it is now known that clays may add valuable properties to paints, and indeed they are essential components of some types of paint.

Types of Clay Used in Paint

KAOLINITE

Kaolins that are essentially pure kaolinite clays are used very widely in paint formulations. In general the kaolins are water washed, chemically bleached, and fractionated to produce a controlled particle-size distribution. Kaolins used in the paint trade range generally in average particle size from 0.5 to 5 μ and have only a trace of residue on a 325-mesh sieve. Clay producers market grades of different particle-size distribution, for, as will be shown presently, the properties in paint vary with the particle size, and the same particle size is not equally acceptable in all types of paint. In the United States, kaolins for the paint trade are mined in Georgia and South Carolina. Elsewhere, they are mined in the Cornwall district of Great Britain, in Germany, France, Czechoslovakia, Japan, and possibly also in other countries.

The amount of kaolin in paint formulations varies with the type of paint. The amount may be only 2 to 5 per cent as in the case of some enamels where it is used as a suspension aid and to assist in the prevention of flooding. On the other hand in some interior wall paints, 70 per cent of the total volume is pigment of which 70 per cent may be kaolin. House paints are prepared containing 2 to 3 lb of clay per gal which means that the paint contains about 25 per cent clay by weight.

It is claimed that kaolinite clays have the following desirable properties in paint formulations.

They impart desirable and controllable surface characteristics. Thus, such clays are used in some formulations to attain the desired sheen. It is thought that kaolinite clays impart a high, uniform sheen because the kaolinite particles generally have thicknesses less than the wave length of light. They permit high pigment loading; this is particularly true in semigloss paints where there is a gradual loss of gloss with increased loading rather than a sharp drop at a given loading value.

Kaolinite clays are rapidly and completely wettable in many vehicles. Actually kaolins seem to improve the ease of dispersion of other pigments which are more difficult to incorporate in the paint. They are non-abrasive, and they give good use performance; this has been shown, for example, in outside water-thinned paint. Such clays provide good brushability and good flow and leveling qualities. They have good suspension properties, which reduces settling on storage and gives good shelf qualities.

Kaolins add to the hiding power. This has been especially shown in water paints and oleoresinous paints. They have satisfactory oil absorption properties. Table 8-5 shows the oil-absorption values obtained

TABLE 8-5

OIL ABSORPTION OF KAOLINS AND OTHER PAINT FILLERS
(After Minerals and Chemicals Philipp Corp.,
Tech. Inf. Sheet 204, 1958)

Kaolin A (average particle size, 5 μ)........... 34.2[a]
Kaolin B (average particle size, 0.5 μ)......... 43.0
Calcium carbonate........................ 15 – 60
Talc.................................... 25 – 57
Diatomaceous earth....................... 24 –110
Precipitated silica........................ 22.6– 35
Mica................................... 24.5– 52
Aerogels................................ 170 –250

[a] Pounds of oil absorbed per 100 lb of pigment.

for kaolins of different average particle size as well as similar values for other pigments. *Oil absorption* is defined as the least amount of oil which is required by a specified amount of pigment to form a paste of given characteristics determined according to a standard procedure (A.S.T.M., D281-31). It is usually expressed as pounds of oil per 100 pounds of pigment. As would be expected the coarser kaolins have the lower oil-absorption value, and consequently they have the lowest vehicle demand and the highest loading potential. The coarser kaolins are sometimes more difficult to disperse and would probably have less hiding power than the finer-grained clays. Probably a certain particle-size distribution rather than actual fineness produces optimum hiding power.

Clays are hydrophilic in nature causing them to mix more easily with water than many other liquids. When used in paints such clays are dried to less than 1 per cent absorbed water, but even so, by the time of actual use they probably have absorbed some water so that they have at least a monolayer of water physically held on their surfaces. In many cases hydrophilic pigments can be dispersed satisfactorily in organic systems, but this is not the case with all organic vehicles. Also, the presence of the water film is thought to cause undesirable properties in some systems. All this has somewhat limited the use of clay pigments in organic liquid systems. To remedy this situation kaolins have been produced, and are now on the market, in which the individual kaolinite particles are coated with a variety of organics. These "surface-modified" kaolins are available in a variety of particle-size distributions. Those clad with cationic surfactants are perhaps most common, but some with other coatings are available. The development of the "surface-modified" kaolins has been an extremely important advance in the kaolin industry. It has been possible to prepare kaolins clad with organics that are specific for certain vehicles.   In other words, the kaolin can be tailor-made for a particular use, so that its surface reacts in the most desirable fashion with the organic liquid or, if it is desired, does not react at all with the organic vehicle. The process used in the production of these kaolins has not been made public, and the coatings used are usually not stated.

As shown in Table 8-6, the surface area determined by nitrogen ab-

TABLE 8-6

SOME CHARACTERISTICS OF ORGANIC-CLAD KAOLINS
(From Minerals and Chemicals Philipp Corp., Tech. Data Sheet 1,026, 1958)

Kaolin	Oil absorption, ml/100 g	Water surface, area sq m/g	Nitrogen surface, area sq m/g	Hydrophobic surface, %
A	36.2	6.7	15.0	55
B	34.0	6.1	11.4	46
C	35.7	9.6	12.9	26
D	38.0	9.8	13.0	25
E	40.0	10.6	12.0	11
F	47.6	13.8	13.6	0
G	49.0	15.1	15.0	0

sorption does not necessarily change very much in the coating of the kaolins, but the water-surface area shows a large change.   Oil absorption also shows a large change, although the amount is controlled by the selection of the coating and the manner of preparation of the clad particles.

Kaolins calcined to temperatures of the order of 1700°F and then very finely ground are also used in paint formulations.   Such calcination completely dehydrates the kaolinite and reduces its water-absorbing tendencies.   It also increases the brightness value to 90 to 92 and the oil absorption to 56 to 58 for a product with 0.005 per cent residue on a 325-mesh sieve and for material with an average particle size of 0.8 μ. Slightly coarser kaolin with an average particle size of 1 μ has an oil-absorption value of 46 to 47.   Calcined kaolins appear to have enhanced hiding power as compared with noncalcined kaolins.   Calcined kaolins are said to be used in a variety of types of paint.

ATTAPULGITE

Clay composed of attapulgite is used in paint because in some formulations it adds desired thickening and thixotropic properties.   It also serves as a flattening agent.   Attapulgite has high oil-absorption values, in the range of 85 to 104 per cent (Minerals and Chemicals Philipp Corp., Tech. Inf. Sheet 204, 1958).

MONTMORILLONITE

Bentonite clays composed essentially of montmorillonite are used extensively in paints. The desirable montmorillonite clays are those which carry sodium as the exchangeable cation and which are highly colloidal and readily and completely dispersible. In the United States such clays are produced in the Wyoming area. In other countries, such as Germany, France, and England, the sodium montmorillonites are prepared synthetically from natural calcium clays by using a cation-exchange reaction procedure. In the United States the sodium value may be enhanced by treatment of the crude bentonites with soda ash.

Bentonites are used in both oil- and water-based paints. In water-based paints the montmorillonite clay acts as a suspending and thickening agent. It can be used, for example, as the carrier for portland cement. Bentonite is used also as an emulsifying agent in water- and oil-paint formulations.

Like kaolinite, montmorillonite is hydrophilic and thus may be difficult to disperse in some oil vehicles. To overcome this difficulty, organic-clad montmorillonite clays are used. Such organic-clad montmorillonites can be tailor-made with a variety of organic compounds to meet the requirements of different vehicles, such as lacquers, epoxy resins, and vinyl resins. These clays are said to give the following desirable effects: improved pigment suspension because of an effective coupling of the adsorbed organic with the free vehicle, which has the effect of reducing the attractive forces of one particle for another; enlarged effective particle size, giving the particle a lower average specific gravity; and improved viscosity and thixotropy control, since each increment of organic-clad montmorillonite in general produces a proportionate rise in viscosity and gelation. The gel structure is said to enhance brushability and spraying characteristics and to permit some control of the penetration of the vehicle into porous surfaces. In some vehicles, the organic-clad clay contributes a mild degree of flattening action. Amounts of clay of the order of 2 to 10 lb per 100 gal are used.

PAPER

Introduction

Paper is a thin uniform sheet of fine intermeshed and felted cellulose fibers. The cellulose for the highest quality paper is obtained from cotton and linen, but for most purposes fibers obtained from a large variety of woods are satisfactory.

A single sheet of cellulose fibers is not well suited to high fidelity printing because of transparency and irregularities of the surface. These deficiencies are corrected by the addition of binding agents, such as starch and resin, and by the mechanical incorporation into the fiber stock of various mineral fillers, such as calcium carbonate, calcium sulfate, and especially relatively pure white clay. When such a sheet is polished by passage through smooth rolls (calendering), it becomes usable for a great variety of printing applications. The amount of filler used ranges up to 35 per cent of the weight of the paper.

Ordinary filled paper still lacks the perfection of surface smoothness required for accurate production of the tiny ink dots in halftone printing. The quality of the filled sheet is often enhanced by coating its surface with a thin film of finely divided mineral pigment suspended in an adhesive mixture, such as starch and casein. Depending on the desired effect, the coating pigment might be calcium carbonate, satin white, titanium dioxide, and especially relatively pure white clay with a specific particle-size distribution. The amount of coating ranges up to 25 per cent of the weight of the paper.

The coating preparation must fulfill the following requirements: It must penetrate and bond satisfactorily to the surface of the paper; it must flow well enough to permit the required degree of spreading at the machine speed; it must have the proper leveling and setting characteristics after being applied to the surface of the paper; and, on drying, a smooth surface must develop that can be calendered to produce a gloss without the application of undue pressure.

The adaptability of clays for paper use is a consequence of such characteristics as softness of texture, absence of harsh impurities, chemical inertness, desirable brightness, satisfactory ink absorption, relatively low adhesive demands, controllable particle-size distribution, ability to produce high gloss, and desirable rheological properties.

Paper-clay Evaluation Tests

The publications of the Technical Association of the Pulp and Paper Industry (Lyons, 1958) describe the tests generally used to evaluate clays for the paper industry. The following statements are taken from these publications, and the reader is referred to them for further details.

Abrasion

A clay-water slurry of specified concentration is circulated through a perforated rubbing block which is in contact with a small section of Fourdrinier wire, simulating the action of the clay on similar wire in the paper machine. Abrasiveness is recorded in terms of loss of wire weight in milligrams. The widest variation in abrasiveness is in filler clays, and the test is generally applied only to filler clays.

BRIGHTNESS

This property is determined usually with a reflection meter in which the per cent reflectance of the clay sample is obtained by comparing it with an opal glass standard of known reflectance. The determination is made at an effective wave length of 458 millimicrons. The clay sample is prepared by drying to not over 105°C. and with a maximum moisture content not in excess of 1.5 per cent.

"MAKE-DOWN" TEST

The perfection of any coated surface depends greatly on how well the clay has been "made down" or dispersed in the coating mixture. No simple laboratory method has been developed for measuring the extent or completeness with which coating clays disperse which can be correlated satisfactorily with plant operating conditions. However, some measure of this property can be obtained by subjecting a fluid clay-water mixture to a definite amount of agitation, blending the dispersed clay-water mixture with an adhesive solution, followed by screening of the complete color ("color" in the paper industry designates the coating mixture). A thin film of the finished color is then spread on a smooth glass plate, and the surface is graded in accordance with the size and number of undispersed clay particles which are visible under 4-5 magnifications.

PARTICLE-SIZE DISTRIBUTION

Using Stokes' law, which relates settling rate in a liquid to density and size of particles and the specific gravity and viscosity of the liquid, the particles' size distribution is determined. The hydrometer method is frequently used. Stokes' law is based on spherical particles and hence results are in so-called equivalent spherical diameters. A sodium polyphosphate or sodium silicate is used as the dispersing agent, and an attempt is made to attain maximum dispersion.

SCREEN RESIDUE

This value is the residue on 200 and 325 mesh screens determined by placing the dry pigment on the screens, wetting with water and washing the pigment through the screen with a stream of water. In order to break up the aggregates that are wetted with difficulty it is necessary to use a brush or the finger tip. Some methods call for the use of acetone or alcohol to wet the clay prior to washing with the stream of water. The test is not very satisfactory as the results depend to a great extent on the amount of brushing or rubbing.

VISCOSITY

The viscosity of coating mixtures is determined with instruments capable of administering varying shearing forces. However, the vast array of coating formulations precludes any standard test formula for viscosity measurements. For ordinary purposes, a recipe containing 42 per cent total solids with 15 parts of casein to 100 parts of clay is quite satisfactory for differentiating clays for brush or "air-blade" types of operation. Similarly, a recipe containing 57.5 per cent total solids with 17 parts of commercially modified starch of medium viscosity to 100 parts of clay, is helpful in differentiating clays for machine coating operations. Extreme care is necessary in obtaining accurate concentrations of clay and adhesive, as well as uniformity in the degree and type of agitation during the compounding of the test color as changes in these factors may seriously alter the flow characteristics of the mixture.

Clay-water systems offer a much better prospect for the establishment of a standard viscosity test. The test is generally made on a mixture containing 70 per cent clay dispersed to maximum fluidity with a sodium polyphosphate frequently tetrasodium pyrophosphate. A viscosity evaluation of this type is particularly useful in predicting the rate of flow through fine screens in operations which require screening of highly concentrated clay-water systems.

Values are frequently presented for two rates of shear, for example, 10 and 100 rpm, and in the form of curves which plot shearing force applied against rpm. The latter are particularly useful in making evident any dilatant or thixotropic properties.

Types of Clay Used and Their Preparation

KAOLIN

Clays composed of kaolinite in as pure a form as possible are wanted for filling and coating papers, except, as will be noted presently, when papers with special properties are desired. Clays easily dispersible in water are necessary, and they should have, in the crude state, a fairly wide particle-size distribution so that a range of products with varying particle size can be prepared commercially. The clay should be as nearly white as possible or capable of easy chemical bleaching to a high degree of whiteness. Gray kaolins, because of the presence of organic pigments, have generally been found unsatisfactory. Kaolins containing halloysite also do not appear to be used in the paper industry. Kaolins of both sedimentary and hydrothermal origin (known in the industry as secondary and primary kaolins) have been found to be excellent for paper use.

Kaolins generally contain appreciable quantities (2 to 4 per cent) of titanium dioxide in the form of extremely minute particles of anatase. Such particles, which may be well under 1 μ in diam, serve to reduce somewhat the brightness of the clay, and much thought has been given to their removal, so far without commercial success.

In the United States, extensive tonnages of kaolins for the paper industry are mined in Georgia and South Carolina from deposits of sedimentary origin; more than one-half of the kaolin mined goes into the paper industry. Large amounts of paper-grade kaolins are mined from deposits of hydrothermal origin in the Cornwall district of Great Britain; they are also mined in Germany, Czechoslovakia, U.S.S.R., Japan, and Australia. In many instances the mode of origin of these deposits is not known definitely.

Dry Preparation Process. The crude clay, naturally containing 20 to 25 per cent moisture, is dried to 1 to 2 per cent water. The dry clay is then fed to a grinding mill equipped with a separator and cyclone collector. The particles of desired fineness are lifted from the grinding chamber by an air current of controlled velocity while the coarser particles are rejected from the upward stream by the separators. The inherent fineness and grit content of the crude clay determines its suitability for air separation. The crude clay must also be of a color requiring no chemical bleaching. In general, dry processed kaolins are suitable only for filling clays.

Wet-preparation Process. This process involves the separation of water-suspended clay fractions with controlled particle-size ranges followed by filtration and drying. An additional step to whiten and bleach the clay by chemical means is sometimes applied to get the requisite brightness and whiteness.

The clay is dispersed in water by blunging, using sodium silicate or a sodium polyphosphate as the dispersing agent. The grit and coarser clay particles are allowed to settle out of the suspension, which is then fractionated to achieve the classification of kaolinite particles of given sizes. For the latter purpose, Bird-type continuous centrifuges are often used in the United States.

Chemical bleaching to remove discoloration caused by iron compounds is accomplished by reducing insoluble oxides of iron to soluble ferrous compounds, frequently by using either zinc or sodium salts of hydrosulfurous acid. Such treatment enhances the brightness by 2 to 7 points.

The clay slips are dewatered by plate and frame filters or by continuous-type drum filters and then dried to the desired moisture content in rotary or tunnel driers. In recent years spray driers have been used to dewater and dry the clay in one operation. Spray drying permits the retention of the dispersing agent, and this has led to the production of "predispersed" clays, which do not require a further addition of chemical dispersing agents when the color is made up in the paper mill.

Calcined Clay. Kaolins calcined to temperatures in excess of that required to completely dehydrate the kaolinite (1000°F) and below that at which new high temperature phases form and the clay begins to vitrify

(1700°F) have been found useful in some paper-coating operations. Following calcination, the clay is ground to extreme fineness. Calcination may increase the brightness to 90 to 92 per cent but also tends to increase somewhat the abrasiveness.

ATTAPULGITE

This type of clay is used in the manufacture of the so-called NCR (no carbon required) paper (Barrett et al., 1951). The clay is used to coat the upper surface of a sheet of paper; the lower surface is coated with minute globules of a certain kind of organic compound. The lower surface of one sheet rests on the upper surface of a second sheet. The pressure of writing serves to break the globules of the organic compound which then penetrates the attapulgite clay coating causing a color reaction, and the mark is made on the second sheet.

According to Allegrini and Claxton (1960), attapulgite clay can be used to reclaim fiber from waxed-paper broke (industrial waste, cuttings, etc.) by shredding the broke, heating it in the presence of the granular clay, and separating the fiber from the adsorbent clay. The clay is regenerated by heating to about 1000°F. The content of wax and polyethylene is reduced to less than 1 per cent from original values of about 27 per cent wax and 6 per cent polyethylene.

MONTMORILLONITE

Bentonite clays composed of montmorillonite of the highly colloidal and easily dispersible type, such as the variety carrying sodium as the exchangeable cation from the Wyoming area, are used for several purposes in paper making. Pitch, tars, waxes, and resinous material from the wood and from waste cuttings and mixed paper may tend to agglomerate to a sufficient size to stick to screens, machine wires, press rolls, etc., and cause defects in the paper. It is claimed that the addition to the pulp slurry of $\frac{1}{4}$ to $\frac{1}{2}$ per cent of such clay, based on the dry weight of paper stock, will prevent the agglomeration of such particles and, hence, correct the difficulty. It is also claimed that the addition of 1 to 2 per cent of such clay at the beater or pulper will increase the retention of pigments by the paper stock and also the uniformity of their distribution throughout the paper.

Specifications of Kaolins for Paper Use

FILLER

Kaolins prepared by either the dry or wet process may be used as fillers. The selection is frequently a matter of cost and the preference of individual paper-mill operators. A compilation of the properties of widely

TABLE 8-7

PROPERTIES OF SOME KAOLINS USED IN PAPER MANUFACTURE

(From Minerals and Chemicals Philipp Corp.)

	Filler clay		Coating clay			
	A	B	C[b]	D	E	F[b]
Particle-size distribution, equivalent spherical diameter, % by weight:						
0 – 0.5 μ	20	4	44	44	30	26
0.5– 1 μ	21	6	28	28	27	29
1 – 2 μ	17	10	20	20	23	23
2 – 5 μ	13	31	8	8	17	20
5 –10 μ	12	30	0	0	3	7
10 –30 μ	7	19	0	0	0	0
Maximum screen residue, wet, 325 mesh..........	0.15	0.15	0.005	0.01	0.01	0.008
GE brightness....	82.5–84	80.5–83	86.5–88	86.5–88	85 –86.5	85 –86.5
pH.............	4.2– 5.0	3.8– 4.6	6.3– 7.0	4.2– 4.6	4.2– 4.6	6.3– 7.0
Maximum viscosity:[a]						
at 10 rpm.....	...	...	500	500	350	300
at 100 rpm....	...	...	200	200	200	180

[a] TAPPI procedure, Brookfield, R.V.F., 70 per cent solids; No. 3 spindle.
[b] Clays C and F are "predispersed."

used kaolins is given in Table 8-7. The brightness varies from about 80 to 84 although sometimes slightly lower values are acceptable. The residue on a 325-mesh screen is generally lower than about 0.15 per cent. The particle-size distribution varies considerably from one kaolin to another (Table 8-7 and Fig. 8-5). Usually there are relatively small amounts of particles coarser than about 10 μ and finer than 1 to 2 μ. A moderate range of particle sizes is desired as it favors increased opacity. Abrasion-test values of 13 to 16 mg are usual. The viscosity characteristics of filler clays are not important, but the clay must be easily dispersible.

COATING

Coating kaolins are usually produced by the wet process and are chemically bleached to attain the desired brightness, which is frequently

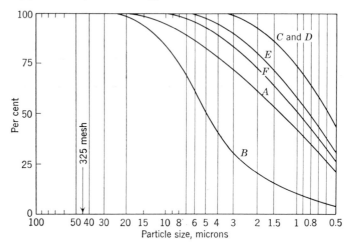

FIG. 8-5. Cumulative particle-size distribution curves of some kaolins used in paper manufacture, data from Minerals and Chemicals Philipp Corp. (1960).

in the range from 85 to 88 per cent.	It is interesting that uncalendered surfaces possess the higher brightness whereas the calendered surfaces have the higher gloss.	Calendering reduces the brightness but enhances the polish or gloss of the surface (Fig. 8-6).

The data presented in Table 8-7 and Fig. 8-5 show that coating kaolins yield only a trace of residue on a 325-mesh screen (less than 0.01 per cent) and a very small quantity of particles coarser than 2 μ.	In the best grades of coating clays the bulk of the particles are finer than about 1 μ.	Maloney (1930) appears to have been the first to point out the improved hiding power and gloss-making character of kaolinite particles

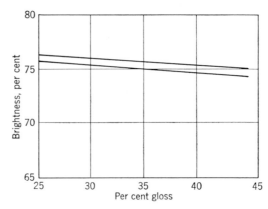

FIG. 8-6. Relation of brightness to gloss with increased calendering, after Anon. (1955).

finer than about 2 μ. It is well known that such fine particles also improve the brightness.

The rheological properties of coating kaolins are extremely important. Clay-water mixtures containing as much as 68 to 72 per cent clay are often required to be sufficiently fluid to permit free passage through relatively fine screens. Also they must have flow properties which will permit spreading at very high coating-machine speeds (1,000 fpm) and leveling after application to the paper surface. The suspensions should not be dilatant, as it is well known (Albert, 1951) that dilatant compositions cannot be applied satisfactorily because they cause "chattering" of the rolls producing a nonuniform surface. A moderate amount of thixotropy is desired—thus Smith and his coworkers (1950) have shown that there is a minimum value below which a coating color will not apply properly.

The change in resistance to flow of clay-water systems becomes very pronounced after the amount of clay reaches about 65 per cent solids. Figure 8-7 shows this abrupt change in viscosity. Such suspensions, even when dispersed to maximum fluidity with a sodium polyphosphate, will vary in character from mixtures too thick to pour to those thin enough to flow readily through a 200-mesh screen. Moreover, the flow properties of such highly concentrated systems are not always consistent with clay fineness and often exhibit irregular and unpredictable trends. The variation is influenced by particle size and shape, their distribution, and perhaps by other characteristics not well understood. An example of the variation between two different kaolins of similar particle sizes is shown in Fig. 8-8.

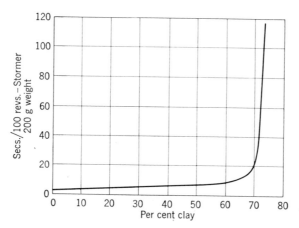

Fig. 8-7. Effect of clay concentration on flow characteristics of kaolin-water system, after Anon. (1955).

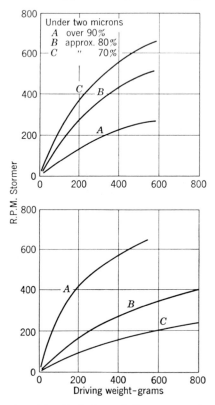

FIG. 8-8. Relation of flow properties to particle fineness of two crude kaolins in 70 per cent clay-water systems, after Anon. (1955).

It is evident that a clay-water mixture is not a simple system. Its properties are made even more complex by the incorporation of adhesive suspension of either starch or casein. Clay-coating mixtures, unless used in extremely dilute suspensions, seldom produce strict Newtonian flow systems, in which the viscosity is proportional to the shearing force. Thus, consistency curves must be determined over a range of shearing forces.

The literature on paper clays contains an abundance of data on rheological properties. In general each paper mill has certain specifications that the vender must meet. Also each vender is prepared to submit viscosity determinations of his clay and generally is prepared to produce a clay that will meet the demanded specifications by particle-size selection, character, and amount of additive in a predispersed clay, etc. Some crude kaolins have inherent properties permitting the production of low-viscosity products, whereas others will not yield such products after any sort of preparation. The kaolin producer, therefore, frequently selectively mines his clays, keeping the low-viscosity kaolins for the coating trade.

Theory of Paper Coating with Kaolins

Kaolinite particles are inherently white flakes with smooth surfaces. In the coating and calendering operations these flakes are plastered on the fiber surface with their plane surfaces parallel. The high degree of parallelism is easily demonstrated by X-ray diffraction analyses of coated papers.

Woodward and Lyons (1951) have shown that kaolinite particles smaller than about 2μ appear as single flakes, whereas larger particles tend to be aggregates of these flakes. This, according to these authors, explains the superior coating qualities of clays with all particles smaller than 2μ.

It must be remembered that this is equivalent spherical particle size, which means that the flakes are considerably thinner than 2 μ, so that the maximum roughness due to the overlap of flakes would be much less than 2 μ.

Murray and Lyons (1956) have shown that, in general, the suitability of a kaolin for paper coating increases as the perfection of the crystallinity of the kaolinite particles increases. They show that crystallinity is not a function of the size of the particle; i.e., particles less than 0.25 μ may be well crystallized. Any montmorillonite in the kaolin decreases its suitability for coating paper.

It would be expected that the optimum particle-size distribution would vary with the paper stock to be coated. Thus, if the cellulose fibers were relatively coarse, the presence of somewhat larger flakes in the color would be desirable to bridge the gap between individual fibers.

Dilatancy is favored by the concentration of particles in a given fine-particle size. An increase in abundance of extremely fine particles causes increased thixotropy and viscosity. The clay producer is faced with the dilemma of producing an extremely fine clay for superior brightness and gloss which, therefore, is less desirable because of its rheological properties.

The variation of viscosity from one kaolin to another is sometimes due to the presence of montmorillonite in the finest particles. A few per cent of montmorillonite will greatly increase the viscosity of kaolin suspensions, as shown in Fig. 8-9. Lyons (1946) has shown that the removal of the finest particles, believed to be montmorillonitic, causes a major reduction in viscosity and desirably alters the flow properties.

There are many kaolinite clays without montmorillonite which have relatively high viscosity characteristics. The explanation of why such kaolins have a much higher viscosity than others is often not clear. X-ray diffraction analyses, particle-size-distribution determinations, electron micrographs, exchangeable-ion-composition measurements, etc., have shown no variation in mineral composition, chemical composition, size or shape of particles, or texture,

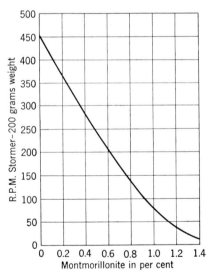

Fig. 8-9. Effect of montmorillonite on the flow characteristics of a 70 per cent kaolin-water system, after Anon. (1955).

which in every case explained the rheological properties.   Millman (1951) has shown that mechanically working a crude clay with added water to yield a puttylike consistency tends to reduce viscosity.   Millman reasons that this working produces a clay of increased fineness composed of particles having a greater ratio of thickness to length, and at the same time it tends to create a particle system which engages the least volume of water.   The highest-viscosity kaolins are believed to be composed of the thinnest flakes.   The mechanical working is thought to break these flakes across the large dimensions thereby producing more equidimensional, somewhat granular, particles.   The process can be carried out in a continuous manner with machines, such as pugmills or extruders.   It is difficult to accept this explanation.   Kaolinite particles possess good cleavage parallel to their basal surfaces, and it would be expected that the working would serve to cleave the particles into even thinner flakes.   Electron micrographs made before and after working generally do not reveal the differences expected from Millman's theory.

It seems likely that the differences in viscosity of pure kaolinite clays reside somehow in the surface characteristics of the kaolinite particles and in variations in their shape which are extremely difficult to detect. The surface characteristics would be a consequence of slight variations in the kaolinite lattice, i.e., small amounts of isomorphic substitution, broken-bond variations, or differences in adsorbed ions tied to the surface. Shape variations can be visualized as frayed edges of some flakes as compared with sharp edges of others (Hemstock, personal communication, 1959).

PELLETIZING ORES, FLUXES, FUELS, ETC.

In the beneficiation of some ores for metallurgical use, it is frequently necessary to pulverize the ore to carry out separations and concentrations. In some cases such ores can not be used until the fine material has been pelletized or agglomerated into larger units.   An example is the taconite iron ore of the Lake Superior district, which must be finely ground to concentrate the iron content.   The fine product can only be used in the blast furnace after it is pelletized into units of the order of 1 in. or more in diam.   Pellets can be prepared by mixing coke, taconite ore, and a small percentage of Wyoming-type bentonite (sodium montmorillonite), then moistening, extruding, or rolling to form the pellets, followed by roasting at 200 to 400°F, and firing at 1650 to 1800°F.   Quicklime may also be used as an ingredient (Bann and Erch, 1952; Haley and Trask, 1957; DeVaney, 1956; Komarek and Chapman, 1952; Stowasser, 1957). The amount of bentonite used is reported to be about 0.5 per cent of the weight of the ore.   It is not known how thoroughly other types of clay have been tried in pelletizing this iron ore. Wyoming-type bentonite provides very high dry strength and high hot strength in molding sands (Chap. 4), and these properties may make it particularly suited in pelletizing the ores.

Klinefelter (1946) has indicated the possible use of Wyoming-type bentonite in combination with corn flour or starch as a binder for nonplastic and poor-binding ore slimes. Combinations containing 2 per cent bentonite were found satisfactory. The pellets were roasted at 200 to 400°F. Abbot and Anderson (1940) disclose a process for pelletizing finely ground flourspar flux by using about 1 per cent of the same type bentonite and sulfite liquor and roasting at 200 to 400°F. Rick and Loetel (1940) disclose the pelletizing of powdered fuel using about 5 per cent bentonite with quebracho extract.

PESTICIDES

Introduction

Many of the chemical compounds useful as pesticides are highly concentrated and are in a physical form requiring further treatment and dilution to permit effective and economic application. In the form of dusts, sprays, solutions, and emulsions, the resulting pesticide formulations are applied by aircraft or ground equipment. In the form of granular materials, the pesticide formulations may be incorporated in fertilizers or spread directly on the ground with suitable equipment.

A number of diluents are available in solid or liquid form to dilute the pesticide chemicals to field strength. In most cases, for additional economy and for practical processing and storage reasons, an intermediate, or master-batch, stage is desired which can be further diluted at a later stage or just prior to application. Solid diluents are usually termed *carriers* when used in the intermediate stage, and the materials used for final reduction are known as *diluents*.

While carriers and diluents generally are considered to be inert, they have a vital bearing on the potency and efficiency of a pesticide dust or spray, since most dusts and sprays contain 1 to 20 per cent active ingredient and 80 to 99 per cent carrier-diluent. The physical properties of the carrier-diluent are now recognized to be of great importance in the uniform dispersion of the toxicant used in the application, in the retention of the pesticide by the plant, and in the preservation of the toxicity of the pesticide. Clays of various kinds are used as carriers and diluents.

Properties of Clays for Pesticides

The particle size must be extremely small, or somewhat larger particles must be easily reduced to extreme fineness when mixed with the toxicant.

Kaolinite clays are prepared so that about 99 per cent is less than 325 mesh and 90 per cent is less than 2 μ. Attapulgite and montmorillonite, which more readily break up into extremely small particles, do not in every case require initial preparation to the extreme fineness of the kaolins.

The clay must provide a pesticide that will deposit in adequate thickness on plant surfaces and stick or adhere to the surface even in the presence of rain and substantially high wind.

The carrier must yield dry-feeling and free-flowing dust bases and wettable products. Some carriers can be compounded with as much as 76 per cent of liquid or low-melting-point, solid toxicants and still provide lump-free, dry, and free-flowing powders.

Pesticide carriers and diluents must be compatable physically and chemically with the active ingredients to avoid deterioration or breakdown of the chemical with the resulting loss of potency. This is particularly true when intermediates and finished pesticides are stored over long periods or in tropical climates. The degree of deterioration varies with the toxicant and, of course, is not the same for all types of clay. Considerable research has been done on this matter, and inhibitors are frequently recommended by the toxicant manufacturers or the carrier producers to provide storage stability and to prevent the loss of toxicity. This property of the clays cannot be resolved without a test of deterioration on the specific toxicant after compounding.

It has been shown (Hunt, 1947) that certain diluents do have some lethal power themselves, probably due to physical rather than chemical properties. Various physical effects are thought to be contributory to this toxicity, for example, starvation (food barrier, digestive clogging, etc.) and desiccation (aridity, adhesiveness, fineness of dust, etc.).

Clays for pesticides are frequently produced with free moisture contents of less than 1 per cent. This is essential for certain toxicants, such as tetraethyl pyrophosphate and methyl parathion, which are subject to rapid hydrolysis. For other toxicants, this is not so critical, and clays of different moisture contents are available to take advantage of the easier compounding when the clay has slightly more moisture.

Types of Clay Used

Clays composed of attapulgite, montmorillonite, and kaolinite are used in pesticide preparations. Producers of each of these types of clay indicate the preferred properties of their clays. There are several hundred United States patents disclosing pesticide formulations which include clays of various kinds. Also there is a voluminous literature from agriculture experiment stations suggesting formulations. The conclusions to be drawn from all these data so far as the clays are concerned are as follows:

all the types of clays used have desirable properties which vary in degree depending on the particular toxicant and the type of application for which the compound is to be used, and the industry in general selects the desired carrier and diluent by actual compounding tests.

Clays composed of the other types of clay minerals do not seem to be used commonly in pesticides. The frequent variability of such clays and the presence of gritty material in many of them might serve to retard their use.

PLASTICS

Introduction

Mineral fillers for use in reinforced polyester resins and other reinforced plastics, according to Wilcox (1954), offer the following advantages: aid in producing a smooth-surface finish, reduce cracking and shrinkage during curing, aid in obscuring the fiber pattern of the glass reinforcement, contribute to high dielectric strength, low water absorption, and high wet strength, resist chemical action and weathering, and offer a means of controlling flow properties. Luce (1960) has pointed out that fillers are sometimes used in plastics merely as extenders but that plastics manufacturers are realizing the importance of filler material as a means of improving the physical properties of their product.

Clay fillers are extensively used in polyester resins where the amount of loading may reach 60 per cent. Such fillers are also used widely in polyvinyl compounds with similar loadings. Examples of the latter usages are in electrical insulation, phonograph records, and floor coverings. Also clays may be used effectively in rigid and flexible urethan foams to provide exceptional cost reductions and, at the same time, to improve such properties as deflection values, uniformity, and finer cell size.

Clays Used in, and Properties of, Clay-filled Resins

Kaolinite clays are used extensively in the filling of plastics. The producers market clays with a variety of particle-size distributions, so that the resin molder is able to select the product best suited to the particular resin and casting operation. It is known, for example, that kaolins with the finest particle size tend to increase viscosity and thixotropy of the mixture, and at the same time they increase concealing power. The selection of the proper kaolin product is made on the basis of actual use tests. In general there are no short-cut evaluation tests.

Kaolinite clays have been found particularly useful because they are relatively easily dispersible in the resin as compared with other mineral fillers. Also they tend to stay in suspension rather than separating out.

TABLE 8-8

EFFECT OF LOADING WITH KAOLIN ON CURE PROPERTIES OF POLYESTER RESINS
(From Minerals and Chemicals Philipp Corp., Tech. Inf. 251-A, 1958)

Per cent loading	Gel time	Cure time	Exothermic peak, °F
0	3.0	5.4	379
10	3.8	6.2	352
20	4.1	6.8	318
30	4.0	7.2	288
40	3.7	7.5	253

All fillers increase the viscosity of the mixture, but in the case of clays this property can be somewhat controlled by the selection of the proper particle-size distribution. The low specific gravity of kaolinite is an advantage it has over other mineral fillers. Also the white color of this type of clay is a desirable property.

Polyester resins experience an exothermic reaction on curing which is accompanied by shrinkage. It is claimed that kaolin fillers reduce the intensity of this exothermic reaction and cause a more uniform cooling and shrinkage of the molded object (Table 8-8).

The chemical inertness of kaolinite clay fillers is coupled with high dielectric strength and generally good electric properties. Table 8-9 illustrates the change in these properties attained with kaolin fillers. As shown in Table 8-10, there is only a slight change in flexural strength with the addition of large amounts of kaolin, and this strength is somewhat larger than that attained with another commonly used filler. The variation in the utility of kaolin in various types of resin is emphasized by the fact that some resins are catalyzed by kaolinite clays whereas others are inhibited.

The use of active surface agents to produce organic-clad kaolins in order to alter the properties of clay-liquid systems, such as printing inks

TABLE 8-9

POWER FACTOR, DIELECTRIC CONSTANT, AND LOSS FACTOR
OF POLYESTER RESINS WITH KAOLIN
(From Minerals and Chemicals Philipp Corp., Tech. Inf. 251-A, 1958)

Resin	Power factor	Dielectric constant	Loss factor
Without filler.....................	0.0192	3.92	0.0755
30% kaolin......................	0.0165	4.19	0.0691
30% surface coated $CaCO_3$........	0.0162	4.55	0.0752

TABLE 8-10

FLEXURAL STRENGTH OF POLYESTER RESINS WITH KAOLIN
(in Pounds per Square Inch)
(From Minerals and Chemicals Philipp Corp.,
Tech. Inf. 251-A, 1958)

Without filler...................... 26,100
Percentage kaolin:
    10............................ 24,000
    15............................ 22,800
    20............................ 23,600
    30............................ 22,900
    35............................ 23,000
Percentage surface coated $CaCO_3$:
    10............................ 22,400
    15............................ 22,100
    20............................ 24,600
    30............................ 23,900

and paints, is well established (see pages 371, 376). Wilcox (1954) has
shown that certain coating materials used on kaolinite particles greatly
alter the dispersion and flow properties of polyester-resin systems. Such
coatings have definitely more effect as dispersion aids than the mere
introduction of the active surface agent in the complete solid-liquid
system, and, at least in special cases, they bring about greater changes
in the flow properties of the complete mix. Materials showing promise
in viscosity reduction have included some classified as cationic, some
anionic, and some nonionic. Table 8-11 lists viscosity data for coated and

TABLE 8-11

EFFECT ON VISCOSITY[a] OF POLYESTER RESINS FILLED
WITH KAOLINS CLAD WITH DIFFERENT ORGANICS
(After Wilcox, 1954)

Kaolin	Loading, %	Viscosity, coated kaolin	Viscosity, uncoated kaolin
Fine grained..............	35	14,500	60,000
Medium grained:			
Coating A.............	45	12,000	24,000
	50	16,000	86,000
Coating B.............	45	11,500	24,000
Coating C.............	45	24,000	69,000

[a] Static Brookfield, 10 rpm, no. 6 spindle.

noncoated kaolins incorporated in a general-purpose resin of rather low viscosity. The viscosity comparison between uncoated and coated fillers showed about the percentage of reduction when other resins were used. The most effective wetting agents with regard to viscosity reduction greatly improve wetting-out and dispersion in the resin and at the same time preserve the desired thixotropy. Certain active materials applied as coatings on kaolinite particles increase rather than decrease the apparent viscosity. Some of the cationic agents tested by Wilcox (1954) show a tendency to catalyze the cure of the resins. Some of the materials greatly reduced the cure time at a temperature of 250°F. Certain nonionic coating agents, equally effective in reducing viscosity and improving wet-out, do not show this catalytic action. Physical properties of laminates filled with surface-coated kaolins are equal or superior to those of comparable laminates filled with noncoated kaolins. Information is not at hand regarding the possible use of other types of clays than kaolins in similar plastics.

PLASTICIZING AGENTS

Clays are used in a wide variety of compounds as plasticizing agents. They are used with cement, asphalt, talc, vermiculite, silica, diatomaceous earth, calcined magnesite, calcite, etc., and in various mortars, putties, mastics, calking compounds, etc. In general there are no specifications for such usages except that the clay must perform satisfactorily and must be economical. In general the clay should be free from grit. If thixotropic characteristics are desired, montmorillonite and attapulgite clays might be most satisfactory. If white color and freedom from alkalies and alkaline earths is required, kaolinite clays would seem most desirable.

RUBBER

Introduction

Kaolins and bentonites are used in compounding rubber. Two varieties of kaolin, designated as *hard* and *soft* by rubber technicians, are used. Hard kaolins produce a high modulus of rupture, high tensile strength, good resistance to abrasion, and stiff uncured compounds, and soft kaolins produce a lower modulus, lower tensile strength, lower resistance to abrasion, and soft uncured compounds. It will be seen presently that hard kaolins have a larger content of fine particles than soft kaolins.

In the United States, kaolins for the rubber trade are mined in Georgia and South Carolina, with the latter state producing the bulk of the hard clays. Great Britain, Germany, and France are also important miners of kaolins for the rubber industry.

Kaolins were first used in rubber simply as diluents (Davis and Blake, 1937), but it was soon learned that they also provided desirable reinforcing and stiffening properties in certain rubber products. Hard kaolins are used in compounds for shoe heels and soles, tubing, extruded stock of all types, wire insulation, gloves, adhesives, tire treads, and inner tubes where certain types of synthetic rubbers are used. When it is desirable to use high pigment loading to reduce costs and when abrasion resistance is not paramount, soft kaolins are used. Examples of products compounded with soft kaolin are household goods, blown sponge, hard rubber, toys, and novelties.

Bentonite used in the rubber industry is largely of the high-colloidal variety composed of montmorillonite carrying sodium as the major exchangeable cation; it is mined in the Wyoming area of the United States.

Montmorillonite clays are used as additives to latex for purposes of thickening and stabilizing (Anon., 1937), as emulsion stabilizers, for example, in rubber-base paints, and in rubber adhesives. In adhesives, the montmorillonite particles serve to separate the latex particles so that they do not cohere to each other.

Hauser (1955) has described the following use of montmorillonite clays in rubber. The viscosity of the natural milk sap, or latex, of the rubber tree is very low as compared with the viscosity of a solution of rubber in an organic solvent, even if the concentration of rubber in latex is many times that of the organic solution. Although this low viscosity has many advantages for the use of latex, it is a serious drawback whenever a too great fluidity of the system is disadvantageous. If a thixotropy-inducing montmorillonite dispersion is added to the latex, the compound will set up to a thixotropic gel as soon as the dispersion has come to rest, and the undesirable effects of the low viscosity may be avoided. Hauser (1955) gives an example of the use of thixotropic latex with the added montmorillonite in the production of "dipped" rubber articles, for example, rubber gloves. It permits the withdrawal of the mold onto which the latex compound has been deposited without the danger, which a low-viscosity latex would exhibit, of the compound flowing down to the finger tips and there forming droplets which would cause increased thickness of the rubber layer on evaporation of the solvent.

Characteristics of Kaolins for Rubber Compounding

Table 8-12 shows the particle-size distribution of typical hard and soft kaolins used in rubber compounding. In hard kaolin, about 90

TABLE 8-12

PARTICLE-SIZE DISTRIBUTION OF SOME KAOLINS USED IN RUBBER COMPOUNDS
(After Anon., 1955)

Diameter, μ	Hard, %	Soft, %		
		A	B	C
Above 10	0.1	8.3	6.6	1.2
10–5	2.8	12.4	9.2	8.2
5–4	1.5	4.5	4.2	4.2
4–3	2.3	6.3	5.7	6.5
3–2	3.4	8.6	8.9	9.4
2–1	9.0	17.1	18.4	15.4
1–0.5	19.0	17.2	16.2	16.0
<0.5	61.9	25.1	30.8	39.0
Above 5	2.9	20.7	15.8	9.4
Under 2	89.9	59.4	65.4	70.5

per cent of the particles are finer than 2 μ, and only about 3 per cent are coarser than 5 μ; in the soft kaolin, only 60 per cent are finer than 2 μ, and about 20 per cent are coarser than 5 μ. In general the clays should be as low as possible in coarse material, usually expressed as the residue failing to pass through a 325-mesh screen. Excessive grit reduces tensile strength, causes premature flexcracking, dulls the knives of trimming machines, and causes wear of dies and rubber-mixing machines, particularly internal mixers. Grit also is a source of dielectric failures in insulated wire compounds. The amount of plus 325-mesh material found in rubber-grade clays varies up to 3.5 per cent but in high-grade clays is less than about 0.3 per cent.

In general hard kaolins are darker than soft kaolins. The brightness of hard clays is in the range of 71 to 78 per cent, and of soft kaolins, in the range of 74 to 82 per cent. Most rubber kaolins are prepared by the dry air-float process, but when higher brightness than the foregoing is necessary, they may be water washed and bleached chemically by processes similar to those used in preparing kaolins for coating paper.

The moisture content determined by drying to 105°C on finished kaolins has a maximum value of 1 per cent.

Clays have very little covering power in rubber because the indices of refraction of the clay minerals and rubber are nearly alike.

Certain compounds of manganese, iron, and copper are quite harmful to the aging properties of natural-rubber compounds—they cause a rapid loss of tensile strength after only a few days. It has been shown experimentally that other compounds of these elements have no deleterious effect at all. In some cases clay with a high total-manganese content may age better than one which shows only a fractional percentage of manganese in a harmful form. It seems impossible to predict whether or not such compounds would be harmful; consequently rubber kaolins must be substantially free of such compounds, or, if chemical analyses show their presence, aging tests must be run to prove that they are not harmful.

Tests of other properties, such as water-settling characteristics, viscosity, oil absorption, and dye absorption, are sometimes run on rubber kaolins. These tests generally do not determine the value of a clay for rubber compounding but serve as control tests for comparative purposes.

Properties of Rubber Compounded with Kaolins

NATURAL RUBBER

Hard kaolins tend to produce a high tensile strength and modulus in comparison with soft kaolins (Table 8-13). Also, the hard kaolins

TABLE 8-13

SOME PROPERTIES OF RUBBER COMPOUNDED WITH KAOLIN[a]
(FROM MINERALS AND CHEMICALS PHILIPP CORP., TECH. DATA SHEET 451)

Property	Hard kaolin	Soft kaolin
Modulus at 300% elongation, psi..........	1,510	975
Ultimate tensile strength, psi..............	2,480	1,820
Elongation at break, %...................	447	470
Set at break, %.........................	57	45
Shore hardness.........................	62	59

[a] Press cured 10 to 70 min at 290°F: tests at room temperature; unaged. Recipe: clean pale crepe, 1,009; zinc oxide, 59; sulfur, 39; altax, 19; tuads, 0.19; stearic acid, 39; clay, 125 g.

have a slower rate of cure. These differences become less evident as the clay loading increases. Hard clays generally produce higher tear values than the soft kaolins, and again this difference diminishes as the clay loading increases. Clays, especially the hard variety, produce good resistance to abrasion. Aside from carbon black, there are only a few nonblack pigments which will exceed clays in this respect. Heat-generating characteristics of clays in rubber reflect reinforcement in the same manner as do most other pigments for rubber. Hard clays produce somewhat higher heats on flexing than do the soft clays.

The energy-rebound properties of natural rubber compounds pigmented with clays are influenced to a significant extent by the type of clay used. Thus, a hard clay produces a stock with lower energy of rebound than a similar stock compounded with soft clay.

Rubber-grade clays differ markedly in their effect on the extrusion properties of rubber compounds. With hard clays, the extrusion rate decreases quite rapidly with an increase in clay loading. In the case of soft clays, a considerably higher loading of clay can be incorporated without decreasing the rate of extrusion. In most cases the difference in rate going from 40 to about 70 volumes of soft clay is not appreciable; in fact, sometimes the rate of extrusion actually increases up to 60 volumes of loading.

When the clays are free from deleterious compounds of copper, iron, and manganese, the aging characteristics of clay stocks are similar to those with other pigments.

Table 8-14 shows water-absorption data for a hard and soft kaolin in

TABLE 8-14

WATER-ADSORPTION DATA ON TWO KAOLINS IN COMPARISON WITH OTHER PIGMENTS
(in Per Cent)
(From Anon., 1955)

Pigment	Weeks in boiling water					
	1	2	3	4	5	6
Hard kaolin................	7.52	11.46	18.55	25.73	72.08	37.96
Soft kaolin.................	9.44	17.25	28.40	39.30	48.09	59.05
Treated precipitated $CaCO_3$...	13.24	22.61	32.54	43.89	55.25	67.30
Gilder's whiting.............	11.97	23.25	37.30	53.85	65.70	79.28
Ground limestone...........	9.91	17.98	26.87	37.59	48.88	59.37

comparison with other pigments. The data show that hard clay is superior to soft clay and that the hard kaolin is also superior to the other pigments in this property.

The accelerator used has a marked effect on some of the physical properties of rubbers compounded with clays. For example, the extrusion rate and plasticity of a clay compound is decidedly altered by the accelerator used.

SYNTHETIC RUBBER—GR-S (BUTADIENE-STYRENE COPOLYMER)

As in the case of natural rubbers, hard kaolins are slower curing than soft ones (Anon., 1955). The superiority of hard over soft kaolins in degree of reinforcement is more pronounced in GR-S than in natural rubber. The modulus characteristics, however, do not differ as markedly between hard and soft kaolins in GR-S. Significant differences in moduli do not become apparent until quite high loadings are reached. In a soft kaolin, the resistance to abrasion is 5 to 10 per cent higher when compared with a hard kaolin than it is when the two are compared in natural rubber.

While many factors contribute toward the improvement of resistance to cut-growth in GR-S tire treads, the inclusion of relatively small amounts of hard kaolin was found to aid materially in reducing the cut-growth rate. In this usage it was found that hard kaolin was considerably better than soft kaolin.

Hard rubber-grade kaolin is a unique reinforcing pigment for GR-S. In the range of 40 volumes of loading, hard clay produces higher tensile properties than most of the other nonblack pigments and the thermal blacks. The soft clays equal the common nonblack pigments in tensile values obtainable.

SYNTHETIC RUBBER—GR-M (NEOPRENE)

Using the Goodrich tear-resistance test as a criterion of reinforcement, it was found (Anon., 1955) that hard rubber-grade kaolins produce outstanding resistance to tear. Such clay further shows the unusual characteristic of increasing tear resistance with increased loading up to and including 80 volumes of pigmentation.

SYNTHETIC RUBBER—GR-I (BUTYL)

Aside from the finest particle-size materials, such as the channel blacks, ordinary pigments for rubber do not increase the tensile strength of butyl rubber compounds. Rubber-grade clays, the other common nonblack pigments, and carbon blacks do, however, improve the tear-resistance of butyl stocks in varying degrees (Anon., 1955).

Clays, as a class, impart reinforcement comparable to that produced by other nonblack pigments. Where the high reinforcement of the fine-particle blacks is not needed or where colored products, such as red inner tubes, are desired, rubber-grade clays definitely serve a purpose.

Another use for clays in butyl rubber is as a processing aid for black-inner-tube compounds. It has been found that small amounts of clay will help "smooth out" the extruded surface of these stocks during tubing.

SYNTHETIC RUBBER—BUNA N

Practically all pigments increase the tensile values of Buna N stocks, with the carbon blacks giving the best results. As a class, the clays compare favorably with the other nonblack pigments. Hard kaolins produce better physical properties than the soft kaolins (Anon., 1955).

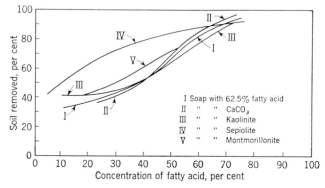

Fɪɢ. 8-10.   Effect of replacement of fatty acid in soap with various materials on soil removal, after Fleury-Larsonneau and André (1942).

Use of Organic-clad Clay Minerals

Clays of various compositions with cation-exchange capacities of from 10 to 100 meq per 100 g in which the inorganic cation has been replaced by a substituted organic onium base have been used as reinforcing agents in natural and some synthetic rubbers (Carter et al., 1950).   Clark and Parker (1949) claim that clay is rendered more suitable for use as a filler for rubber by coating the clay particles with a strongly adhering organic layer.   The layer consists of the product of the reaction of an organic base, such as an amine or basic dyestuff, with the acidic clay particles. No information is at hand regarding the actual use of organic-clad clay particles in rubber compounds.

Theory of the Action of Clay in Rubbers

The literature contains little specific information on the possible causes of the effects that clay has on the properties of rubber compounds. Barron (1948) states that the effects of fillers are related to the particle size, particle shape, particle surface structure, and wettability.   Greider (1923) showed that the particle size of clays is the outstanding considera- tion in determining their suitability in rubber.   Smaller particles tend to produce greater reinforcement.   Perhaps the clay particles should, at least, approach the particle size of the rubber micelles.

The kaolins used in rubber are composed of flake-shaped particles. Hofmann (1954) has shown that halloysite composed of elongate tubular particles provides a little less reinforcement than kaolinite clays of com- parable particle size.   Some fillers other than clay used in rubber are not flake-shaped, and it appears that shape is not an exceedingly important factor.

It is generally agreed that any rubber filler must be easily wettable and dispersible in the rubber. The surface of the filler and the rubber must react in some way to produce a tight bond. It is not clear just what sort of bond is desired or what the nature of the filler surface should be, but apparently kaolinite possesses the desired properties.

Clay minerals other than kaolinite are composed of flake-shaped particles which may be very small. They do not appear to have been used, probably because they are generally not white and have variable chemical compositions which may in some cases include detrimental elements.

SOAPS AND CLEANING AND POLISHING COMPOUNDS

Soaps

A large literature exists concerning the use of clays in soaps and detergents, which has recently been summarized by Déribéré and Esme (1951). According to them, certain clays are used in soaps as a partial replacement for the fatty-acid component because of their emulsifying action, their affinity for carbon particles, and their detergent effect. Information is not available on any actual use of clays in soaps. It is said to be possible to use as much as 40 per cent clay in soaps; however, it would seem probable that the percentage would rarely go above about 5 to 10 per cent.

Fleury-Larsonneau and André (1942) determined the relative efficiency of montmorillonite, kaolinite, and sepiolite in soaps in actual washing tests. They prepared a soap with 30 per cent of the fatty acid replaced with clay and mixed this soap in various proportions with one containing no clay, and then they determined the amount of soil removed in 1 hr of washing. Figures 8-10 and 8-11 show their results. The data in the

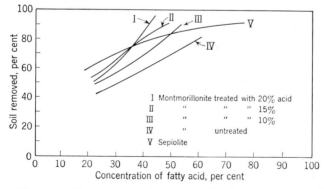

Fig. 8-11. Effect of acid treatment of montmorillonite clay on its soil removal properties in soap, after Fleury-Larsonneau and André (1942).

curves suggest that kaolinite is inert and serves only to dilute the soap. On the other hand, montmorillonite has some detergent action, and sepiolite has even more. The curves in Fig. 8-11 show the effect of an acid treatment of the montmorillonite on its detergent action in soap. The acid treatment improves the value of the montmorillonite, making it equal or even superior to the sepiolite. This improvement can be explained by the improved decolorizing power (i.e., adsorptive power for some carbonaceous material) developed by such acid treatment. The decolorizing ability of all montmorillonites, however, is not enhanced by acid treatment; therefore not all montmorillonites would be improved for use in soaps by such treatment.

Various publications (Hirschmann and Bechtner, 1938; Anon., 1950) have pointed out desirable properties of highly colloidal sodium montmorillonite clays (e.g., Wyoming-type bentonites) as ingredients in soaps, particularly in paste soaps and those used in power laundries. It is claimed that such clays improve detergent action of soap and may be used as builders. They are said to act as dispersing agents to improve the efficiency of soaps by lowering the surface tension of the solution and forming suds. Sodium montmorillonites have water-softening action by exchangeably replacing calcium and magnesium with sodium. During washing the clay helps to keep the dirt in suspension. Like soap, such clay emulsifies oil and grease.

Cleaning and Polishing Compounds

The properties of clay minerals mentioned above have led to the suggested use of clays in a variety of cleaning and polishing compounds. Thus, Collingridge (1938) describes the use of montmorillonite or kaolinite clays in shoe-dressing compounds. Auch (1936) and Small (1942) present formulas for automobile cleaners and polishing agents carrying sodium montmorillonite clay. Small (1941) gives a formula for a metal cleaner containing the same type of clay. Leonard (1949) presents a procedure for cleaning rugs whereby dry sodium montmorillonite is wetted with a dry-cleaning solvent enough to make the mass damp to the touch and is placed on a rug, allowed to stand for some hours, and then removed. The solvent dissolves the soil and permits it to be adsorbed by the clay. Attapulgite clays have gelling and suspending properties which should make them useful in some cleaning and polishing compounds.

Certain types of clay are used in polishing compounds where they serve as the actual polishing agent rather than merely as suspending and bodying agents. The clays used for this purpose are moderately calcined so that they do not readily break down to extremely small particles. Attapulgite seems to have desirable attributes for polishing compounds because its acicular form and rather poor cleavage give it mild abrasive action. The easier cleavage of the other clay minerals would be expected to give them less abrasive action in the necessary calcined form.

THERAPEUTIC MUDS

Mud and organic-mud baths have been a favored remedy in some parts of the world, especially in Europe, for the treatment of certain ailments, such as those of the heart and nervous system and rheumatics. Mertz (1940), Stockfisch and Benade (1930), and Hynie and Koutek (1933) describe the geologic character of muds used in Europe for this purpose. These authors point out that any therapeutic value of such muds probably resides in their nonclay components, e.g., sulfurous compounds, radioactive materials, or salines. In some cases the heat given to the body by the mud may be of prime importance.

A wide variety of muds are used. Many are volcanic in origin and are naturally hot because of an association with hot waters. Others are sediments, some with high contents of organic materials, which are heated just prior to use.

Clay mineral analyses do not seem to have been made on therapeutic muds. However a description of the properties of such muds seems to make it clear that, under some conditions, any type of clay may be used. Frequently such descriptions mention the high water-holding capacity of the muds and their stickiness and high plasticity, which suggests that in many cases montmorillonite is an important component. The volcanic muds associated with hot springs would probably also have much montmorillonite.

WATER CLARIFICATION

In the clarification of potable waters, colloidal matter is removed by filtration and/or sedimentation processes. Alum is commonly used to flocculate the colloidal material to enhance its settling and filtration rate. In some cases the alum alone is not completely effective, and, according to Nordell (1951), it may be desirable to add a highly colloidal, easily dispersible clay to the water prior to the addition of the alum. The alum flocculates the clay which serves to gather up and collect the colloidal material that would not otherwise settle (Olin and Peterson, 1937).

Bentonites from Wyoming and attapulgite clays from Georgia and Florida have been used for this purpose because they possess the necessary dispersion and adsorptive properties. According to Olin (1944), when Wyoming bentonite is used, it should be added in about a 5 per cent suspension in an amount to give 15 to 125 ppm to the water.

Slocum (1932) and later Weir (1938) claimed that the clay treatment also reduced and removed bad odors and tastes and had a softening effect on the water. However, Baylis (1933) says that clay is not likely to be very effective in odor removal. Weir (1939) claims that the use of clay in combination with activated carbon is more effective than either one alone.

According to Olin and Freeman (1941) and Olin et al. (1942), similar treatment of paper-mill wastes, sewage, and industrial wastes is satisfactory for their purification.

WATER IMPEDANCE

Wyoming-type bentonite, composed of montmorillonite carrying sodium as the exchangeable cation, is used extensively to impede the movement of water through earthen structures and to retard or stop similar movement through cracks and fissures in rock and concrete structure. For example, such bentonite is used to stop the seepage of water from ponds and irrigation ditches. It is used to waterproof the outside basement walls of homes (Mielenz and King, 1955).

According to Weaver (1946), there are two broad classifications under which such bentonite is used in water impedance. It is used as a grout, in which a bentonite suspension is injected under pressure into a porous strata, a fissure, or crack, or along the foundation of a building. It is also used in a "placement" method, in which the bentonite may be placed to form an unbroken blanket between the earth and the water or mixed with the surface soil of the structure to render the soil impervious. In the case of placing a bentonite blanket to seal a pond or lake, the pond need not be drained in every case, as granular bentonite may be added to the water surface—it will settle to the bottom of the pond forming the impervious blanket.

When the bentonite is mixed with the soil, it is said that about 1 part bentonite to 5 parts of soil is adequate. When a blanket is prepared, it should be 3 to 4 in. thick, which requires about 100 lb of bentonite in a finely pulverized condition per 100 sq ft. In a grouting operation, the bentonite is mixed with sufficient water to yield a pumpable slurry. For waterproofing walls it may be desired in paste or putty consistency.

According to Weaver (1946), soils with a high clay content and rocky soils are not suitable for sealing with bentonite. Very clayey soils may not form a dense layer when attacked by water, and when rocks are present, the water tends to pass along their surface washing bentonite away and causing seepage. Fine sandy soils and sandy loams which form a dense blanket are most effectively sealed.

The reaction of water and bentonite is very sensitive to variations in the electrolyte content of the system. Thus, in highly saline or acid waters the impedance property of the bentonite is greatly reduced. Also montmorillonite clays which do not carry sodium do not have this property to a marked degree.

The explanation of the water-impedance property probably lies in two characteristics of the sodium montmorillonite. In the first place such montmorillonite tends to disperse into extremely small particles so that the interstices of the soil would be filled and a very dense soil mass would be formed. That is, it would tend to fill the pores and break connections between them. In the second place, a mass or clump of sodium montmorillonite, even a very small one, tends to absorb water up to a certain point, forming a gelatinous mass. Without vigorous agitation the gelatinous mass takes up no more water; i.e., it is impervious. From a more fundamental standpoint, water is taken up between the individual unit layers of montmorillonite to a definite thickness when sodium is present. When this stage is reached, the clay has a gel consistency. In general, such a gel must be agitated vigorously in order that the gel structure be broken and more water may be absorbed on the layers of montmorillonite. Stated in other terms: the sodium montmorillonite tends to pull water between each unit layer until a given water-layer thickness is reached. At this point the hydration power of the montmorillonite surface (and also that of the sodium) is satisfied. The structure of the adsorbed water is such that the montmorillonite flakes are held together. This means that no more water is taken up, and the montmorillonite with the water does not swell further or disperse; it is impervious and stays in place between the soil and water in a pond. Violent agitation is required to break up the water structure and hence the bond between the montmorillonite particles so that the montmorillonite units can be further dispersed in water.

When the montmorillonite carries other cations than sodium, e.g., calcium, the clay is not so thoroughly dispersible. What is more important is that the maximum extent of hydration of the montmorillonite surfaces is less in the presence of an abundance of water and that the structure of the water gives less bond between the montmorillonite units when the adsorbed water layers are relatively thick.

REFERENCES

Anonymous, The De-inking of Paper with the Aid of Beidellite, *Paper Trade J.*, **105**(20), 24 (1937).
———, Use of Bentonite in Rubber, *Rubber Age*, May (1937).
———, Bentonite as a Soap Builder, *Soap and Sanit. Chemicals*, **26**, 61–62 (1950).
———, "Kaolin Clays and Their Industrial Uses," J. M. Huber Corp., New York (1955).

Abbot, F. C., and C. O. Anderson, "Metallurgical Flux and Method of Producing It," U.S. Patent 2,220,385 (1940).

Albert, C. G., Physical and Colloidal Chemistry of Clays, *J. Am. Leather Chemists' Assoc.*, **35**, 25–36 (1940).

———, Particle Structure and Flow Properties of Coating Clays, *J. Tech. Assoc. Pulp & Paper Ind.*, **34**, 453–458 (1951).

Allegrini, A. P., and A. W. Claxton, Dewaxing of Waxed Paper Broke by Adsorption, *J. Tech. Assoc. Paper & Pulp Ind.*, **43**, 164A–165A (1960).

Alton, W. H., and H. I. Jones, "Delustering Textiles," U.S. Patent 2,057,469 (1936).

Amphett, C. B., Ion Exchange in Clay Minerals, *Endeavor,* **17**, 149–155 (1958).

Archibald, F. R., and C. F. Jackson, Alumina from Clay by the Lime-sinter Method: I, *Trans. AIME,* **159**, 227–240 (1944).

——— and C. M. Nicholson, Alumina from Clay by the Lime-sinter Method: II, *AIME Tech. Pub.* 2390 (1948).

Auch, R. H., Auto Polish, *Soap,* **12**, 98–101 (1936).

Austin, C. R., J. L. Nomes, and J. D. Sullivan, Basic Factors Involved in Bloating of Clays, *AIME Tech. Pub.* 1486, *Mining Technology,* **6**, (1942).

Bann, T. E., and L. J. Erck, Laboratory Procedures for Determining Pelletizing Characteristics of Iron Ore Concentrate, *Trans. AIME,* **196**, 803–811 (1953).

Bardollet, M. S., and H. S. Paine, Clarification of Starch Conversion Liquors in the Manufacture of Corn Syrup, *Ind. Eng. Chem.,* **19**, 1245–1246 (1927).

Barr, M., Activated Attapulgite, *J. Am. Pharm. Assoc., Pract. Pharm. Ed.,* **19**, 85–87 (1958).

Barrer, R. M., and N. MacKenzie, Sorption by Attapulgite: I, Availability of Intracrystalline Channels, *J. Phys. Chem.,* **58**, 560–568 (1954).

——— and D. M. MacLeod, Intercalation and Sorption by Montmorillonite, *Trans. Faraday Soc.,* **50**, 980–989 (1954).

Barrett, K., R. Green, and R. W. Sandberg, "Manifold Record Material and Process for Making It," U.S. Patent 2,550,469 (1951).

Barron, H., "Modern Rubber Chemistry," D. Van Nostrand Company, Inc., Princeton, N.J. (1948).

Baylis, J. R., Bleaching Clays, *Water Works & Sewerage,* **80**, 287–288 (1933).

Bernstein, I. M., Objective Analysis of Clays in Ink Formulations, *Am. Ink Maker,* March (1956).

Blakely, R. M., J. P. Jowsey, and H. L. MacGregor, The Effect of Sodium Bentonite in the Diets of Turkey Poults, *Poultry Sci.,* **34**, 1181 (1955).

Bogue, R. H., "The Chemistry of Portland Cement," 2d ed., Reinhold Publishing Corporation, New York (1955).

Briggs, G. M., and M. R. Spivey-Fox, Vitamin A Deficiency in Chicks Produced by Adding High Levels of Bentonite to Synthetic Diets, *Poultry Sci.* **35**, 570–576 (1956).

Brownmiller, L. T., and R. H. Bogue, The System $CaO\text{-}NaO_2\text{-}Al_2O_3\text{-}SiO_2$, *Am. J. Sci.,* **23**, 501–524 (1932).

Carter, L. W., J. G. Hendricks, and D. S. Bolley, "Elastomer Reinforced with a Modified Clay," U.S. Patent 2,531,396 (1950).

Chambers, G. P. C., Some Industrial Applications of the Clay Mineral Sepiolite, *Silicates inds.,* April, (1959).

Clark, N. O., and T. W. Parker, "Improvements in or Relating to the Treatment of Clay," Brit. Patent 630,418 (1949).

Claxton, A. W., The Functional Behavior of Clays in Adhesives, *J. Tech. Assoc. Pulp & Paper Ind.*, **40**, 180A–186A (1957).

Collingridge, G. S., Shoe Polishes and Creams, *Chem. Age*, **39**, 3–5 (1938).

Conley, J. E., H. Wilson, and T. A. Klinefelter, Production of Lightweight Concrete Aggregate from Clays, Shales, Slates, and Other Materials, *U.S. Bur. Mines Rept. Invest.* 4401 (1948).

Conoway, G. R., "Thermal Stretching Cellulose Yarn," U.S. Patent 2,395,396 (1947).

Copson, R. L., J. H. Walthall, and T. P. Hignett, Extraction of Alumina from Clays by the Lime Sinter Modification of the Pederson Process, *Trans. AIME*, **159**, 241–254 (1944).

Cordon, W. A., and M. E. Hickey, Properties of Concrete Made with Typical Lightweight Aggregate, *U.S. Bur. Reclamation, Materials Laboratory Rept.* C-385 (1948).

Cronan, C. S., Ceramic Sponges Store Radioactive Wastes, *Chem. Eng.*, **66**, 76–78 (1959).

Curado, J. G., and D. H. Praeg, "Printing Ink," U.S. Patent 2,750,296 (1956).

Davis, C. C., and J. T. Blake, "Chemistry and Technology of Rubber," American Chemical Society Monograph 74 (1937).

Deolin, H. B., and H. A. Mattill, The Chemical Determination of Tocopherols in Muscle Tissue, *J. Biol. Chem.*, **146**, 123–130 (1942).

Déribéré, M., and A. Esme, "La bentonite," 3d ed., Dunod, Paris (1951).

DeVaney, F. D., "Process of Preparing Indurated Pellets of Iron Ore Fines," U.S. Patent 2,743,172 (1956).

Edwards, J. D., F. C. Frary, and Z. Jeffries, "Aluminum and Its Production," McGraw-Hill Book Company, Inc., New York (1930).

Esme, A., L'emploi des argiles colloidales en papeterie, *La Papeterie*, November (1928).

Esselbaugh, N. C., Effect of Bentonite on Loaf Volume and Weight of Hard and Wheat Bread, *Cereal Chem.*, **25**, 280–286 (1948).

Fantus, B., Fuller's Earth: Its Adsorptive Power and Its Antidotal Value for Alkaloids, *J. AMA*, **64**, 1838–1845 (1915).

Feild, T. A., "Vinyl Resin Textile Article," U.S. Patent 2,499,477 (1950).

Fiero, G. W., The Effect of Clay on Rancid Fats, *J. Pharm. Assoc.*, **18**, 491–493 (1929).

Fischer, R., and W. Iwanoff, The Use of Various Adsorbents for the Detection, Determination, and Purification of Organic, Mainly Physiological, Active Compounds, *Arch. Pharm.*, **281**, 361–377 (1943).

Fleury-Larsenneau, A., and M. André, Etude du pouvoir de savon charges, *Chim. & ind.*, **47**, 333–350 (1942).

Goodman, L. S., and A. Gilman, "The Pharmacological Basis of Therapeutics," 2nd ed., The Macmillan Company, New York (1955).

Greider, H. W., The Resilient Energy and Abrasion Resistance of Vulcanized Rubber, *Ind. Eng. Chem.*, **15**, 506–511 (1923).

Grim, R. E., "Clay Mineralogy," McGraw-Hill Book Company, Inc., New York (1953).

———, J. S. Machin, and W. F. Bradley, Amenability of Various Types of Clay Minerals to Alumina Extraction by the Lime Sinter and Lime-Soda Sinter Processes, *Illinois State Geol. Survey, Bull.* 69 (1945).

Haley, K. M., and H. V. Trask, "Metaliferous Agglomerates Having Improved

Green Strength and Method of Forming the Same," U.S. Patent 2,807,534 (1957).

Hall, H. H., and R. E. Lothrop, Use of Clarified Honey in Culture Media, *J. Bacteriol.,* **27,** 349–355 (1934).

Halperin, Z., Tartrate Recovery from Winery Wastes, *Chem. & Met. Eng.,* **52,** 116–119 (1945).

Hanna, W. C., Unfavorable Chemical Reactions of Aggregates in Concrete and a Suggested Corrective, *Proc. Am. Soc. Testing Material,* **47,** p. 986 (1947).

Hanut, C. J., The Effect of Various Agents on the Action of Snake Venoms on Blood Coagulation, *Ann. physiol. physiochem. biol.,* **14,** 893–913 (1938).

Hauser, E. A., "Flexibilizing Clay Film," U.S. Patent 2,266,638 (1941).

———, "Inorganic Film Products and Method of Making Same," U.S. Patent 2,266,636 (1941).

———, "Waterproofing Flexible Body," U.S. Patent 2,266,637 (1941).

———, "Modified Gel-forming Clay and Process of Producing Same," U.S. Patent 2,531,427 (1950).

———, "Silicic Science," D. Van Nostrand Company, Inc., Princeton, N.J. (1955).

Hirschmann, W. B., and P. Bechtner, Bentonite, *Soap Sanit. Chem.,* **14,** 24–26 (1938).

Hofmann, U., Fullstoffe und keramische Rohmaterialien, "Rapport Europées congrés electronmicroscopic," pp. 161–172, Gent (1954).

Holden, E. G., "Preservation of Baked Cereal Food," U.S. Patent 2,443,138 (1948).

Hunt, C. R., Toxicity of Insecticide Dust Diluents and Carriers to Larvae of the Mexican Bean Beetle, *J. Econ. Entomol.,* **40,** 215–220 (1947).

Hursh, R. K., J. E. Lamar, and R. E. Grim, Illinois Clays and Shales as Mortar Mix, *Illinois State Geol. Survey, Rept. Invest.* 100 (1944).

Hynie, O., and J. Koutek, Geologie der wichtigsten Schlammarten Europas. *Knihovna státníko geol. ústavu Československ. rep.,* **16,** Prague (1933).

Jordan, J. W., "Lubricants," U.S. Patent 2,531,440 (1950).

———, Organophilic Bentonites I., *J. Phys. Chem.,* **59,** 294–505 (1949).

Jordan, R. M., Tests Indicate Bentonite in Lamb Rations, Beneficial, *Feedstuffs,* p. 46B, May (1953).

Kerr, J. M., Preliminary Tests on Clay Sinters to Retain Reactor Wastes, *Bull. Am. Ceram. Soc.,* **38,** 374–376 (1954).

Klinefelter, T. A., Evaluation of Some Binders for Use in Pelletizing Slimes, *U.S. Bur. Mines Rept. Invest.* 3846 (1946).

Komarek, G., and W. J. Chapman, "Briquettes and Method of Making Same," U.S. Patent 2,582,386 (1952).

Kruge, R. W., M. M. Sparks, and E. C. Tunma, Lightweight Aggregate Concrete, *Proc. Am. Concrete Inst.,* **45,** 625–642 (1949).

Lacy, W. J., Decontamination of Radioactively Contaminated Water by Slurrying with Clay, *Ind. Eng. Chem.,* **46,** 1061–1065 (1954).

Lea, F. M., The Chemistry of Pozzolans, *Proc. Symposium Chem. Cement,* pp. 460–490, Stockholm (1938).

Lemetayer, E., and P. Uhry, Prevention and Treatment of Tetanus Intoxication in Rabbits by Intravenous Injection of Charcoal Suspension and Specific Antiserum, *Compt. rend. soc. biol.,* **125,** 823–826 (1938).

Leonard, E. A., Rug Cleaning, *Soap Sanit. Chemicals,* **25,** 46–48 (1949).

Lesser, M. A., Bentonite, *Drug & Cosmetic Ind.,* **49,** 390–392 (1941).

Lothrop, R. E., and H. S. Paine, Removal of Colloids from Honey with Bentonite, *Ind. Eng. Chem.*, **23**, 328–332 (1931).

Luce, C. C., Clay Fillers in Structural Reinforced-plastics Parts, *Plastics Technol.*, **6**, 40–43 (1960).

Lyons, S. C., "Method of Improving Kaolin and Products Thereof," U.S. Patent 2,524,816 (1946).

———, "Paper Coating Pigments," chap. V, pp. 57–115, Technical Association of the Pulp and Paper Industry, Monograph 20 (1958).

Machalske, F. J., "Process of Producing Elementary Silicon and By-Products," U.S. Patent 1,062,982 (1913).

Maloney, W. T., "Clay Product and Process of Preparing Same," U.S. Patent 2,158,987 (1939).

Masucci, P., "Antigenic Composition," U.S. Patent 2,332,521 (1943).

Matagrin, A., Le desencrage du papier imprime, *La Papeterie*, pp. 98 and 219 (1943).

Mattiello, J. J., "Protective and Decorative Coatings," vol. III, pp. 611–654, McGraw-Hill Book Company, Inc., New York (1943).

McCarter, W. S. W., K. A. Krieger, and H. Heinemann, Thermal Activation of Attapulgus Clay, *Ind. Eng. Chem.*, **42**, 529–533 (1950).

Mertz, E. L., Brief Account of Soils Applicable for Mud and Organic Mud Baths, *Danmarks Geol. Undersøgelse,* ser. 4, **2** (14) (1940).

Mielenz, R. C., K. T. Greene, and N. C. Schieltz, Natural Pozzolans for Concrete, *Econ. Geol.*, **46**, 311–328 (1951).

——— and M. E. King, Physical-Chemical Properties and Engineering Performance of Clays, *Calif. Div. Mines Bull.* 169, pp. 196–254 (1955).

———, L. P. Witte, and O. J. Glantz, Effect of Calcination on Natural Pozzolans, *Am. Soc. Testing Materials, Spec. Tech. Pub.* 99, pp. 43–91 (1950).

Miller, C. F., "Carbonization of Cellulose Esters," U.S. Patent 2,287,696 (1942).

Millman, N., Viscosity Control of Concentrated Clay Suspensions, *Paper Trade J.*, **132** (7) (1951).

Milton, R. M., "Molecular Sieve Adsorbents," U.S. Patents 2,882,243; 2,882,244 (1959).

Murray, H., "The Structure of Kaolinite and Its Relation to Acid Treatment," Ph.D. thesis, University of Illinois (1951).

——— and S. C. Lyons, Correlation of Paper Coating Quality with Degree of Crystal Perfection of Kaolinite, *Natl. Acad. Sci. Publ.* 456, pp. 31–40 (1956).

——— and J. M. Smith, Lightweight Aggregate Potentialities of Some Indiana Shales, *Indiana Geol. Survey Rept. Progr.*, **12** (1958).

Nordell, E., "Water Treatment for Industrial and Other Uses," Reinhold Publishing Corporation, Inc., New York, 1951.

Nishita, H., A. J. Kowalewsky, R. T. Steen, and K. H. Larson, Fixation and Extractability of Fission Products Contaminating Various Soils and Clays, *Soil Sci.*, **81**, pp. 317–326 (1956).

Olin, H. L., "Purification of Water," U.S. Patent 2,362,022 (1944).

———, R. J. Box, and R. E. Whitson, Bentonite as a Coagulant for Sewages and Industrial Wastes, *Water Works & Sewerage*, December (1942).

——— and H. F. Freeman, Purification of Water with Bentonite, *Paper Trade J.*, November (1941).

——— and H. W. Peterson, The Use of Bentonite as a Coagulant in Water Treatment, *J. Am. Water Works Assoc.*, **29**, 513–517 (1937).

Pask, J., and B. Davies, Thermal Analysis of Clays and Acid Extraction of

Alumina from Clays, *U.S. Bur. Mines Tech. Paper* 664, pp. 56–78 (1945).

Petersen, T. H., "Lightweight Aggregate Concrete, Housing and Home Finance Agency," GP Office (1950).

Price, W. H., and W. A. Cordon, Tests of Lightweight Aggregate Concrete Designed for Monolithic Construction, *Proc. Am. Concrete Inst.*, 45, 581–600 (1949).

Richmond, H. A., "Process of Treating Aluminous Ores," U.S. Patent 1,245,383 (1917).

Rick, G. G., and C. E. Loetel, "Fuel Briquettes and Method of Making Same," U.S. Patent 2,217,994 (1940).

Riley, C. M., Relation of Chemical Properties to the Bloating of Clays, *J. Am. Ceram. Soc.*, 34, 121–128 (1951).

Rosner, G. J., "Manufacture of Improved Doughnut Sugar and the Resulting Product," U.S. Patent 2,846,311 (1958).

Salmon, W. D., N. B. Guerrant, and I. M. Hays, The Effect of Hydrogen Ion Concentration upon Adsorption of the Active Factors of Vitamin B Complex by Fuller's Earth, *J. Biol. Chem.*, 80, 91–101 (1928).

Sawyer, E. W., J. A. Polon, and H. A. Smith, "The Stabilization of Suspension Fertilizers with Colloidal Attapulgite," paper at Convention of National Fertilizers Solutions Association, St. Louis (1959).

Saywell, L. G., Clarification of Vinegar, *Ind. Eng. Chem.* 26, 379–385 (1934).

———, The Bentonite Process of Clarifying Wine, *Calif. Wine Rev.*, January (1935).

Schwiete, H. E., The Influence of the Clay Minerals on the Formation of Dust in Burning Cement Clinker, *Zement-Kalk-Gips,* 9, 351–357 (1956).

Seidell, A., Improved Method for the Preparation of Vitamin-activated Fuller's Earth, *U.S. Public Health Repts.,* 37, 801–803 (1922).

Silva, F. J. R., Colloidal Bentonite as a Clarifying Agent, *Sugar J.,* October (1948).

Slocum, E. M., The Use of Bleaching Clays in Water Purification, *J. Penn. Water Works Operators' Assoc.,* 4, 53–64 (1932).

Small, C., Metal Polish, *Chem. Ind.,* 49, 488–490 (1941).

———, Automobile Cleaners and Polishes, *Chem. Ind.,* 50, 806–809 (1942).

Smith, J. W., R. T. Trelfa, and H. O. Water, Casein Adhesives in Roll Coating, *J. Tech. Assoc. Pulp & Paper Ind.,* 33, 212–218 (1950).

St. Clair, H. W., S. F. Ravety, A. T. Sweet, and C. E. Plummer, The Ammonium Sulfate Process for Production of Aluminum from Western Clay, *Trans. AIME,* 159, 255–266 (1944).

Stockfisch, K., and W. Benade, Die Charakterisierung der Heilschlamme und verwandter Stoffe, *Mitt. Preuss. geol. Landesanstalt,* 11, Berlin (1930).

Stowasser, W. F., New Pellet Hardening Method Uses Grate and Kiln Firing, *Mining World,* 19, 59–60 (1957).

Sweet, A. T., and G. D. Gardini, Elimination of Iron in Ammonium Sulfate Process for Production of Alumina from Clay, *U.S. Bur. Mines Rept. Invest.* 4183 (1948).

Thiebaut, J. L., "Sediments argilo-calcaires du bassin de Paris," Nancy, France (1925).

Tuthill, L. H., Concrete Operations in Concrete Ship Program, *Proc. Am. Concrete Inst.,* 41, 137–177 (1945).

Uren, L. C., Cements for Oil and Gas Wells, *Petrol. Eng.,* September (1942).

Venezia, M., Food Processing and Packing, *Marketing,* p. 204, July (1948).

Voet, A., and A. E. Yelmgren, "Anti-misting Printing Ink," U.S. Patent 2,754,219 (1956).

Walthall, J. H., P. Miller, and M. M. Striplin, Development of a Sulfuric Acid Process for Production of Alumina from Clay, *Trans. AIME,* **41,** 55–138 (1945).

Weaver, C. D., Water Impedance with Bentonite by the Placement Method, *Proc. Soil. Sci. Soc. Am.,* **11,** 196–254 (1946).

Weber, F. C., "Process of Treating Kaolin for the Production of Carborundum and Alumina," U.S. Patent 728,528 (1903).

Weir, P., The Use of Clay in Coagulation and Taste and Odor Control, *J. Am. Water Works Assoc.,* **30,** 1528–1539 (1938).

———, Use of Bleaching Clays in Water Purification, *AIME Tech. Pub.* 1018 (1939).

Wells, S. D., Making New Paper from Old Paper Stock, *Paper Trade J.,* **74,** 47–50 (1922).

White, C. K., Alumina from Clay Plant at Salem, Oregon, *Mining Congr. J.,* **31,** 32–34 (1945).

White, W. A., "Lightweight Aggregate Resources of Illinois," manuscript, Illinois State Geological Survey (1959).

Whiting, J. A., "Anthelmintic Compositions and Processes of Preparing Same," U.S. Patent 2,428,444 (1947).

Wilcox, J. R., Controlling Flow Properties with Fillers, *Proc. Soc. Plastics Ind.,* **9,** sec. 27, February (1954).

Wilson, J. A., Colloidal Clay in Leather Manufacture, *Hide and Leather,* **90,** 32–33 (1935).

Wolf, L., Zur Chemie des Kaolins, *Ber. deut. keram. Ges.,* **14,** 393–403 (1933).

Woodward, L. A., and S. C. Lyons, The Mechanism of Gloss Development in Clay Coated Sheets, *Tech. Assoc. Pulp and Paper Ind.,* **34,** 438–442 (1951).

Woody, R. J., Literature on the Extraction of Alumina from Clay, with Short Discussion, *Wash. State Coll. Mining Exp. Sta. Bull.* E-1 (1943).

Wollman, M. S., and E. B. McGowan, "Textiles," The Macmillan Company, New York (1926).

Index

Absorbent, floor, 367
Acid-activated clays, 322–323
Activity, classification, 219
  clay mineral values, 207–209
  concept, 219–227
Adhesives, 333–334
Adsorbed water, adsorbed ions, 37
  dehydration, 34–35
  density, 36
  physical state, 35–36
  plasticity, 63–71
  structure, 35–37
  types, 34
Adsorbents, 362–363
Air-set strength (molding sands), concept, 190, 196–197
  definition, 144
  halloysite clays, 169–173
  illite clays, 169–173
  kaolinite clays, 169–173
  montmorillonite clays, 169–173
Allophane, composition, 10
  definition, 2, 10
  dehydration curve, 88
  differential thermal curves, 91
  drying shrinkage, 76
  high temperature phases, 106
  structure, 10
Allophane clay, activity, 207
  firing shrinkage, 113
  liquid limit, 207, 211–212
  permeability, 242
  plastic limit, 208
  plasticity index, 207, 214
Alpha alumina, 103
Alsifilm, 334–335
Alum manufacture, 339
Aluminum ore, bauxite, 335
    Bayer process, 335
  clay, acid process, 336–339
    alum manufacture, 339
    clay mineral properties, 336–338
    ammonium sulfate process, 339–340

Aluminum ore, clay, electrochemical processes, 346
  lime-sinter process, 340–342
  lime-soda sinter process, 343–347
Amorphous materials, 2
Analytical procedures, 45–47
Anauxite, 14
  differential thermal curves, 91
Ancient sediments, clay mineral composition, 42–43
Angle internal friction, 235
Animal bedding, 346–347
Anion exchange, 32–34
  capacity of clay minerals, 33
  cause, 33
  replaceability, 34
Anorthite, 109
Atomic-waste disposal, 347–348
Attapulgite, cation-exchange capacity, 30
  composition, 26
  differential thermal curves, 93
  electron micrograph, 27
  high temperature phases, 111–112
  shape and size, 26–28
  structure, 25–27
Attapulgite clay, activity, 207
  animal bedding, 346
  cleaning and polishing compounds, 402
  consolidation, 259
  decolorizing oil, 321–322
  desiccants, 361–363
  drilling muds, 287–289
  dry strength, 82
  drying shrinkage, 76
  fertilizers, 366
  firing shrinkage, 113, 116, 120
  floor absorbent, 367
  liquid limits, 207, 211–212
  medicines, pharmaceuticals, cosmetics, 372–373
  paint, 376
  paper, 382
  pesticides, 390

413

Attapulgite clay, plastic limits, 207
plasticity index, 207, 213–214
pozzolanas, 356
water of plasticity, 57
water clarification, 403–404
Attapulgite-sepiolite clay, 148
Atterberg limits, 58–59, 205–216
clay mineral values, 59, 207–209, 224–225
concept, 219–227
definition, 58, 205
drying, 216–217
exchangeable cations, 211–212
particle size, 214–216
Atterberg plasticity index (*see* Plasticity index)

Ball clay, 132
Bauxite, 133
Beer clarification, 360–361
Beidellite, 21
Bentone, 369
Bentonite, catalyst manufacture, 309–310
cement, 352
clarification of wines, cider, beer, 359
composition, 43–44
decolorizing oil, 322–323
definition, 43
drilling muds, 283–291
food, 367–369
geologic age, 44
greases, 369–370
medicines, pharmaceuticals, cosmetics, 372–373
molding sands, 146–147
origin, 43
pelletizing ores, fluxes, fuels, 388
permeability, 242–244
plasticity, 55–60
sensitivity, 237
water adsorption and swelling, 248–250
water clarification, 403–404
water impedance, 404–405
Beta cristobalite, 109–112
Beta quartz, 109
Biotite, dehydration curves, 102
differential thermal curve, 92
high temperature phases, 103
Boehmite, 133
Bonding action (molding sands), 179–201
Brick, adobe, 130
common, 129
face, 130
paving, 131
Bulk density (molding sands), concept, 193–195

Bulk density (molding sands), definition, 143
halloysite clay, 158–159
illite clay, 159–160
kaolinite clay, 159–160
montmorillonite clay, 157–158
relation, to dry strength, 169
to green strength, 152–156, 169
to plastic limit, 160

Catalysts, gasoline manufacture, clays used, 309–310
concept, 315–318
preparation, 310–311
properties, 311–315
types, 308–309
use, 307–308
miscellaneous reactions, condensations, 319
dechlorinations, 319
dehydrations, 319–327
essential oils, 318
glyceride oils, 318
hydrogenation, 319
isomerization and cyclization, 319
oxidations and reductions, 319–320
Cation exchange, 30–32
capacity of clay minerals, 30
cause, 30–31
definition, 29
organic reactions, 38
replaceability, 32
Cement, portland, clays used, 349–350
composition, 349
lightweight aggregate, 353–355
manufacturing process, 348
pozzolanas, clay mineral properties, 355–359
definition, 355
Cement and concrete additives, 351–352
Ceramic properties, definition, 52
drying, 75–86
factors determining, 53
firing, 86–125
green, 71–75
lamination, 74–75
plasticity, 54–71
Ceramics, definition, 52
processes, 53
Chain structural unit, 9
Chemical logs, 297
Chinastone, 131
Chlorite, cation-exchange capacity, 30
composition, 23
degraded form, 24
dehydration curve, 90
differential thermal curves, 93

Chlorite, high temperature phases, 105–106
  structure, 22–24
Chlorite clay, activity, 208
  dry strength, 82
  drying shrinkage, 76
  firing shrinkage, 118
  liquid limit, 208–212
  plastic limit, 208
  plasticity index, 208–214
  pozzolanas, 359
Cider clarification, 360–361
Clarification of wines, cider, beer, 359–361
Clay material, concepts of composition, 1
  definition, 1
  factors controlling properties, 2–5
    clay mineral composition, 2
    exchangeable ions and soluble salts, 3
    nonclay mineral composition, 2–3
    organic material, 3
    texture, 3–5
  industrial importance, 4
Clay mineral concept, definition, 1–2
  history, 1–2
Clay minerals, acid solubility, 336–338
  analyses, procedures, 45–47
  cation-exchange capacity, 30
  definition, 2
  dehydration, 88–94
  differential thermal curves, 91–93
  high temperature phases, 96–112
  occurrence, 39–44
  origin, 39–44
  petroleum discovery, 278–280
  petroleum refining, 307–330
  properties, bonding, 151–203
    catalytic, 312–315
    ceramic, 52–134
    decolorizing, 320–326
    drilling mud, 280–293
    miscellaneous, 38, 333–410
    pozzolanic, 355–359
  reaction with organic compounds, 38–39
  secondary oil recovery, 297–304
  structure, 10–28
  well-logging, 293–297
Cleaning compounds, 402
Clinochlore, 118
  limit values, 208
Coating seeds, 361
Cohesion, 235–236
Compressibility (*see* Consolidation)
Compressibility coefficient, 254
Compression index, 253
Compression strength, unconfined, classification, 228
  clay mineral values, 229–230
  concept, 179–201

Condensations (catalysis), 319
Consolidation, concept, 259–262
  definition, 251–252
  primary, 255
  relation, to clay mineral composition, 253–262
    to exchangeable cations, 256–259
  secondary, 255–261
Cordierite, 109
Corundum, 103
Cosmetics, 372–373
Cristobalite, 99–102, 109, 111–112

Dechlorination, 319
Decolorization (of oil), acid-activated clays, 322–323
  clay materials used, 321–325
  clay specifications, 323–324
  process, 320–321
  theory, 325–326
Degraded illite, 22
Dehydration (catalysis), 319
Dehydration curves, allophane, 88
  chlorite, 90
  glauconite, 90
  halloysite, 88
  hectorite, 89
  illite, 90
  kaolinite, 88
  montmorillonite, 89
  nontronite, 89
  palygorskite, 90
  sepiolite, 90
De-inking newsprint paper, 361
Density, 266–267
Desiccants, 361–363
Diagenesis, 42, 279
Diaspore, 133
Dickite, 14
Differential thermal curves, allophane, 91
  anauxite, 91
  attapulgite, 93
  biotite, 92
  chlorite, 93
  glauconite, 92
  halloysite, 91
  illite, 92
  kaolinite, 91
  montmorillonite, 92
  muscovite, 92
  nontronite, 92
  palygorskite, 93
  pyrophyllite, 93
  quartz, 93
  sepiolite, 93
  talc, 93

Differential thermal curves, vermiculite, 93
Dinnerware, 132
Dioctahedral structure, 18, 103, 105, 107
Drilling fluids, clay mineral properties, 283–291
  concept, 288–291
  function, 281–282
  oil-base muds, 292–293
  oil-emulsion muds, 291–292
  properties, 281–283
Dry strength, ceramics, 82–86, 262–263
  adsorbed ions, 85
  clay mineral values, 82
  definition, 82
  effect of montmorillonite, 83
  texture, 84–85
  molding sands, concept, 197
  definition, 144
  halloysite clay, 163–168
  illite clay, 163–168
  kaolinite clay, 163–168
  montmorillonite clay, 160–168
  relation, to bulk density, 169
    to green strength, 169
Drying, ease of, 80–81
  adsorbed ions, 81
  clay mineral composition, 80
  texture, 81
Drying scum, 76
Drying shrinkage, 75–89, 262–263
  clay mineral values, 76
  concept, 78–79
  definition, 75
  relation, to texture, 76–78
  to water of plasticity, 76
Durability (molding sands), clay minerals, 177–179
  concept, 201–202
  definition, 145–146

Efflorescence, 126
Electric well logs, 293–296
Electron micrographs, attapulgite, 27
  halloysite, 15
  kaolinite, 13
Emulsifying agents, 364
Emulsion-oil drilling muds, 291–292
Enstatite, 111, 112
Essential oils, 319
Exchangeable ions and soluble salts, 3, 29–30
  hydration, 32
  ionization, 31
  montmorillonite, 16

Exchangeable ions and soluble salts, relation, to adsorbed water, 37
  to consolidation, 256–259
  to drilling muds, 286–289
  to dry strength, 85
  to drying shrinkage, 76
  to green strength, 72
    molding sands, 154
  to liquid limit, 211–212
  to permeability, 242–243
  to pH, 32
  to plastic limit, 206–209
  to plasticity, 66–68
  to plasticity index, 213–214
  to water adsorption and swelling, 250

Fabrics, 364
Fertilizers, 365
Fillers, miscellaneous, 367
Fireclay, 147
Firing color, 122
Firing expansion, 114–120
Firing properties, 86–125
  dehydration, 88–94
  dimensional changes, 112–121
  fluxes, 95–96
  general statement, 86–97
  high temperature phases, 97–112
  inheritance, 96–105
  reheat volume changes, 129
  specific gravity changes, 120–121
Firing shrinkage, clay mineral values, 113
  texture, 113–114
Flint clay, 13, 133
  firing shrinkage, 115
  plasticity, 55, 60
Floor absorbent, 367
Flowability (molding sands), clay minerals, 176–177
  concept, 195–196
  definition, 145
Fluxes, pelletizing, 389
Food, 367–369
Foundry molding sands, air-set strength, 144, 169–173
  bulk density, 143, 157–160
  clays used, 146–148, 179
  concept of clay bonding, 179–201
  dry strength, 144, 160–169
  durability, 145–146, 177–179
  factors controlling properties, 142
  flowability, 145, 176–177
  green strength, 143, 148–157
  hot strength, 144, 174–175
  oil base, 202
  permeability, 145

Frost heaving, cause, 245
    relation to clay minerals, 246-247
Fuels, pelletizing, 388
Fuller's earth, 321
Fusion temperature, 121-122

Gamma alumina, 99, 103
Gamma Fe$_2$O$_3$, 103
Gamma-ray logs, 296
Gibbsite, 133
Glauconite, 21
    dehydration curve, 90
    differential thermal curve, 92
Glaze properties, 127-128, 134
Glyceride oils, 319
Greases, 369-370
Green strength, ceramic, clay mineral values, 72-73
    concept, 73-74
    definition, 71
    relation, to plasticity, 71, 73
        to texture, 73-74
    molding sands, concept, 189-193
        definition, 143
        halloysite clay, 150-157
        illite clay, 151-157
        kaolinite clay, 151-157
        montmorillonite clays, 149-157
        relation, to bulk density, 153-156
            to dry strength, 169
            to plastic limit, 156

Halloysite, cation-exchange capacity, 30
    composition, 14
    dehydration curves, 88
    differential thermal curves, 91
    high temperature phases, 101-102
    nomenclature, 16
    shape of particles, 15-16
    size of particles, 15
    structure, 14-16
Halloysite clay, 148
    activity, 207-208
    air-set strength, 169-173
    aluminum ore, 336-346
    bulk density, 157-158
    catalyst manufacture, 310
    dry strength, 82, 163-168
    drying shrinkage, 76
    firing shrinkage, 113-114
    fusion temperature, 121
    green strength, 72
        molding sands, 150-157
    liquid limit, 207-208, 211-212
    plastic limit, 207-208

Halloysite clay, plasticity index, 207-208, 213-214
    water of plasticity, 57
Hectorite, 287
    dehydration curve, 89
    differential thermal curve, 92
High temperature phases, 97-112
    allophane, 106
    chlorite, 105-106
    halloysite, 101-102
        impurities, 102
    illite, 102-104
    kaolinite, 98-101
        crystallinity, 100
        impurities, 100
    montmorillonite, 107-111
        adsorbed cation, 110-111
        anhydrite structure, 107
    sepiolite-attapulgite, 111-112
Hot strength (molding sands), concept, 199-201
    definition, 144
    kaolinite clays, 174-175
    montmorillonite clays, 174-175
Hydrogenation, 319
Hydrothermal origin of clay minerals, 40

Illite, anion-exchange capacity, 33
    cation-exchange capacity, 30
    composition, 20
    definition, 22
    degraded form, 22
    dehydration curves, 90
    differential thermal curves, 92
    dry strength, 82
    drying shrinkage, 76
    green strength, 72
    high temperature phases, 102-104
    size and shape, 20-22
    structure, 20-22
    water of plasticity, 57
Illite clays, 147-148
    activity, 207, 209, 215
    air-set strength, 169-173
    aluminum ore, 336-346
    atomic waste disposal, 347
    consolidation, 259
    dry strength, 163-168
    durability, 177-179
    electric logs, 293-296
    fertilizers, 365
    firing shrinkage, 113-114, 117
    flowability, 176-177
    green strength (molding sands), 151-157
    lightweight aggregate, 353
    liquid limit, 207, 209, 211-212, 215

Illite clays, plastic limit, 207, 209, 215
  plasticity index, 207, 209, 213–215
  pozzolanas, 355–359
  secondary recovery (oil), 298–300
  shear resistance, 234–235
  vitrification range, 123–124
  water adsorption, 224–225
    and swelling, 248–250
Ink, 370
Internal friction, angle, 235
Ion exchange, definition, 29
  importance, 29–30
Isomerization, 319

Kaolinite, anion-exchange capacity, 33
  cation-exchange capacity, 30
  composition, 11–12
  dehydration curves, 88
  differential thermal curves, 91
  dry strength, 82
  drying shrinkage, 76–77
  green strength, 72
  high temperature phases, 98–101, 117
  organic-clad, 371, 376, 393–394, 400
  shape of particles, 13
  size of particles, 12
  stress-strain plasticity, 60–61
  structure, 10–14
  variations in crystallinity, 12
  water of plasticity, 57
Kaolinite clays, 131–132
  activity, 207–209, 215
  adhesives, 334
  air-set strength, 169–173
  aluminum ore, 336–346
  bulk density, 159–160
  catalyst manufacture, 310
  catalysts, 309–310
  cement, 249–352
  compression strength, unconfined, 229
  consolidation, 256–259
  dry strength, 163–168
  durability, 177–179
  electric logs, 293–296
  fabrics, 364
  firing shrinkage, 113–115, 117
  flowability, 176–177
  fusion temperature, 121
  green strength (molding sands), 151–157
  hard, 396
  hot strength, 174–175
  ink, 370–371
  leather, 371
  liquid limit, 207–209, 211–212, 215
  medicines, pharmaceuticals, cosmetics,
    372–373

Kaolinite clays, paint, 374–376
  paper, 380–388
  permeability, 241–242, 298–300
  pesticides, 390
  plastic limit, 207–209, 215
  plasticity index, 207–209, 213–215
  plastics, 391–394
  pozzolanas, 355–359
  rehydrated, fired properties, 125
  rubber, 394–401
  secondary recovery (oil), 298–300
  shear resistance, 233–235
  soaps, 401–402
  soft, 396
  vitrification range, 123–124
  water adsorption, 224–225
    and swelling, 248–250
Keppler plasticity number, 62

Lamination, 74–75
Lateritic soil, 41
Leather, 371
Leucite, 103
Lightweight aggregate, clays used, 354
  manufacturing process, 352–353
  theory, 353–354
Liquid limit (*see* Atterberg limits)
Liquidity index, definition, 227
  relation, to clay minerals, 227
    to consolidation pressure, 227–228
    to sensitivity, 236

Medicines, 372
Metakaolin, 99, 102
Mixed-layer minerals, 28
  identification, 45
Moisture expansion, fired products, 126–
  127
Molding sands, 141–203
  air-set strength, 144, 169–173
  bulk density, 143, 157–160
  clays used, 146–148, 179
  concept of clay bonding, 179–201
  dry strength, 144, 160–169
  durability, 145–146, 177–179
  factors controlling properties, 142
  flowability, 145, 176–177
  green strength, 143, 148–157
  hot strength, 144, 174–175
  mulling, 193
  oil-base, 202
  permeability, 145
Molecular sieves, 363

Montmorillonite, anion-exchange capacity, 33
  cation-exchange capacity, 30
  composition, 18–19
  dehydration curves, 89
  differential thermal curves, 92
  high temperature phases, 107–111
  organic-clad, 334, 369, 377, 400
  shape and size of particles, 19
  structure, 16–20
Montmorillonite clays, acid-activated, 322–323
  activity, 207–209, 215
  air-set strength, 169–173
  alsifilm, 334
  aluminum ore, 336–346
  animal bedding, 346
  atomic-waste disposal, 347
  bulk density, 157–158
  catalyst manufacture, 309–310
  cement, 349–352
  clarification of wines, beer, cider, 359–360
  cleaning and polishing compounds, 402
  coated seeds, 361
  compression strength, unconfined, 229
  consolidation, 256, 258–259
  decolorizing oil, 322–323
  de-inking, newsprint, 361
  desiccants, 362–363
  drilling mud, 283–291
  dry strength, 82, 160–168
  drying shrinkage, 76
  durability, 177–179
  electric logs, 293–296
  firing shrinkage, 113–114, 117
  floor absorbent, 367
  flowability, 176–177
  food, 367–368
  green strength, 72
    molding sands, 149–157
  hot strength, 174–175
  liquid limit, 207–209, 211–212, 215
  medicines, pharmaceuticals, cosmetics, 372–373
  paint, 377
  paper, 382
  permeability, 241–242, 298–300
  pesticides, 390
  plastic limit, 207–209, 215
  plasticity index, 207–209, 213–215
  pozzolanas, 355–359
  rubber, 395
  secondary recovery (oil), 298–300
  shear resistance, 233–235
  soaps, 401–402
  stress-strain, plasticity, 60–61

Montmorillonite clays, therapeutic muds, 403
  water of plasticity, 57
  water adsorption, 224–225
    and swelling, 248–250
  water clarification, 403–404
  water impedance, 404–405
Mortar mix, 350–351
Mulling (molding sands), 193
Mullite, 96, 99–104, 109, 112
Muscovite, differential thermal curve, 92
  firing shrinkage, 119
  high temperature phases, 103

Nacrite, 14
Neutron-gamma logs, 296–297
Nonclay mineral composition, 2–3
Nonliquid adsorbed water, 35–36
  relation, to Atterberg limits, 219–227
    to bonding (molding sands), 179–199
    to consolidation, 259–260
    to drilling muds, 288–290
    to green strength, 73–74
    to plasticity, 63–71
    to secondary recovery (oil), 302–303
Nontronite, 18
  activity, 208
  anion-exchange capacity, 33
  dehydration curve, 89
  differential thermal curves, 92
  firing shrinkage, 116, 120
  liquid limit, 208
  permeability, 242
  plastic limit, 208
  plasticity index, 208, 213

Occurrence of clay minerals, 39–44
Octahedral structural unit, 7–8
Oil-base foundry sands, 202
Oil-base drilling muds, 292–293
Oil reclaiming, 329
Olivine, 105
Ores, pelletizing, 388
Organic-clad kaolinite, 371, 376, 393–394, 400
Organic-clad montmorillonite, 334, 369, 377, 400
Organic material, 3
  reaction with clay minerals, 38–39
  relation to plasticity, 71
Origin of clay minerals, 39–44
Oxidation (catalysis), 319

Paint, attapulgite properties, 376
  kaolinite properties, 374–376

Paint, montmorillonite properties, 377
  organic-clad kaolins, 376
  organic-clad montmorillonite, 377
  types and composition, 373–374
Palygorskite, 27
  dehydration curve, 90
  differential thermal curves, 93
Paper, clays used, attapulgite, 382
  kaolins, preparation, 381–382
    properties, 380
    specifications, coating, 383–386
      filler, 382–383
    montmorillonite, 382
  composition, 377–378
  paper-clay evaluation tests, abrasion, 378
    brightness, 379
    make-down, 379
    particle size, 379
    screen residue, 379
    viscosity, 379–380
  theory of kaolin coating, 386–388
Particle-size distribution, 3–5
Pelletizing ores, fluxes, fuels, 388–389
Penetration resistance, definition, 263
  relation, to Atterberg limits, 264–265
    to clay mineral composition, 263–266
    to particle size, 264–265
Permeability, clay mineral values, 241–243, 280
  coefficient, 240
  concept, 243–245
  exchangeable cations, 242–243
  molding sands, 145
  relation to type of fluid, 245
  reservoir rocks, 297–304
  secondary recovery (oil), 297–304
Pesticides, 389–390
Petroleum, decolorization, 320–326
  drilling fluids, 280–293
  producing operations, 297–303
  refining, 307–318, 326–330
  search for, 278–280
  well logging, 293–297
Pharmaceuticals, 372
Phlogopite, firing shrinkage, 118
  high temperature phases, 103
Plastic limit, Atterberg, bulk density, 160
  clay mineral values, 206–210
  concept, 219–227
  definition, 58, 205
  drying, 216–217
  exchangeable cations, 206–209
  green strength (molding sands), 156
  particle size, 214–216
  texture, 210
Plasticity, 54–71

Plasticity, adsorbed ions, 66–67
  Atterberg limits, 58–59, 205–216
  clay mineral structure, 65–67
  concept, 63–71
  definition, 54
  heating, 62
  liquid, 64, 69–70
  methods of measurement, 54
  organic material, 71
  stress-strain curves, 55
  stress-strain values, 59–62
  surface area, 68
  texture, 67–68
  water of, 56–58
  weathering, 70
Plasticity index, Atterberg, clay mineral values, 206–210, 213–214
  concept, 219–227
  definition, 58, 205
  drying, 216–217
  exchangeable cations, 213–214
  particle size, 214–216
  Rieke, 59
Plasticizing agents, 394
Plastics, clay use, 391
  kaolin properties, 392–394
  organic-clad kaolins, 393–394
Podsolic soil, 41
Polar organic-clay mineral reactions, 38–39
Polishing compounds, 402
Porcelain, 132
Porcelain-enamel properties, 128–129, 134
Portland cement (*see* Cement)
Pozzolanas, 355–359
Preconsolidation, 262
Prilling material, 365
Prochlorite, 208
Pyrophyllite, differential thermal curve, 93

Quartz, differential thermal curve, 93
Quickclay, 236–237
  concept, 239–240

Radioactive-waste disposal, 347–348
Radioactive well logs, 296–297
Recent sediments, clay mineral composition, 42, 279
  diagenesis, 42, 279
Reduction (catalysis), 319
Refractories, 132–134
  high alumina, 133
  ladle, 133
  plastic, 134

Reheat volume changes, 129
Rehydrated kaolinite, fired properties, 125
Reservoir rocks, clay mineral composition, 280–301
  permeability, 280, 297–304
  secondary recovery, 297–304
Resistivity well log, clay mineral influence, 293–294
  concept, 295
  definition, 293
Rieke plasticity index, 59
Rubber, clays used, 394–395
  kaolin specifications, 395–396
  properties with kaolin, 397–398
  synthetic, with kaolin, 398–400
  theory of action of clays, 400–401

Saponite, 18–21
  firing shrinkage, 116
Scum, 126
Sea coal, 141
Secondary recovery (oil), clay mineral influence, 298–301
  concept, 301–303
  definition, 297–298
  water-composition influence, 298–301
Sediments, clay mineral composition, ancient, 42–43, 279–280
  recent, 42
Self-potential well logs, clay mineral influence, 293–295
  concept, 295
  definition, 293
Sensitivity, classification, 236
  clay mineral values, 231
  concept, 238–240
  definition, 236
  relation, to clay minerals, 237–238
    to liquidity, 236
Sepiolite, cation-exchange capacity, 30
  composition, 27
  dehydration curve, 90
  desiccants, 363
  differential thermal curves, 93
  drilling mud, 287
  firing shrinkage, 116
  high temperature phases, 111–112
  soap, 401
  structure, 27
Septechlorite, 24
Sewerpipe, 131
Shear strength, clay mineral values, 231–235
  concept, 235–236
  relation, to activity, 234
    to liquidity, 232

Shear strength, relation, to overburden pressure, 232–235
  to plasticity index, 235
Sillimanite, 112
Smectite, 290
Soap, 401–402
Soil mechanics, 204–277
Soil stabilization, cement, 270–271
  lime, 268–270
  lime-flyash, 270
  organic compounds, 271
Soils, clay mineral composition, 41–42
  factors controlling forming processes, 41–42
  factors controlling properties, 272–274
  profiles, 41
Specific gravity, changes on firing, 120–121
Spinel, 103–104
Stabilizing agents, 364
Stoneware, 131–132
Structure of clay minerals, adsorbed water, 35–37
  allophane, 10
  attapulgite-palygorskite, sepiolite, 25–28
  chlorite, 22–24
  halloysite, 14–16
  illite, 20–22
  kaolinite, 10–14
  montmorillonite, 16–20
  relation to plasticity, 66–68
  vermiculite, 25
Surface area relation, to Atterberg limits, 216
  to plasticity, 68
Suspending agents, 364
Swelling, concept, 251
  pressure, 250
  relation, to clay mineral composition, 247–250
    to exchangeable cations, 250
Synthesis of clay minerals, 39–40
Synthetic rubber, fillers, 398–400

Talc, differential thermal curve, 93
Temper (molding sands), 143, 195
Tempering water, 141, 143
Terra cotta, 131–132
Tetrahedral structural units, 8–9
Texture, relation, to Atterberg limits, 214–216
  to dry strength, 84–85
  to drying shrinkage, 76–78
  to green strength, 73–74
  to plastic limit, 210
  to plasticity, 67–68

Texture, significance, 3–5
Therapeutic muds, 403
Thixotropy, 236–238, 282
Thuringite, 208
Tile, drain, 130
  roof, 130
  structural, 130
Translucency, 127
Trioctahedral structure, 18, 103, 105

Underclay, 133, 147

Vermiculite, anion-exchange capacity, 4
  atomic-waste disposal, 346
  cation-exchange capacity, 30
  composition, 25
  differential thermal curves, 93
  structure, 25
Vitamins, 368–369
Vitrification, 97–122
  fluxes, 124
  range, 123–125
Void ratio, definition, 251–252
  relation, to consolidation, 252–259
    to permeability, 244

Water, adsorbed (*see* Adsorbed water)
  of plasticity, 56–58

Water, of plasticity, clay mineral values, 57
  definition, 56
  relation to drying shrinkage, 76
    to exchangeable cations, 57
    to particle size, 57
Water adsorption (*see* Swelling)
Water adsorption rate, clay mineral values, 223–225
  relation to Atterberg limits, 223–225
Water clarification, 403–404
Water impedance, 404–405
Weathering, factors controlling, 40–41
  origin of clay minerals, 40–42
  profiles, 41
  relation to plasticity, 70
Well logs, chemical, 297
  electric, 293–296
  radioactive, 296–297
Whiteware, 131
Wines, clarification, 359–361

X-ray diffraction, analytical procedure, 45–47
  glycol treatment, 46
  oriented aggregates, 45–46

Zeolites, 1
Zschokke plasticity number, 61